Kaitlin
Wlodkowski

Kaitlin
Wlodkowski

Dive into a book.

The unknown awaits—

an inky ocean canyon with glowing fish

or a pharaoh's  pyramid, filled with treasure.

You may even discover something

about yourself that you never knew before.

Imagination

charts your course through

Cover, Introduction, and Title Page Illustrations by Piotr Kaczmarek.

Acknowledgments appear on page 586.

Printed in the U.S.A.

ISBN: 0-395-51925-X

EFGHIJ-D-998765432

BEYOND THE REEF

Senior Author
John J. Pikulski

Senior Coordinating Author
J. David Cooper

Senior Consulting Author
William K. Durr

Coordinating Authors
Kathryn H. Au
M. Jean Greenlaw
Marjorie Y. Lipson
Susan Page
Sheila W. Valencia
Karen K. Wixson

Authors
Rosalinda B. Barrera
Ruth P. Bunyan
Jacqueline L. Chaparro
Jacqueline C. Comas
Alan N. Crawford
Robert L. Hillerich
Timothy G. Johnson
Jana M. Mason
Pamela A. Mason
William E. Nagy
Joseph S. Renzulli
Alfredo Schifini

Senior Advisor
Richard C. Anderson

Advisors
Christopher J. Baker
Charles Peters

HOUGHTON MIFFLIN COMPANY BOSTON
Atlanta Dallas Geneva, Illinois Palo Alto Princeton Toronto

THE SPIRIT OF SURVIVAL

BOOK 1

THEME BOOK
Courage at Indian Deep
by Jane Resh Thomas

EXPLORING THE OCEANS

BOOK 2

THEME BOOK
The Great Barrier Reef: A Treasure in the Sea
by Alice Gilbreath

BECOMING

BOOK 3

THEME BOOK
. . . and now Miguel
by Joseph Krumgold

BOOK 4

TIMELESS TALES

BOOK 6

THEME BOOK
The Cow-Tail Switch, and Other West African Stories
by Harold Courlander and George Herzog

NOVEL
469

The Summer of the Swans

BOOK 7

by Betsy Byars

THEME BOOK
The House of Wings
by Betsy Byars

ADVENTURE

BOOK 1

THE SPIRIT OF SURVIVAL

**DOG SLEDS
RACE TO SAVE
NOME, ALASKA
AND MORE . . .**

CONTENTS

THE
SPIRIT OF SURVIVAL

MAYDAY

MAYDAY

42

From *Shadow Shark*
by Colin Thiele

MAYDAY

62

From *Race Against Death*
by Seymour Reit

82

Long Claws
by James Houston

SURVIVAL

I wonder if

we will ever be rescued.

The thought of floating

out here until I die

is horrifying.

I think about sharks . . .

AT SEA

My trip to a resort in Haiti began at New York's La Guardia Airport, two weeks after my fourteenth birthday. All the people going to the resort had congregated around the check-in counter. While waiting around, I met Anna Rivera and Delia Clarke, who would be passengers on the doomed plane, and Delia's daughter, Krista. Anna was concerned about how she could get malaria pills.

I had a great time during my week in Haiti, waterskiing, snorkeling, swimming, and suntanning — things I don't get to do much in New York City. During the week, the Haitians went on strike a number of times to protest against the government. At the end of the week American Airlines, on which we were supposed to fly, canceled all flights to and from Haiti indefinitely because of the political unrest.

The resort gave those of us who were supposed to fly home Saturday a choice: Either stay in the village for free until the airline restored service, or go by chartered airplane to Santo Domingo, in the Dominican Republic, and catch a connecting flight from there. I

by Ariane Randall

wanted to stay since I was having such a good time and there would be a July Fourth celebration, but my father decided that we should get out of the country while we still could. This story proves that all parents should listen to their children.

The next day, July 4, twelve guests gathered to wait for the bus. As it turned out, we wouldn't be leaving for another two hours, so I took the opportunity to sunbathe and go for a last dip in the pool. Finally the bus arrived, and I said good-bye to the friends I'd made.

At the airport the plane never came, due to engine trouble. Finally the resort chartered four small planes, and a few hours later four of us — Delia Clarke, Anna Rivera, my father, and I — boarded the last of them. It was a dinky-looking plane, a Piper Cessna, with only three rows of seats. My father and Anna sat backward in the second row, and Delia and I faced them in the third row. Delia was slim and pretty with short brown hair. She told me she'd lost seventy pounds a few years before. (Later I guessed that kind of will-power helped give her strength after we crashed.) Anna was also nice-looking. She was going home to New York.

WEST INDIES

Atlantic Ocean

CUBA

DOMINICAN REPUBLIC

HAITI

JAMAICA

Port-au-Prince

Santo Domingo

Caribbean Sea

We took off at 8:36 P.M. It was soon after that my dad looked out the window and noticed the stars were all wrong. From the location of the Big Dipper and other stars, he could tell that we were going west, toward Cuba, as opposed to east, toward Santo Domingo. He asked Anna, who spoke Spanish, to ask the pilot why we were going in the wrong direction, but she was reluctant. She didn't want to question authority. I don't know why I didn't use my Spanish to question him myself. The plane was getting cold, but I went to sleep for two hours, during which time, I have been told, we continued going 180 degrees in the wrong direction.

When I woke up, I noticed that we were over water, with no land in sight. The lights on the wings were not functioning properly. They started and stopped — and then stopped altogether. Most of the instruments on the dashboard were not lit up. This was something I hadn't paid too much attention to before but now scared me. The pilot was not getting a response on his radio, and Anna noticed we were running out of gas. The next thing I knew the pilot was saying, "Mayday! Mayday!"[1] into the radio. Anna cried, "We're going to crash!" I started looking desperately for my life jacket behind and under the seat, but I couldn't find it. Anna found hers. Delia did not. The last thing I saw the pilot doing was tossing his life jacket to my father, who gave it to me and then pulled me on his lap. The plane circled three times around an oil tanker and began the swift descent, gliding toward the sea.

We hit the water, and there is a terrible crashing sound as my side of the plane breaks off and water rushes in. I climb out onto the wing. As I stand there I realize my glasses are gone. I fish around in the water and come up with half the frame. I toss it away. The plane is sinking, and my father comes out with the two ladies but no pilot. We swim away from the wreck as the tail disappears beneath the water. Now we are four people and two life jackets in the vast, dark Caribbean Sea. The pilot is nowhere to be seen.

---

[1]**mayday:** an international radio-telephone signal word used by airplanes and ships in trouble.

The water is warm, and we swim together, realizing it's the safe thing to do and it's comforting. I am the least hurt, having received a blow to the head, probably from my dad's chin. He has a gash on his chin and is bleeding heavily (later we found out he'd lost a quart of blood). And he has bruises, especially on his legs. Delia seems to have broken her nose, and there is blood coming from it. She is not in pain, though. Anna has several cuts about her face, a broken arm, and a concussion that has caused partial amnesia. She keeps asking what has happened, and we tell her that the airplane has crashed. She will ask again the next minute.

Anna and I have inflated our life jackets. They have lights on them that shine brightly. We all hold on to each other, mainly so that the two without life jackets can remain afloat but partly for security. I'm wearing boxer shorts, a T-shirt over my new red bikini, and Chinese slippers, which I keep on the whole time. My father's pants and shoes are bogging him down, so he takes them off.

We think we see a boat light, but it soon disappears. I wonder if we will ever be rescued. The thought of floating out here until I die is horrifying. I think about sharks and ask Anna and Delia not to splash about so much because it will attract "the wrong kind of fish." Sharks can smell blood a mile away, and three of us are bleeding. There is a silent agreement not to mention the pilot or sharks.

Pretty soon we are all telling each other how glad we are to be together and how much we love each other. We talk about ourselves. Anna is single (we find out later she has a sister). She works with bilingual children and has a new job waiting for her on Monday. She is worried that her job won't be kept for her if we are not rescued soon. Delia has two boys back in Connecticut, where she works in a real estate office. She's happy that her daughter, Krista, was not on our flight. My father, Francis, a Russian history professor, will be teaching in the fall. I'll be a sophomore in high school, and if I make it back, I'll have the best what-did-you-do-for-your-summer-vacation essay to hit my teachers in a long time.

All of a sudden a light appears. It looks like a boat light, and we are filled with hope. It appears to be coming steadily toward us. Delia is the only one who can really see since both my father and I have lost our glasses and Anna is fading toward unconsciousness. Anna's injuries are so serious I think she's going to die, but she seems to get better as time goes on. After a half hour (I have my waterproof watch on) the boat light starts to fade. If no boat comes, I decide that I'll swim for land in the morning . . . if there's land anywhere in sight.

We think we see another boat light, but it turns out to be the planet Venus. I feel sick and throw up a lot, which makes me feel better. I drift off into something like sleep. Around 4:30 A.M. Delia spots something that looks like land but might be mist. We wait for dawn to be certain.

When dawn comes, we see it is definitely land. We talk about what to do. Delia and Anna cannot swim well, if at all. If we all go at their pace, there is no way we will reach shore by night. We must make a decision: If my father and I swim for shore, it seems likely we'll make it and be able to tell the Coast Guard where to find Anna and Delia. Or my father might be able to find a boat and come back himself, and in the meantime they could continue to swim. The alternative is to stick together and hope for rescue. My father and I think that splitting up will increase our collective chances of survival. Anna and Delia are reluctant — they feel safer in a group — but they acknowledge that splitting up would be better. Anna and Delia have the better life jacket. We separate, not really saying good-bye because we expect to see each other again soon. Even after we swim far away and can't see them, we hear their voices carrying over the waves.

I keep my father posted on the time. Hours pass, and the nearer we get, the more we realize that we still have many miles to cover. We stop every twenty minutes or so for a rest break, during which I float on my back, which is not so hard to do with a life jacket. I'm not feeling very strong, and I hold on to my dad's shirttails and kick or just let him pull me.

It is noon, and we are still a good distance from land. I no longer hear the voices of Delia and Anna. Every now and then my father tells me he loves me a million, trillion times. I say I will tell him how much I love him when we get to land. I'm too tired to speak just now.

It is two o'clock. I have more energy now and a determination to get to land before dark. My dad is getting weaker but still pushes on. I get salt in my mouth all the time, and my tongue is numb from it. It also gets in my eyes, but I have learned to open them quickly afterward, and for some reason this gets rid of the sting. My hair is all matted. We have not had fresh water or food in thirteen hours, but I'm not hungry or thirsty.

It is three o'clock, and I'm starting to hallucinate. I see dolphins, seals, an occasional shark or two, sailboats, and buoys. I say to my dad, "We can do it." And he says, "Yes . . . we can do it." We keep telling each other "I love you" and that we'll make it to shore. I'm guiding my father now, because he keeps his eyes closed most of the time because of the brine[2] and starts to go in the wrong direction unless I correct him. Two pieces of sugarcane float by us, and like the twig brought back to Noah's Ark, they seem like a sign of hope. I think I see palm trees behind me, but they are not really there. At six o'clock we are maybe a mile from shore and feel certain we will make it before nightfall.

But an hour later, with the shore in sight, the sky has become gray with thunderclouds. We think we see thousands of tiny sailboats, and my dad yells for me to swim fast to them. I try hard as the wind blows and it gets stormier. I look back. I can't see my

---

[2]**brine:** water that contains a lot of salt.

dad. "Daddy! Where are you?" I scream. No one answers, and I'm crying for the first time. "Help! Somebody please help! Daddy, where are you?" The rain is coming down hard and fast. I stick my tongue out to see if I can get some. It doesn't work too well. I fight with the waves to keep moving toward land. I ask God why He has put this test before me. I tell Him it won't work: I will come through this with flying colors; I'll ace this test.

When the storm passes, I just want to sleep. The problem is that I then drift with the current, which seems to be going out to sea. Sea snails are biting my legs, but I don't have the strength to brush them off. I don't know what has happened to my father. I try the signal we planned — a high shriek — in case we got separated, but he doesn't answer. I fight to keep awake but slowly drift off.

All the girls I hung out with at the resort are inside my head telling me to swim this way or that. I'm trying to swim toward a hotel, where I can go to sleep. I just want to relax, but I can't because I'll drown. The straps of my life jacket are cutting into me, so I take it off and let it float away. My mouth is burning from the salt — I don't want to die now — if I have to die, can't I at least have a Coke to drink? — something nice-tasting before I drown.

I dream I am destined to drown. Everyone says so, but I'm still trying to find a way out. I dream I inhaled something that burned out my lungs and throat. Then I'm being pulled. I'm being pulled out of the water into a dugout canoe. By two men. Are they capturing me? I must get out. I pick up a piece of wood from the bottom of the boat and try to clobber one of them with it. But he stops me and hits me back.

What a nice way for me to greet my Haitian rescuers — for that's who they were. I saw that they had picked up my dad, too, in another canoe. I heard my dad asking them to start a search for Anna and Delia. The villagers of Bariadelle fed us mangoes and fresh water and crowded around us to watch. They were trying to talk to us in Creole.[3] I could scarcely talk and was confused, but I did manage a *merci beaucoup.*[4]

From Bariadelle we were driven to Dame Marie and deposited in a French Canadian mission station. By this time my body had gone into shock. I had a high fever, a severe sunburn, and a throat infection that made it difficult to swallow anything without coughing. We were taken to a doctor, but by morning my fever was gone. I found out that I'd lost three pounds. (What a crash diet!) My father had lost fifteen. We were driven to a hospital in Anse d'Hainault and eventually, passing through fourteen roadblocks and over sixty miles of bumpy mountain roads, to the city of Jérémie. There my father was able to phone my mother and brother and tell them that we were all right. There was still no news of Anna and Delia.

Back in New York the phone never stops ringing. People call to find out if all this really happened to us. Sometimes I ask myself the same question. But what about Anna and Delia? I think of their voices over the waves as we swam away. What happened to them? What will happen to their families?

It is a miracle my father and I survived. When people ask me what I feel about the whole experience, I say that when you've almost missed life, you see it differently. To be with my family and friends, just to be able to go shopping to replace my lost clothes, each day seems like an amazingly good thing.

Shortly after Ariane Randall and her father were rescued, the U.S. Coast Guard began the search for the two missing women and the pilot. The search continued for three days, but Delia Clarke, Anna Rivera, and the pilot, Elia Katime, were never found.

---

[3]**Creole** (krē′ōl′): a language based on French and the native language of Haiti.
[4]**merci beaucoup:** thank you very much.

Thinking and Discussing

How do the steps that Ariane and her father take help their chances of survival during the emergency at sea?

How does Ariane's attitude toward life and other people change as a result of the plane crash?

Choosing a Creative Response

Thinking Quickly The author describes how she and the other victims of the crash act quickly during the emergency. In a group discussion, identify their good decisions, and then try to come up with other solutions to the problems they face.

Filming an Adventure Imagine that you plan to film "Survival at Sea." List each person in the story, and name the actor you might cast in the role. Explain what qualities the actor and the character share that make your choice a good one.

Creating Your Own Activity Plan and complete your own activity in response to "Survival at Sea."

Thinking and Writing

Ariane describes being rescued by two Haitians in a dugout canoe. If you were one of her rescuers, what would you do and say? How would you feel? Rewrite the event from the rescuer's point of view.

Writing AN EYEWITNESS M·E·M·O·I·R

As you read the selections in "Spirit of Survival," think of a true-life adventure that you have witnessed or have followed closely in the news. Write an eyewitness memoir in which you recall the details of this time when people were faced with a desperate situation. Include your impressions of the way the victims responded to the crisis, and present alternatives to the ways in which they dealt with their problems. If you have another idea, write about that one instead.

1. *Prewriting*

   Before you begin writing your eyewitness memoir, recall all the details of the adventure about which you are writing. Who were the participants? What was the setting? What made the situation adventurous?

   2. *Write a First Draft*

   Write a first draft, trying to write your ideas as quickly as you can. Do not worry about spelling, punctuation, or correct sentences now. Let your ideas flow as you describe the setting, make your characters come alive, and bring the plot to a gripping climax so your readers will appreciate the adventure of your memoir.

3.   *Revise*

Read your first draft to a partner, and answer the following questions. Do the characters, plot, and dialogue capture the adventure as it really happened? Is the memoir exciting? Is it suspenseful? Listen to your partner's comments, discuss them, and make any necessary changes.

4.   *Proofread*

Reread your adventurous eyewitness memoir carefully, correcting any errors in spelling, grammar, capitalization, and punctuation, using proofreading marks. You may want to exchange stories with your partner to see if you can spot any errors in each other's work.

5.   *Publish*

Make a neat copy of your memoir. Decide how you want to share the memoir with your classmates. You may want to tape-record it, using exciting sound effects. Allow others to experience the adventure.

THE

from *Call It Courage* by Armstrong Sperry

When Mafatu was only three, he and his mother were
caught in a great hurricane that swept through Hikueru, his
home island. Ever since, the memory of his mother's loss to the
fury of the merciless sea has filled him with terror.

Now, the other boys and girls laugh at him and call him
the Boy Who Was Afraid. His father's silence shames him. His
only friends are the yellow dog Uri and an albatross he has
befriended and named Kivi.

When the boys mock him and call him coward,
he realizes what he must do: He must prove his
courage to himself and to others. He must face
Moana, the sea god, and he must
conquer his fear.

SEA

ay broke over a gray and dismal world. The canoe lifted and fell idly on the glassy swells. Mafatu looked back over his shoulder, searching the horizon for a last glimpse of Hikueru; but the atoll[1] had vanished, as if to hide itself forever from his concern.

The matting sail slatted uselessly. But there seemed to be no need of a sail: the little canoe was riding one of the mysterious ocean currents that flow in their courses through the length and breadth of the Pacific: the *Ara Moana*, Paths of the Sea, as the Ancients called them. They were the ocean currents that had carried the Polynesian navigators from island to island in the childhood of the world. Mafatu was drifting farther and farther away from his homeland.

With wide-flapping wings Kivi rose from the bow of the canoe. In ascending spirals the bird climbed higher and higher, until at last he was no more than a gray speck against the lighter gray of the sky. Mafatu watched his albatross disappear and felt a desolation flood his heart. Now there was only Uri to keep him company in this hostile world of sky and sea. Uri. . . .

[1]**atoll** (ăt′ôl′): an island formed by coral.

The yellow dog lay curled up in the shadow of the bow, opening one eye from time to time to look at his master. Wherever Mafatu went, Uri, too, would go.

All around, as far as the eye could reach, were wastes of leaden water. The canoe was the moving center of a limitless circle of sea. The boy shuddered. His fingers gripped the paddle convulsively. He thought of Kana and the other boys — what would they say when they learned that he had disappeared? And Tavana Nui — would there be sorrow in his father's heart? Would he believe that Moana, the Sea God, had claimed his son at last?

It was an ominous, oppressive world at this season of storm. Half a mile distant a whale heaved its varnished hulk to the surface, to throw a jet of vapory mist high into the air; then it submerged, leaving scarcely a ripple to mark its passage. A shoal of flying fishes broke water, skimming away in a silver shimmer of flight. A dolphin sped after them, smooth-rolling in pursuit, so close that the boy could hear the sound of its breathing. This world of the sea was ruled by Nature's harsh law of survival. Mafatu knew the sea with an intimacy given to few. He had seen fleets of giant mantas whipping the lagoon of Hikueru to a boiling fury; he had seen the mighty cachalot[2] set

upon by killer-whales and torn to ribbons almost in the blink of an eye; once he had seen an octopus as large as the trunk of a tamanu,[3] with tentacles thirty feet long, rise from the mile-deep water beyond the barrier reef. . . . *Ai*, this sea!

Mafatu opened one of the green drinking nuts and tilted back his head to let the cool liquid trickle down his parched throat; more

---

[2]**cachalot** (kăsh′ə lŏt′): the sperm whale.
[3]**tamanu**: a large East Indian tree.

refreshing than spring water, cool on the hottest days, and as sustaining as food. The boy scooped out the gelatinous meat for Uri and the dog ate it gratefully.

The ocean current which held the canoe in its grip seemed to have quickened. There was a wind rising, too, in little puffs and gusts. Now the canoe heeled over under the sudden attack, while Mafatu scrambled onto the outrigger to lend his weight for ballast; then the wind dropped as suddenly as it appeared, while the canoe righted itself and the boy breathed freely once again. He searched the skies for Kivi. His albatross might have been one of a thousand sea birds flying against the roof of the sky, or he might have vanished utterly, leaving his friends here in solitary space. The bird had led Mafatu out through the reef-passage at Hikueru into the open ocean, and now, it seemed, had deserted him.

A storm was making, moving in out of those mysterious belts which lie north and south of the equator, the home of hurricanes. The wind shifted a point, bringing with it a heavy squall. Mafatu lowered the sail on the run and gripped the steering paddle with hands that showed white at the knuckles. All around him now was a world of tumbling water, gray in the hollows, greenish on the slopes. The wind tore off the combing crests and flung the spray at the sky. Like advance scouts of an oncoming army, wind gusts moved down upon the canoe, struck at it savagely. So busy was Mafatu with the paddle that there was no time for thought. He called a prayer to Maui, God of the Fishermen:

"Maui é! E matai tu!"

Somehow the sound of his own voice reassured him. Uri lifted his head, cocked his ears, thumped his tail for a second. The canoe rose to the swells as lightly as a gull and coasted like a sled down the frothing slopes. What skill had wrought this small canoe! This dugout, hewn from the mighty tamanu tree. It swooped and yielded, bucked and scudded, one with the fierce element whose back it rode.

The sky darkened. A burst of lightning lit up the sea with supernatural brilliance. An instantaneous crack of thunder shattered the world. Lightning again, striking at the hissing water. Mafatu watched it with fascinated eyes. Now it was all about him. It ran to the end of the boom in globes of fire that exploded and vanished, and in the awful moment of its being it revealed mountain shapes of dark water, heaving, shouldering. . . . How long could this frail craft of wood and sennit resist? Under the combined attack of wind and sea it seemed that something must inevitably give way. The wind shrilled a fiercer note. Spray stung the boy's flesh, blinded his eyes, chilled his marrow.

The sail went first — with a split and a roar. Fragments swept off on the back of the wind. The cords that held the mast hummed like plucked wires. Then with a rending groan the mast cracked. Before Mafatu could leap to cut it clear, it snapped off and disappeared in a churn of black water. The boy clung to the paddle, fighting to keep his canoe from turning broadside. Water swept aboard and out again. Only the buoyancy of tamanu kept the craft afloat. Uri cowered in the bow, half submerged, his howls drowned by the roar of the elements. Mafatu gripped his paddle for very life, an unreasoning terror powering his arms. This sea that he had always feared was rising to claim him, just as it had claimed his mother. How rightly he had feared it! Moana, the Sea God, had been biding his time. . . . "Someday, Mafatu, I will claim you!"

The boy lost all sense of time's passage. Every nerve became dulled by tumult. The wind howled above his head and still Mafatu clung to the lashed steering paddle; clung fast long after strength had vanished and only the will to live locked his strong fingers about the shaft. Even death would not loose the grip of those fingers. He held his little craft true to the wind.

There was a wave lifting before the canoe. Many the boy had seen, but this was a giant — a monster livid and hungry. Higher,

higher it rose, until it seemed that it must scrape at the low-hanging clouds. Its crest heaved over with a vast sigh. The boy saw it coming. He tried to cry out. No sound issued from his throat. Suddenly the wave was upon him. Down it crashed. *Chaos!* Mafatu felt the paddle torn from his hands. Thunder in his ears. Water strangling him. Terror in his soul. The canoe slewed round into the trough. The boy flung himself forward, wound his arms about the mid-thwart.[4] It was the end of a world.

The wave passed. Stunned, gasping, Mafatu raised his head and looked about. For a second he could not believe that he still breathed and had being. He saw Uri wedged under the bow, choking for air. He pulled the dog free. Then he saw that his string of drinking nuts had vanished. His fish spear was gone. The knife that hung about his neck by a twist of bark had been torn away. Even his *pareu* of fiber tapa fell from his body as water soaked it through. He was naked, defenseless, without food or weapon, hurled forward on the breath of the hurricane. Numb of all feeling, empty as a shell, still he clung to life, and the hours droned by. . . .

So gradual was the storm's easing that at first the boy was unaware of it. The wind was blowing itself out, moving off into the empty spaces of the world. Uri crept toward the prostrate boy, quailing beside him, whimpering softly.

Night came and passed.

There was no morning mist to dim the splendor of the sunburst across the swinging seas. Far away the wings of an albatross caught its gold as it wheeled and planed against the roof of heaven. The only hint of recent storm lay in the rough and tumbling waters. As the sun climbed through the hot hours of morning, it burned into the boy's body like the sacred fires of the great marae of Hikueru. Mafatu's skin blistered and cracked. His tongue swelled

---

[4]**mid-thwart** (mĭd′thwôrt): the middle of a board forming a seat, or **thwart**, across a boat.

in his throat. He tried to call out a prayer to Maui, but his voice was thick; the sounds which came forth were no more than a hoarse cry. The canoe, stripped of sail and mast, without a paddle to guide it in the swift-racing current, twisted and shifted in the rushing waters.

As one hour merged into another there came moments of fitful, choking slumber, a growing agony of thirst for the boy and his dog. The sun burned into them like an inescapable eye. The current which held Mafatu's canoe fast in its grip was bearing it swiftly on toward its mysterious destination.

And thus the day passed, while night once more descended, bringing blessed release from the sun.

Now the air was luminous with promise of another day. Out of the sultry mists the sea emerged, blue and violent. With the coming of this new day terror raised its head. Mafatu tried to fight it back, to deny its existence; but it gripped his heart with clammy fingers, tightened his throat. He flung himself flat on the floor of the canoe and buried his face in his arms. He must have cried out then. His voice was but a hoarse croak, yet it stirred Uri to life: the dog's ragged tail gave one feeble thump. With the ghost of a whimper the animal laid his hot nose against the boy's hand.

The brave thump of his dog's tail touched Mafatu profoundly. He caught the animal to him, while a new assurance, a new strength, flooded his being. If Uri could have courage to die, surely he, Mafatu, could not do less! In that instant he heard a whir and fury in the sky above, a beat of wide wings. . . . Looking upward, the boy's dulled eyes made out the widespread wings of an albatross, circling above the canoe.

"Kivi!" Mafatu cried hoarsely. "*Ai*, Kivi!"

Even as he spoke, the bird wheeled slowly, then flew off straight ahead for the distant horizon. The boy noticed then that the sea current was carrying him almost due southwest. Kivi's flight moved in exact parallel. Once more it seemed as if his albatross were leading him onward, just as he had led the canoe out of the passage of Hikueru.

Mafatu scanned the rim of the horizon; it looked as hard as the cut edge of a stone. But suddenly the boy's heart gave a great leap and he started forward. *It couldn't be!* It was a cloud. . . . But the sky was cloudless. Far off in the sea-shimmer lay something that was neither sea nor sky. The swells, lifting higher, now revealed, now concealed it. That shadow on the horizon — it was land! The boy flung himself forward, shaking uncontrollably.

He seized Uri in his arms and lifted him up, laughing, crying: "Uri! Uri! It's land. *Land!*"

The dog sniffed at the air and a little whimper broke from him.

What island could this be? Was it Tahiti, the golden island, whose language was akin to that of Hikueru? Or was it, perhaps, one of the terrible dark islands of the eaters-of-men?

Now the current had a westward drift, and it was to the west that the dark islands lay. . . .

All day, as the canoe drifted onward, the boy watched the distant shadow-shape of land, not daring to take his eyes from it lest it vanish into the sea. Hunger and thirst were lulled into forgetfulness. There was only this one reality, land — escape from the sea. Weak as he was, he still clung to the thwart, his lips whispering a silent prayer of gratitude. With waning afternoon, the island took more distinct form as the canoe drifted nearer. It was high and peaked, its valleys blue-shadowed against the paler tone of the sky. Hour by hour, with every lift of the swells, the island rose higher and higher, filling Mafatu's soul with wonder. Hikueru, the only land he had ever seen, was as flat as his hand; but a great single peak crowned this strange island. Trees rose green and fair, tier upon tier of them, from the shoreline into the foothills of the purple mountain. Uri had caught the scent of the land now and was quivering with delight.

Then from far off came the first muffled thunder of the reef: the boom of the surf high-bursting on the barrier coral. That sound — was it the voice of Moana? "Someday, Mafatu, someday." . . . Involuntarily the boy shuddered. Would his ears never be free of the Sea God's threat?

Mafatu was powerless to guide his craft. He sensed that the current had quickened. He could only watch helplessly as the little canoe, swift as the following gulls, rushed to meet the tides of the island where they met and churned in a cross sea of conflict. Now across the swells came a sound like a chorus of ghostly fishermen weary with their day's toil: sea birds, always complaining, never at rest; while softer, yet rising above it was another sound — the voice of the reef itself, quieting with sundown, like the reassuring hush of a mother to her child.

Night stole up from the face of the sea, enveloping the world. There was no moon, but the black sky was spangled with unguessed millions of stars: other worlds, other suns. To the watching boy, with land in the offing, they seemed closer and more friendly. The bottom star of the Southern Cross[5] pointed to the end of the world. . . . A soft land breeze, heavy with a scent of flowers, wafted out across the dark waters, tantalizing, bitter-sweet.

Weak with thirst, the boy drifted now into a merciful sleep. He struggled against it, like a weary swimmer fighting a rip-tide, but his head drooped and his eyes closed.

He was aroused at midnight by a thunderous tumult in his ears. Of a sudden he felt the canoe under him lifted and flung high into the air. Then down it crashed into splinters upon the reef. Boy and dog were hurled headlong into the boiling surf.

---

[5]**Southern Cross:** four bright stars arranged like a cross, visible in the Southern Hemisphere.

The shock of cold water brought Mafatu half back to consciousness. Blindly he struck out, fighting for survival. Uri — where was he? No sign of the dog. The boy was aware that the canoe must have been flung over the barrier-reef, for here the water was scarcely troubled by wind or tide. Now he was swimming, swimming. . . . Somewhere ahead a strip of beach, salt-white in the darkness, lured him onward. His muscles did it of themselves. Only a will to live. A strip of sand white in the night. . . . He caught the gleam of a shark's belly, close at hand, but on he swam. His unhampered limbs moved freely through the water.

Of a sudden there was something solid beneath his feet. Sand. Mafatu stumbled, staggered, fell to his knees in the shallows. His lips moved in dry, soundless speech. Lying there with the water rippling and breaking over him, he pulled himself half upright, swayed onward. The palms, trooping to the edge of the beach, were motionless in the night air. All the world seemed to hold its breath as this boy climbed up out of the sea.

He fell to the sand once more, then, guided by he knew not what impulse, he dragged himself to the edge of the jungle. A murmur of water reached his ears, soft as a chuckle of pleasant laughter. Water, sweet water. . . . Down the face of an age-worn rock a small cascade lost itself amid ferns and cool mosses. A ragged, strangling cry broke from Mafatu's throat. He stood upright to full height. Then he crashed to the mossy bank. One cheek lay in the cool water.

The moon lifted above the rim of the palms. It outlined in silver the form of a boy thin with hunger, naked as the daystar. It revealed a small wet dog, dragging himself across the beach to his master's side.

Mafatu lay without moving. Before Uri drank, he touched the boy's cheek with his hot muzzle.

MAFATU'S WORLD

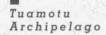

Tuamotu
Archipelago

The name of Mafatu's world, Polynesia, means "many islands." This huge area of the Pacific Ocean includes thousands of small islands. The island where Mafatu lived, Hikueru, is in the Tuamotu archipelago, or group of islands.

Mafatu's canoe was carved from the trunk of the tamanu tree. It included a single-hulled body that was balanced by a wooden outrigger, or float. Mafatu could safely sail in it from island to island if the distance was not too great.

Early Polynesians like Mafatu also made long sea voyages by canoe to explore and settle their part of the Pacific. For these ocean-going trips, they used double-hulled canoes, two hulls with a wooden framework connecting them. They often built a shelter on this framework for passengers and animals. With their knowledge of the special patterns of the winds, waves, clouds, and stars, the Polynesians were able to find their way across the trackless ocean.

Thinking and Discussing

How do Mafatu's feelings change as the storm increases and then dies down again? Why do you think the author describes these changes in the sea to dramatize Mafatu's fears? Do you think it is an effective device? Why or why not?

What does Mafatu learn about himself as a result of his struggle with the sea? Do you think he conquers the sea? Explain your answers.

Choosing a Creative Response

Reading Dramatically The author uses vivid words and images to make Mafatu's experience in the storm seem real and dramatic. Choose a passage describing what Mafatu sees and hears. Practice reading the passage aloud, and then read it to the class. Try to express the excitement of the passage by using gestures and varying your tone of voice. To add to your dramatic reading, you may want to prepare a tape recording of sounds of the sea as well as other sounds suggested by the passage.

Creating Your Own Activity Plan and complete your own activity in response to "The Sea."

Exploring Language

In "The Sea," the author compares the sound of sea birds to "a chorus of ghostly fishermen" and says that Mafatu feels "empty as a shell." How do these comparisons improve the story? Find and list other comparisons used in the story. Then create some comparisons of your own for these story phrases.

Yet human beings battled on. They refused to give in. They struggled and improvised. That was one of the most enduring things about them.

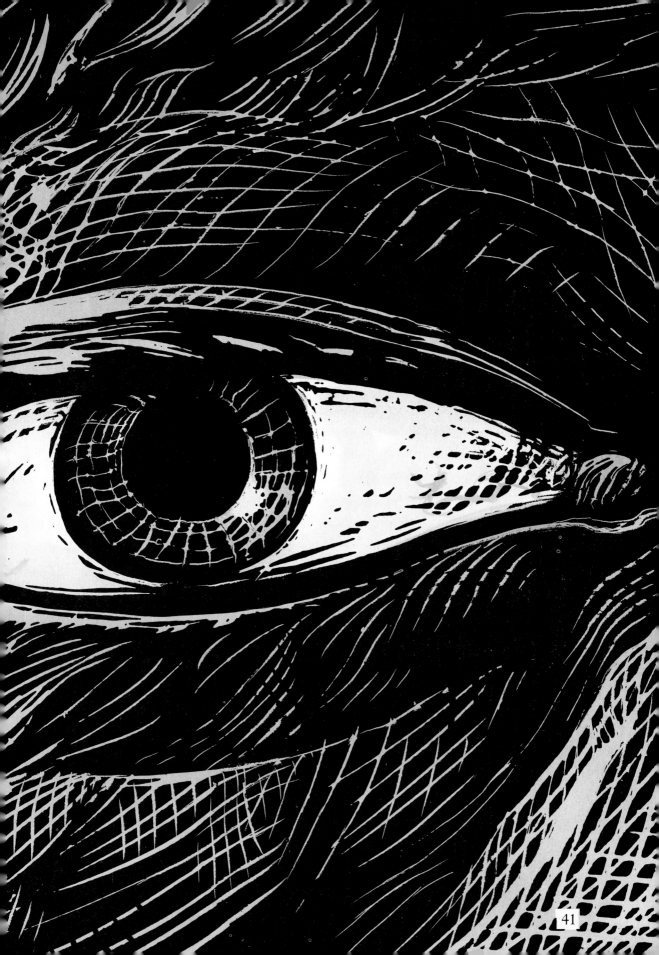

AUSTRALIA

Twelve-year-old Joe has come to live with his cousin Meg Blake and her family in tiny Cockle Bay, on the coast of South Australia. Joe and Meg are excited at the chance to go to Wayward Island with Meg's father, Uncle Harry, to round up his sheep.

SHADOW

A mile from Wayward Island, the boat runs out of gas. When Uncle Harry refuels, the gasoline explodes. The three make it to the island in a life raft, but Uncle Harry is badly burned and may die unless he gets to a hospital. Meg injures an eye.

In three or four more days, someone from Cockle Bay might realize that the three are in trouble. However, that may not be soon enough for Uncle Harry's survival.

by Colin Thiele   illustrated by Bill Russell

Meg, Joe admitted, was far ahead of him in her thinking. By the time the sun was about to set, they had finished most of their jobs. There was a heap of firewood near the door — most of it from old posts and rails — and an S.O.S. sign in letters ten feet wide on the grass nearby. A distress flag was fluttering from a pole on the chimney. They had brought in the clothes from the line and were drying them out finally in front of the fire.

Meg had dragged a bunk into the kitchen, saying that she would sleep there all night so that she could be near her father. Joe could use the spare room. Then they boiled water in the kettle and made some tea, ladling out a precious dash of condensed milk into each mug. Normally Joe hated tea, but when there was nothing else to eat or drink, it had a wonderful mental effect. It somehow persuaded his stomach that it was having its hot evening meal. So

SHARK

he cupped his hands around the mug to share its warmth, blew on it briskly and unnecessarily, and sipped slowly to prolong the drink as long as he could.

Meg took the third mug and walked quietly into the next room with it. "A cup of tea, Dad?" She asked softly.

Her father looked up. "That you, my girl?" he croaked.

"I've brought you some tea."

He frowned and tried to focus his gaze on her. "Your face," he said. "What on earth have you done to your face?"

"The explosion, Dad, remember?"

He seemed to be disoriented, his mind out of kilter. She wondered if he was really only half conscious.

"Would you like a cup of tea?"

She sat on the bedside and tried to hold the cup to his swollen lips. He sipped and coughed and sipped again. Before long he pushed it aside. "Hurts my mouth," he said. She brought in two more painkilling tablets from the kitchen and watched while he swallowed them slowly with a bit more tea.

"It hurts, doesn't it?" she asked. "Bad?"

"Burns are bad."

"Maybe the painkillers will help."

"Maybe."

"Try to rest."

She got up and tiptoed out of the room again. Joe watched her as she sat down beside the fire. She was crying so softly that for a minute he wasn't even aware of it until he saw her shoulders shake and heard a sob. "Meg," he said, "why don't you lie down for a while?"

She looked up, her back hunched in misery. "We've got to get help, Joe," she said. "Dad's really bad, and he's going to get worse. We've just got to get help."

Joe had never felt so helpless. "What can we do? Nothing. Nothing except wait until your mom or Andy Jones gets worried and sends someone over. And that won't be until Thursday or Friday."

"That'll be too late."

They stared at one another despairingly. "If only we had a radio," Joe said. "Or even a signal of some sort — a rocket."

Meg sat forward suddenly. "A signal. Joe, you're a genius."

Although he felt pleased at her praise, he was still nonplussed. "But we haven't got a signal."

"We'll make one."

"How?"

"With the lamp and a box."

Joe couldn't picture what she was talking about.

"And a shutter," she said.

"A what?"

"A shutter of some kind. We'll make an Aldis lamp."[1]

At last he began to understand. He knew what an Aldis lamp was and he had read stories about their use on warships.

"Moses," he said. "D'you think it would work?"

"We'll make it work."

She stood up and started rummaging around, peering into every corner with her one eye like a shortsighted terrier. There were no suitable boxes or cans, but in the end she found a strong carton with the top cut on three sides so that it swung like a hinged lid. "This'll do," she said. "The lid'll be the shutter."

"You're ahead of me," he said. "How the heck is that going to work?"

She was impatient. "Like this." She seized the carton and let it lie on its side. "You stand the lamp in it when it's lying in this position. Then you just lift up the lid to let the light shine out and swing it down to cut it off again."

"I'm starting to see the light."

She jerked her head in disgust at his pun. "Lord save us."

"A blinking light will be better than a steady one."

"Of course. It'll blink out S.O.S."

He looked at her in astonishment. "S.O.S.?"

"Yes, you jerk. In Morse."

"Morse?"

"Sure. Morse code."

---

[1] **Aldis lamp:** a hand-carried signal lamp used to flash messages, especially from ships and aircraft.

"How do you do that?"

"With three dots, three dashes, and three dots. Like this." She tapped on the table with the handle of a knife, calling the code as she did so. "Dot-dot-dot, dash-dash-dash, dot-dot-dot."

He was impressed. "I didn't know that."

"Well, you do now."

"And it's the same with a light — short flashes and long flashes?"

"Sure." She turned the carton toward him and swung the lid up and down three times as quickly as she could. "Dot-dot-dot. Just like that. Then three slower swings so that the light shines out a bit longer each time for the dashes, and last of all three more short flashes for the final dots."

"How did you learn all that?"

"All what?"

"This stuff about Aldis lamps and Morse code?"

She shrugged. "Everybody here knows that. All the skippers have to — in case their radios fail. You don't think Dad would have taken me out on his boat if I couldn't even send an S.O.S.? You can do it with a flashlight."

He eyed the box approvingly. "I reckon it would work — as long as there was someone out there to see it."

She agreed. "That's the catch. This lamp won't shine very far."

"We could turn it up really high — the wick, I mean."

She shook her head. "No, it'll smoke like mad and use up too much kerosene. You'll blacken the glass and then it won't shine at all."

Joe sighed. "Then we need a reflector — a mirror or something."

She glanced at him admiringly. "Sometimes you're brilliant, Joe. That's a marvelous idea."

She went over and took down the old mirror that was hanging from a hook near the kitchen door. It was the only one in the place except for a tarnished piece fixed onto the door of the bedroom wardrobe.

"That's too big," Joe said. "It'll never fit into the box."

They measured it roughly. It was just the right width but twice as long as it should have been.

"We'll have to break it in half," Meg said.

Joe scoffed. "If you hit it with a hammer or something, you'll smash it into a million bits."

She grinned. "Don't try to teach your cousin to suck eggs." She took a piece of string, dipped it in the fuel tank of the lamp, and tied it neatly around the middle of the mirror. Then she struck a match and lit the kerosene-soaked string. It flared up all around in a smoky flame for a minute or two and finally fell away in strands of ash. As the last bit of flame petered out, Meg lifted the mirror and plunged it into the tub of cold rinsing water that stood by the door. The glass broke neatly in halves.

Joe was astonished. "Gosh, Meg, how did you get to know a thing like that?"

She grunted as she polished one of the pieces with a rag and fitted it into the box. "That's an old country trick. We use it to take the tops off bottles so that we can use them for pickles and home-made jam."

Next she polished the lamp glass until it gleamed in the fire-light, and then cut a small hole in the carton above the spot where the lamp was going to stand, so that the smoke and fumes could escape. Last of all she lit the wick and pushed the lamp into position.

"There," she said, swinging the lid up and down. "That's the Special Patent Blake Signaling Lamp."

"It works," he said enthusiastically. "It looks exactly as if the light is blinking on and off. The mirror really makes it flash."

"Good. It ought to be visible for a few miles, don't you think?" She pulled the lamp forward and blew out the flame.

"Farther than that."

"It would be better still if the land here weren't so low. Even the knoll behind the house is nothing but a pimple."

"Yes, it needs higher ground."

"A lot higher. Like a beacon."

He turned toward her suddenly. "What about the headland — Black Bluff? They could almost see it from the mainland then, I reckon."

"That would be perfect — like a little lighthouse. But who's going to go up there in the middle of the night?"

"I will."

As soon as he had said it, he regretted opening his mouth. What on earth was he saying? Who in his right mind would want to go up to the edge of those fearful cliffs in the cold and dark, trying to flash a pitiful little signal into the night? Yet once he had committed himself, he couldn't renege. He very much wanted Meg to think well of him, but if he went back on his word, she would think he was a coward and a fool.

She turned toward him in amazement. "Will you? Really?"

He gulped. "Sure."

She sensed his dread. "It'll be cold and lonely up there, Joe — and dangerous. We can take turns if you like."

"No," he said, desperately defending his pride, "you have to stay here. You have to be with your father."

She glanced quickly at the door of the bedroom. "Yes, I'd better. He should really be having plenty of fluid, and I think he should be exercising his arms and legs every so often."

"How do you know that?"

"I read it somewhere. He should be in the hospital having drips and injections and things."

"For the burns?"

"Yes." She hesitated and then asked a curious question. "Joe, how much of Dad's skin do you think has been burned?"

"What do you mean?"

"What percentage of it?"

"Not much." He thought for a minute. "His face, neck, hands, some on his legs, and a bit on his chest and shoulders. His pants and heavy jacket shielded the rest."

"How much?"

"Ten or fifteen percent."

She seemed relieved. "Are you sure?"

"It wouldn't be any more than that. Probably less. Why?"

"Because if it were thirty or forty percent he would probably die."

Joe looked away. "It's not as much as that, nothing like it." He thought for a moment and added a new thought. "I reckon the burns are not very deep either — just on the surface. He was pitched into the water so fast that he didn't have time to be badly burned."

She put some more wood on the fire to give more light. "I hope you're right, Joe."

He went over to the box with the lamp in it. "You stay with him. I'll go up to the headland."

He practiced flipping the lid up and down. "Dot-dot-dot, dash-dash-dash, dot-dot-dot. Is that about right?"

She smiled. "That'll do. It doesn't matter if it's a bit ragged. If you keep repeating it often enough, any ship that sees it is sure to get the message."

"What'll they do then? Radio?"

"If it's a local boat, they'll let Cockle Bay know, and if it's a big cargo ship they'll radio Adelaide or Melbourne and let them know there's a distress signal on Wayward Island. They'll relay it on."

She picked up his dry clothes from the bunk by the fire. "Here, put these on. You'd better take my coat too, as well as your own, and I'll get you the old blanket from the spare bed. It'll be as cold as an iceberg up there on the bluff."

He went to blunder off into the other room but suddenly realized that it was darker than pitch and there were no lights. She lit the candle from a burning sliver in the fireplace and went to get the blanket. When she returned, she filled a glass with water and carried it toward her father's room. "I'll give Dad a drink. You can change in here."

He was grateful for the warmth as he changed hastily, piling on as much warm clothing as he could — jeans, shirt, sweater, two coats, and the old overalls on top of everything else. They almost fitted him now, filled out by the things underneath. She came back just as he finished struggling with the straps. Then he worked the blanket into a long roll and hung it around his neck like an enormous scarf.

"Ready?"

"Yes."

She picked up two boxes of matches and handed them to him. "Keep these in your pocket. The wind'll blow out the lamp a dozen times before you've finished."

"Thanks," he said wryly.

"Do you know the way?"

"I hope so."

"Go up past the drafting yards, across the pasture paddock for a mile or so, over the little humps, down into the dip by the water troughs, and up the slope the way we always go to the top of the headland."

"I think I can manage it."

"There's not much moonlight, so you'll have to watch your step."

"I'll try."

50

"Whatever you do, don't go too far to the right. There are loose stones on the slope there right down to the edge of the cliffs."

He picked up the carton and the lamp. "Wish me luck."

She came over and put her hand on his arm, looking at him intently with her seeing eye. "Be careful, Joe," she said earnestly. "Please be careful."

He felt buoyed up, warmed by her concern. "You bet."

"Don't stay too long."

"Just long enough for someone to get the message."

"I'll wait up for you. I'll go in and sit with Dad."

He lumbered out of the door into the night, where the darkness enveloped him as if he had suddenly walked into a vast black cave.

Joe now started out on his own personal Calvary. His heart quailed as he stumbled up past the sheep pens in the gloom, straining desperately to see even the most obvious things. Although his eyes adjusted slowly to the darkness, it was still impossible to walk with certainty. His feet struck unseen stones or clumps of grass or stepped unexpectedly into ruts and holes, so he constantly jolted his spine and kinked his neck.

Clutching the box and lamp, he developed a shambling, shuffling walk in self-protection. All around him the landscape of the night was strange and frightening. Nothing seemed familiar anymore. The daytime paddocks were seas of darkness, the hollows were black and edgeless gulfs, the knolls and headlands were vague humps against the faint starlight of the sky.

He wondered how he could possibly have thought the island was beautiful. It now seemed a savage place, aloof and malicious. Several times he was on the point of turning back, convincing himself that it was too dark, too threatening, too dangerous. But the fear that Meg would call him a coward, and the knowledge that her father was lying there in agony waiting to be rescued, drove him on.

He finally negotiated the pasture paddock, stumbled through the dips and hummocks beyond it, and descended toward the hollow where the spring-fed water ran.

"Be careful down there," Meg had said. "Don't get bogged, and don't fall into the sunken troughs. It might be better if you crossed farther up."

But where was farther up? He was getting confused. The low-lying ground was darker than dark, and the starlight was too faint to guide him. He hoped there were no open wells or patches of quicksand near the springs, or he would most likely take his last step and disappear from the earth forever.

It was the Black Bluff itself that saved him from disaster. He saw its silhouette against the sky and recognized the long slope of the shoulder that he and Meg had climbed before. It gave him a sense of direction. He was able to veer upstream, cross the hollow safely, and move onto higher ground.

And so at last, straining and panting, he neared the top of the headland — a boy shrunk to a speck in that vast primordial landscape, crawling like a black mite up the side of the sky. As he reached the summit, the wind seized him, buffeting his body and clutching at his clothes. The sound of the sea seemed frighteningly near, crashing at his feet, but he knew that it was really far beneath him at the bottom of the hideous gulf of darkness nearby.

He put down the carton with the lamp in it and fumbled in his pocket for the matches. Then, crouching protectively on knees and

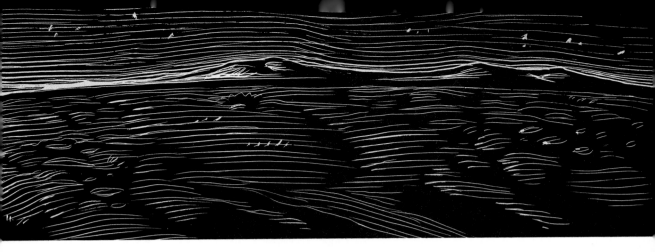

elbows, he lifted up the cardboard flap and struck a light. It was blown out in an instant. Twice more he tried, and twice more it had gone before it had even flared. Panic swept him — a fear that despite the agony of his journey he would fail to send a signal after all.

He took the rolled-up blanket that was coiled around his neck, draped it over the carton like a tiny pup tent, and crawled under it with his head and shoulders. There, after a good deal of groping and fumbling, he was able to strike another match and hold the flame against the wick long enough for it to catch. Then he hastily lowered the glass chimney and imprisoned the flame in calm and safety. Success. Elation. He positioned the lamp carefully under the vent that Meg had cut in the cardboard and pointed the mouth of the box vaguely toward the wide strait that separated Wayward Island from the mainland. The Special Patent Blake Signaling Lamp was ready to begin.

Lying on his left elbow, he took the hinged lid in his right hand and raised and lowered it quickly three times to give three short flashes. Dot-dot-dot. He paused momentarily and then raised the lid more slowly three times to give three longer flashes. Dash-dash-dash. Another brief pause and finally three more short flashes. Dot-dot-dot. He had sent out one complete S.O.S.

After a few minutes he decided that he should be counting the number of distress signals he was sending. He began to do so aloud, mumbling to himself rhythmically: "Dot-dot-dot, dash-dash-dash, dot-dot-dot. One. Dot-dot-dot, dash-dash-dash, dot-dot-dot. Two . . ." When he had counted up to ten he paused to wrap the blanket around his shoulders more closely, shielding his ears and the back of his head from the icy bite of the wind. After another ten he changed the angle of the carton, arguing that its position would be critical to a moving boat because the crew would be in a direct line of sight with it for only a short while.

By the time he had counted to a hundred he was numb. His right arm was aching and his body was shriveled with cold. The wind seemed to have rubbed his cheeks as smooth as polished pebbles. He stood up, stretched his cramped limbs, and peered down at the lamp through the open vent. It was still burning brightly, but he had no idea how long the kerosene was going to last, especially as the tank had been less than half full to start with. The thought made him uneasy and strangely afraid.

He rubbed his hands and cheeks, blew on his fingers, and crouched down to begin another cycle. He calculated that if he allowed a pause of five or ten seconds after each complete S.O.S., he could send out four signals a minute, or twenty in five minutes. A hundred would take him almost half an hour.

As he worked he kept changing the direction in which the mouth of the carton pointed. It was like varying the aim of a gun. He tried to guess the position of Cockle Bay so that he could point toward it, but then he told himself not to be stupid. It would have needed a lighthouse beam of a million candlepower to reach the mainland. What could he expect of a stable lamp in a cardboard box?

As the cold ate into his bones, he found it harder and harder to keep going. He had to set himself shorter goals — at first twenty signals followed by a rest to rub himself warm, then ten, and finally only five. But he finished another cycle of a hundred at last and sat hunched in his blanket, crouching low like a wounded animal in a makeshift hide. His lacerated finger where he had torn the nail from the quick in his desperate struggle to open the life-raft locker was hurting terribly in the cold — a fierce pulsing pain like a hot skewer being driven regularly under the nail.

He began to feel the hopelessness of everything. What was the use? Who was ever likely to see a pitiful little wink of light in that endless wilderness of ocean? In a fit of anger he seized the box and pointed it toward the west, toward the void of the Great Bight, and sent off his message like a plaintive cry. S.O.S., it went. S.O.S., S.O.S., S.O.S. With a sob he turned it wildly to the south and flashed his plea toward the wastes of Antarctica, and then north again toward the Australian mainland.

In his mind's eye he began to have dreams of rescue, visions of great ships coming into sight, liners lit up in the night, all signaling back urgently to him. He couldn't read their Morse, but that was unimportant. The message was always clear: His distress signal had been seen and help was on the way.

But then the reality of his plight came back to him — the cold and the helplessness, the pain and loneliness. In his despair he couldn't even remember whether he was sending out the right message, whether perhaps it should have been three dashes first and three dots in the middle. A fierce gust of wind suddenly whipped over the crest of the bluff and almost overturned the carton, lamp and all. The flame fluttered madly as if in panic. Joe dragged his possessions back a few yards down the slope, to the shelter of a rock he had glimpsed in the beam of light. It was no bigger than a sheep, but it gave him some protection. Once there he lay down in the blanket with his arm around the carton, waiting and thinking.

He decided that he would have to stay for at least one more cycle of a hundred signals. Who could know how near or how far a rescue vessel might be? A container ship or a tanker could be coming from the west at this very moment, just over the horizon, with the crew vigilant and the lookout alert. A tuna clipper could be heading for home after its last trip for the season, or a fishing boat making for Cockle Bay with Stewy Sampson or Tiny Mazerakis[2] at the helm. Any one of them might catch a glimpse of that winking light high on the top of Black Bluff and tingle with alarm at what it was saying, at its terrifying universal message: *Save Our Souls, Save Our Souls, Save Our Souls.* Joe knew that he had to try again. He would wait awhile and then try again.

He looked down at the lamp through the vent. It was idiotic to waste fuel while he was waiting. What would Meg think if the light failed just as a ship passed by? He reached inside, turned the wick back to a glimmer, and blew sharply down the glass chimney. The rind of blue light disappeared in an instant, and darkness enveloped him fearfully again.

He lay quite still, peering into nothing. The night was full of menace. The wind mourned in the rocks, the sea surged spitefully, the tussocks hissed and whipped the bony slopes below. There were other sounds too, strange unidentifiable sounds suggesting stealthy movements in the night. He looked around quickly, afraid that something or someone was creeping up behind him, but it was impossible to see anything an inch beyond his nose.

His scalp prickled at the thought of unknown things, evil things, on the Bluff beside him. Ghosts perhaps. Hadn't a sealer or whaler long ago gone over the cliff to his death, so Uncle Harry said? He had been pushed, murdered in this wild, lonely place, and was his ghost now wandering about vindictively forever on this hill? And the little girl who had died back at the cottage, and the sailors who had been drowned? Surely in a place like this their ghosts would wander endlessly looking for peace and rest.

---

[2]**Stewy Sampson or Tiny Mazerakis:** friends of Uncle Harry's.

After a while Joe couldn't bear it any longer. His nerves were raw. He hastily fumbled for the matches and lit the lamp again. As he held the flame to the wick, he could see his hand trembling. He took the carton and his blanket and went up onto the exposed knob of the Bluff once more. He felt insignificant. In all that infinity of sea and sky he was less than a dust mote. Even the island he was standing on was no more than the head of a pin. In such a vastness of space, how could human beings be so presumptuous about their importance? How could they think they mattered? And how could he and Meg and poor Uncle Harry hope to be rescued?

Yet human beings battled on. They refused to give in. They struggled and improvised.³ That was one of the most enduring things about them.

Joe wrapped the blanket around his frozen shoulders, knelt beside his ridiculous cardboard box, and began the agony all over again: S.O.S., S.O.S., S.O.S. His finger burned with pain, his arm ached, and his eyes watered in the wind. At times they were so bleary that he had to wipe them constantly with the ball of his hand, fearful that he wouldn't even see a ship if it passed right in front of his nose. Perhaps his eyes were not only wet from the wind but from tears of frustration too.

He wondered whether he would ever reach a count of a hundred this time. It was like climbing an impossible mountain, an Everest far beyond his reach. He struggled to twenty and then to thirty. It would have been so easy to give up at that point, to say he had done his best, and to blunder back to the cottage, to Meg, to the beckoning kitchen fire. The fire. The thought of its warmth almost tipped the balance. But then he remembered the responsibility that lay on his shoulders, his promise to Meg, his duty to Uncle

³**improvised** (ĭm′prə vīzd′): done without advance planning, with whatever is available.

Harry. He wrapped the blanket more tightly, steadied his chattering teeth, and went on doggedly once more. His count rose to forty, crept painfully to forty-five, and at last reached fifty. It was a milestone that deserved recognition. He stood up in the buffeting wind, wiped his eyes, rubbed his cheeks, and ran briskly on the spot to stir up his circulation.

As he knelt down again to continue the cycle, he wondered whether he shouldn't be angling his message at the sky as well as the sea. There were airways up there, flight paths for the big jet airliners traveling between Adelaide and Perth that often passed almost directly overhead. But he rejected the idea. The lamp would slide backward and tilt on its side, with the flame blackening and cracking the glass chimney and the fuel draining away from the wick. He would have to go on as he was.

Slowly the count crept up to sixty and then to seventy and on to seventy-five. He was so numb with cold that he was past thinking. The movements of his hand were as jerky and automatic as the arms of a robot, his counting as mechanical as a machine. But he kept on relentlessly, refusing to let his body give up until the next goal had been reached. And so he rose slowly up the mountain of numbers he had to climb until he reached the summit, the final century. Then he stood up and peered all around at the cold and unresponsive darkness for the last time before snuffing out the lamp, picking up the blanket and box, and shambling off down the shoulder of Black Bluff toward the cottage.

He knew he had failed, but he was past caring. Nobody had answered his light, nobody had even seen it. He had tried, God knew how he had tried, but the world had ignored him. Perhaps he had expected too much in the first place. What was the use of a little lamp in the Antarctic Ocean? It was like lighting a match in outer space and asking someone on Earth to see it.

He fell twice on the way home, but luckily neither the lamp nor the mirror was broken. He lost his way after crossing the fresh-water gully and veered too far to the right. He was within a few hundred yards of the south coast before he realized what had happened, and so he had to turn at right angles and head back across the island toward the opposite shore. Even then he didn't know where he was until a light shone out clearly ahead. Meg, bless her, had put the lighted candle in the window to guide him home. Joe lifted his leaden legs and quickened his step. He suddenly understood the old stories about lighted windows that guided the fishermen home from the sea and the hunters home from the hill.

She was waiting at the door when he stumbled in. She hadn't slept, hadn't even rested. Most of the time she had sat silently by her father's bedside, keeping him warm with extra blankets as he went more deeply into shock, moving quietly back and forth from the bedroom to the kitchen to stoke the fire or heat the water. She looked at Joe anxiously as he took off the blanket and put down the box.

"Any luck?"

He shook his head. "Didn't see a thing. No boats, nothing."

She lowered her gaze in disappointment. "It was worth a try."

"How's your dad?"

"Bad."

"I should have stayed up on Black Bluff, but I couldn't stand it any longer."

"You stayed long enough. I was getting worried about you. I didn't like the thought of you sitting up there by yourself on that cliff in the dark."

"I didn't like being there," he answered honestly.

"Better stay by the fire and thaw out. Would you like some hot tea?"

He almost drooled. "Anything warm, anything for my stomach. It's starving."

Her tone was rueful. "We'll be starving for a long time yet."

He stood by the fire, gratefully warming his body. As she bent to lift the hot water, the firelight caught her face and lit up the great bruise there — the contused blue-black flesh, the closed eye, the swelling.

"You look awful," he said. "You ought to be in bed."

"I wanted to wait for you."

He watched her as he sipped his drink. She was tough. Many a person in her position would have given up long ago. He remembered hearing once that women and girls were better at enduring pain, that they could cope with hardship, that they had some kind of inner strength. Well, maybe Meg was like that. She was proving it now.

While he drank she slipped into her father's room once more and returned as silently as she had gone. "He seems to be a bit easier," she said. "Or maybe he's in a coma." She paused. "You'd better go to bed. It's after midnight. Take the blanket."

"What about you?"

"I'll lie down here on the bunk by the fire."

He blundered into the door as he went out. "Can you find your way?" she called. "The bed's near the window."

"I'll strike a match," he answered.

A few minutes later they were both asleep. Outside, the huge sky arched impersonally above the little cottage where they lay, the wind moaned, the island crouched obsequiously in its endless ocean. They were locked in a prison of solitude and silence, and nobody in the whole world had any inkling of their fate.

On the third afternoon, Meg finally attracts the attention of a passing helicopter by sending an S.O.S. signal with a mirror and flashes of sunlight. After the helicopter flies Uncle Harry to a hospital, a boat takes Joe and Meg back to Cockle Bay.

Thinking and Discussing

What physical and emotional obstacles must Joe overcome in carrying out his goal? How does he meet his goal? Do you think Joe has failed because there has been no response to his signals? Why or why not?

At what places in the story are you most aware of the importance of time to the success of Joe's mission? How does the author create a sense of urgency? How does that affect the reader?

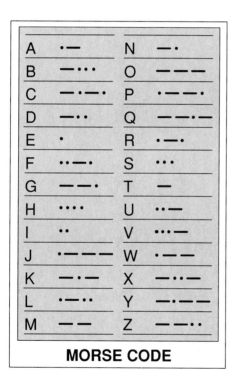

A	· —	N	— ·
B	— · · ·	O	— — —
C	— · — ·	P	· — — ·
D	— · ·	Q	— — · —
E	·	R	· — ·
F	· · — ·	S	· · ·
G	— — ·	T	—
H	· · · ·	U	· · —
I	· ·	V	· · · —
J	· — — —	W	· — —
K	— · —	X	— · · —
L	· — · ·	Y	— · — —
M	— —	Z	— — · ·

MORSE CODE

Choosing a Creative Response

Sending a Message If Joe wanted to send a longer message, how might he do it? Prepare your own rescue messages in Morse code. Using a flashlight or other signaling method, practice sending and receiving messages with a partner or group.

Designing a Signaling Device Meg and Joe develop a simple signaling lamp. Alone or with a partner, create a design for your own signaling device.

Creating Your Own Activity Plan and complete your own activity in response to "Shadow Shark."

RACE
AGAINST

In the winter of 1925, a deadly diphtheria epidemic strikes
Nome, Alaska, and causes the deaths of several children. Curtis
Welch, Nome's doctor, knows that only fresh serum can prevent
the spread of the highly contagious disease, but Nome is icebound,
and no boats or planes will be able to get through for many
months. The serum is brought by rail to Nenana, a town 670
miles east of Nome; but a team of sled dogs must race the serum
the rest of the way. Leonhard Seppala, Alaska's champion sled
driver, is mushing east from Nome to meet a relay driver. Then
he must make the final journey west back to Nome as a
dangerous blizzard approaches.

ALASKA

DEATH

by Seymour Reit

**January 31, 1925
10:30 A.M.**

Curtis Welch shook his head in despair. They couldn't hold on much longer. Where was Seppala with the serum? What was happening to the relay teams? The drivers had to get through — they *had* to. Without antitoxin,[1] Nome would lose

---

[1]**antitoxin** (ăn'tē tŏk'sĭn): an animal serum, or fluid, containing antibodies that fight diseases.

the battle. Every day the terrible disease grew stronger. Every day they came closer to the point where the epidemic would go out of all control.

Dr. Welch felt that they were sitting on a time bomb — and that it was getting ready to explode.

Many miles away, the serum race went on. As Leonhard Seppala hurried east, other drivers were mushing west, toward the waiting town. They pushed stubbornly from outpost to outpost, battling the cold. And each tiring run brought the medicine a little nearer.

Leonhard Seppala with his lead dog Bonzo after winning a dog sled race

They mushed hour after hour, night and day. From Kokrines to Ruby, thirty miles . . . from Ruby to Whiskey Creek, twenty-eight miles . . . from Whiskey Creek to Galena, twenty-four miles . . . from Galena to Bishop Mountain, eighteen miles . . . from Bishop Mountain to Nulato, thirty miles. . . .

The first half of the trip, along the Yukon River valley, had been the easiest. But now the temperature was dropping, and fierce gales were beginning to blow. The sharp winds made the cold even worse. Here and there, huge snowdrifts blocked the way. Every mile was a challenge, and the teams found the going harder and harder. As each sled reached its relief point, the huskies were limping and the drivers were exhausted.

These drivers were rugged men. Some were native Eskimos. Some were Alaskan Indians. Others were pioneers who had come

64

north to hunt for gold, and decided to stay. Some of their names were Titus Nikoli, Sam Joseph, Bill McCarty, Harry Pitka, Ed Nollner, and Victor Anagick.

The sled dogs, or huskies, were rugged, too. Some were an Eskimo breed called "malamutes." Some were Siberian dogs, bred for running in harness. Others were half-wolf — tough and savage. But they all had traits in common. They had broad chests, short necks, and strong legs. They had power and stamina. They could go for days with almost no food and little rest. Huskies never held themselves back. And now they fought through the blinding snow — because it was their work and it had to be done.

All over the United States, people followed the events in Alaska through the newspapers. Every day there were big headlines:

DIPHTHERIA
STILL
RAGING IN NOME

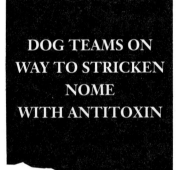

DOG TEAMS ON
WAY TO STRICKEN
NOME
WITH ANTITOXIN

NOME RELIEF
DOGS
REACH HALFWAY
POINT

There was also an editorial in *The New York Times.* It told of the country's sympathy for the people of Nome. This terrible epidemic, said the writer, showed the importance of serum in fighting disease. Some older doctors, the editorial went on, didn't believe in using antitoxin. They called it a "new-fangled" idea. But the tragedy in Nome proved, once and for all, that modern medicine held the answer. Diphtheria shots worked. Only serum could stop the epidemic.

All over America, in their warm, comfortable homes, people read about the serum race. They followed the news stories flashed from Alaska by radio — stories of courage and suspense.

But words printed in a newspaper couldn't tell everything. Words in a paper couldn't really explain the suffering of the sled drivers. Or the weariness of a hard-working doctor. Or the panic that was slowly creeping through Nome.

January 31, 1925
5:30 P.M.

The men almost missed each other in the blinding, swirling snow. But just in time, Leonhard Seppala saw the other sled coming toward him. It was the sled carrying the serum west.

Hank Ivanoff, the relay driver, greeted Seppala with a wave of his hand. The wind was howling so loudly it was hard for the men to talk. They shifted the package of serum to Seppala's sled. Ivanoff also gave Seppala the tattered paper with Dr. Beeson's instructions. Then, with a nod, a quick handshake, a pat on the shoulder, the two drivers parted company.

Now it was time for the tough run back to Nome. Seppala swung his sled around and shouted at the dogs. Their first goal was the town of Golovin, ninety-one miles away. So far, the serum had travelled 500 miles from the rail station at Nenana. But it still had 170 miles to go — and these would be the hardest.

Seppala's dog, Scotty, had been left at a relay point, and Togo was now in the lead. Togo was a Siberian husky. He was small for a sled dog, but a born pack leader. Seppala felt — and many drivers agreed — that Togo was just about the smartest dog in all of Alaska. He also had a special talent. No matter what the trail was like, whether smooth or hilly, Togo was able to travel in a perfectly straight line. He never went off his course — and this saved the team a great deal of time and energy.

Led by the tough little Siberian, the dogs pushed into the teeth of the storm. Togo yelped to his mates, spurring them on. Seppala squinted through the dusk. The Arctic wind whipped ice and snow into his eyes, making it hard for him to see.

Before long, they came to the edge of Norton Bay — and now Seppala had to make an important choice. The safest plan was to stay on solid ground, and to circle all the way around the bay. But this would add many hours to the trip. The bay was frozen, and they could take a shortcut straight across the ice. But it was a dangerous route. In this kind of gale, the ice could begin to crumble and crack. On their way across, the sled might be trapped. If the ice broke, they could easily freeze or drown. And, of course, the serum would be lost.

Standing on the bank in the howling wind, Seppala thought of his own family back in Nome. He thought of Dr. Welch and the brave nurses, and all the others who were working hard and waiting anxiously — waiting for a certain package that meant so much to all of them.

"We're sure counting on you, Len," Mr. Summers had said . . .

The veteran made his decision. He would trust in Togo's instincts — and his own experience. He would save time and take the shortcut. Seppala shouted to the team. Without a second's pause, the faithful Togo started across the ice.

Now the wind came thundering with the force of a locomotive. There were no guide points for Togo to follow. He had to find his way by using his nose — and his uncanny sense of direction. As they mushed along, Seppala kept his eyes on the ice just ahead. He listened for sounds of cracking. He watched for "ice spears." These were broken chunks of ice, sometimes pushed up by the water churning underneath. The chunks were as sharp as razors, and could slash a dog's feet badly. On his sled, Seppala had small flannel coverings which he could tie around their paws, if he had to. Anxiously, he watched the route which Togo was taking.

In most spots the ice was rough. But here and there, it became as smooth as glass. On one of these smooth glassy patches, a sudden gust blew the sled sideways. The dogs slipped, lost their balance, and tumbled over. There was a mad scramble. Seppala lost valuable time untangling the harness and getting the team started again. Then they went on, moving quickly but carefully.

It took several hours for the huskies to work their way across the frozen bay — but to the tired driver it seemed more like weeks. In the darkness, they climbed up at last on the far bank. They had made it safely.

Once on solid ground, Seppala headed for shelter in a nearby Eskimo hut. He moved the dogs into a shed and fed them some dried fish. Then he carried the serum into the hut, where his Eskimo friend had a fire going in the stove. Carefully, Seppala put the package near the stove. Then he fell on a cot, exhausted.

After an hour's rest, he decided to go on again. The old Eskimo warned him to wait. Outside, the storm was building into a full-scale blizzard. But Seppala shook his head. Saving time was all that mattered now.

"Golovin . . ." he mumbled wearily, "got to reach Golovin . . ."

Soon after the team started off, the storm grew more violent. Seppala could barely see more than a few yards in front of the sled. He noticed that the dogs were beginning to stiffen up. This was a danger sign. He stopped the sled and massaged their tired, frozen limbs. Then he brushed away the coating of ice that had formed on their muzzles.

Once more the team pushed forward, numb with cold. Seppala kept shouting words of encouragement. Not just to keep up the dogs' spirits, but his own as well. They struggled on through the blackness, trapped in an icy, howling whirlwind. Finally, Seppala saw lights up ahead, and knew that they had made it to Golovin.

The old veteran was relieved. Then he began to worry. This was one of the worst blizzards he had ever known. And he felt completely worn out. Even with fresh dogs, he wondered how he could go all the way to Nome. Staggering into the town, Seppala didn't know that there had been a change of plan. He didn't know about Kaasen and Balto. Or that Charlie Olson was waiting right there at Golovin with fresh, well-rested dogs — ready to continue the race.

For Leonhard Seppala, Togo, and the other valiant huskies, the ordeal was over. Their trip through the storm had been the longest run of any relay team. Now, thanks to them, the serum was closer to Nome than ever.

But there was still a long way to go, and the storm was getting worse every minute.

February 1, 1925
8:00 P.M.

Sergeant Anderson pulled off his earphones and turned to Dr. Welch, who was sitting near him in the radio shack. Anderson looked worried.

"There's a lot of static, but I got through to Bluff," he said. "It sounds bad, Doc. They're right in the middle of a rip-roaring blizzard. The winds are up to fifty miles an hour."

Curtis Welch stood up and shook his head wearily. He walked over to the window and looked out at the storm. Fifty-mile winds — why, that was hurricane force! He thought of the drivers and dog teams, out there somewhere in the blinding gale. And suddenly he felt very helpless.

At that moment, fifty miles away, another man was staring out the window. Gunnar Kaasen, in the mail cabin at Bluff, watched the snow. He could see only a few yards into the darkness. The thermometer, hanging outside, showed 30 degrees below zero. Well, that was cold — but he'd known it a lot colder. The wind was another matter. The wind really worried him.

Kaasen and the dogs had made their run from Nome without too much trouble. He had taken all thirteen dogs with him — six pairs, plus Balto. He had just given them an extra meal of seal tallow,[2] for warmth and energy. And now they were resting in the big kennel next to the cabin.

Gunnar Kaasen began pacing up and down. Anxious thoughts crept through his mind. All he could do now was to wait — and worry. Had Seppala made it into Golovin? Could Charlie Olson get through this blizzard? Olson's run was fairly short — but it could be very rough in this kind of weather. He might have had a bad accident. Right now, he might be lying somewhere on the trail, freezing to death.

The heroic Gunnar Kaasen pictured here with one fearless member of his famous dog sled team

Kaasen paced back and forth, back and forth, over the rough wooden floor. And the more he paced, the more tense he became.

Suddenly the huskies began to yelp and bark. Kaasen ran to the door and threw it open. He could just make out a sled crawling through the darkness. It stopped outside the cabin. Charlie Olson

---

[2]**tallow** (tăl′ō): animal fat.

staggered in, his face coated with ice. The driver almost fell, and Kaasen had to help him into a chair.

"The serum . . ." he gasped. "Get . . . package . . . Take care of dogs . . ."

Kaasen pulled on his gloves and his sealskin coat, and hurried out. He unhitched the dogs and moved them into the kennel, which was big enough to hold both teams. Then he untied the parcel, carried it inside, and put it near the stove.

Olson was exhausted. Kaasen gave him some hot coffee. Little by little, the driver's strength came back. And soon he was able to talk.

"It's a lucky thing they sent us out, Gunnar," he said. "Seppala just barely made it. He was all played out. His dogs were so tired they fell right over in their harnesses. I never saw anything like it."

Olson held his hands toward the warm stove. "I had a rough time, too," he went on. "The gale blew my sled off the trail four or five times. Knocked it clean over."

The driver studied his fingers. They were a dead, ashy white.

"I took my gloves off to put blankets around the dogs," he explained. "My hands got frozen. I may lose a couple of fingers."

Kaasen examined Olson's hands with an expert eye.

"No, Charlie — I think you'll be all right," he said, "but you'll have a lot of pain when your circulation starts coming back."

Olson shrugged. He didn't mind the pain. He didn't even mind losing a few fingers. Like the other relay drivers, his thoughts had become locked on a single idea. Nothing mattered any more, except getting the serum to Nome.

In a little while, Kaasen checked his watch. Then he put on his heavy parka again.

"I'll get started," he said. "It's now or never."

Charlie Olson nodded. "Right, Gunnar. The storm won't get any better, that's for sure."

Kaasen's goal was Port Safety, the town nearest to Nome. While Olson watched from the doorway, Kaasen quickly lashed the package on the sled. Then he collected his dogs and hitched them in place. He had to take off his gloves to handle the harness buckles — and noticed that, in just a few minutes, his fingers began to get numb.

When all was ready, he turned and waved good-bye to Olson. Then he walked to the head of the waiting team. He crouched down next to Balto and silently stroked the dog's head. The husky lifted his muzzle and wagged his bushy tail. Between man and dog there seemed to be a special bond — a secret understanding that went beyond speech or gesture.

After a moment, Kaasen stood up. He trotted to the rear of the sled and stepped on the crossbar.

"Mush!" he shouted. "Pull, Balto!"

The husky lunged against his straps and the sled began to move. As the dogs started, Kaasen kept shouting, trying to urge them on. But the mocking wind swept his words away into the frozen blackness.

February 1, 1925
10:30 P.M.

Head down . . . nose to the ground . . . find the spoor[3] . . . ears sharp and alert . . . listen for commands . . . keep the team working . . . bark and growl to spur on the slackers . . .

Balto, the leader, plowed through the storm, feeling a surge of power. The ruff stood up on his strong neck. His muscles rippled smoothly, meeting every demand made on them. Ice dust, sharp as

---

[3]**spoor** (spŏŏr): the track or trail of an animal, especially of a wild animal.

a thousand needles, stung his face. He narrowed his eyes to protect them — but he studied the trail as keenly as ever.

By instinct, his mind reached out in two directions. He was aware of the trail ahead, with all its dangers. He was also aware of the driver on the crossbar, who had to be obeyed.

Soon a heavy snowdrift blocked their way. Balto tried to push through. But the snow was thick and deep, and the dogs floundered up to their chests. Gunnar Kaasen tugged on the sled handles and backed the team out. Then he shouted "Gee!" and Balto swerved to the right. Slowly, painfully, the team worked its way around the drift. In a few minutes, Kaasen shouted, "Haw!" Balto swung quickly to the left. He moved on, testing the ground, until he found the trail again.

This happened time after time during the long night. Each time they circled a drift, or skirted a patch of weak ice, Balto brought them back to the right place. Gunnar Kaasen smiled with satisfaction — Balto was proving himself.

As the miles passed, Kaasen felt the cold spreading under his clothes. He hopped off the bar and jogged behind the sled. It made his blood flow fast, and he felt warmer. But it only lasted a moment. Like the other relay drivers, he wore many layers of clothing. And for a good reason. The heat from his body stayed trapped in these layers, giving him a cushion of warmth. But when a fierce wind blew, it went right through the layers. It blew away his cushion of body heat, and there was nothing to stop the cold. This was known in the Far North as "wind chill."

Now Kaasen felt the chill creeping across his skin. It seemed to crawl into his chest, his stomach, his muscles — into his very bones. He tried running again. He shook his hands, and moved his stiff fingers in their sealskin gloves. He slapped his cheeks, which were beginning to feel numb.

The sled crept through the darkness, and the storm closed in. Soon Kaasen could only see as far as his wheel dogs. These were the two dogs nearest to the sled. Kaasen knew that, somewhere in front, Balto was leading them faithfully. But the driver no longer had any control. He was cut off in a wild gray nightmare. The sled handles were his only contact with reality — and he gripped them tightly.

Balto threw a quick look over his shoulder. He, too, felt alone. All he could see now were the two dogs directly behind him. Everything else was lost in the whirlwind. The husky yelped loudly, to reassure the others. Then he pushed on.

Head down . . . nose to the ground . . . find the scent . . . stay alert . . . keep the team moving . . . whatever happens, follow the trail . . .

The sled bumped and tilted. Kaasen knew that they were moving up a steep hill. As they struggled upward, he kept breathing through his nose. His chest felt ready to burst, and he longed to open his mouth wide and take in great gulps of air. But he knew that it would mean frozen lungs — then death.

It seemed like days before the sled crested the hill and started down the far side. The tired dogs half-slid through the thick, powdery snow. At the bottom, Kaasen set his brake and the team rested. But in this kind of storm, even resting was an effort.

Ten minutes later, they were moving again. They mushed for miles through heavy woods, and reached a snow-covered plain. In summer, this was a swampy marshland, but now it was frozen solid. On the open plain, the Arctic wind went mad. An angry gust lifted the sled and the dogs, and flung them aside. The team fell in a wild tangle of harness. Kaasen tumbled head over heels, as though slapped by a huge invisible hand.

With a groan, the driver pulled himself to his feet. He staggered over to the dogs and began to untangle their gear. When he straightened up the sled, he glanced into it — and his heart almost stopped beating.

The package of serum wasn't there!

The weary man couldn't believe his eyes. He realized, with a sick feeling, that he had tied it hurriedly, back at Bluff. The ropes must have worked loose. And, as the sled bounced over the trail, the package had fallen out!

But *where* did it happen? Did he lose it hours ago? Or just now, when the sled was blown over?

In a panic, Kaasen threw himself into the snow. It was too dark to see well, so he groped blindly, his heart pounding. He had to find the serum! He couldn't lose it now — not when they were so close to their goal!

Balto and the other huskies stood by obediently, while Kaasen floundered in the drifts, feeling with his gloved hands.

"Let me find it," he whispered. "Please let me find it!"

Kaasen fought against terror. The serum *had* to be here, somewhere! Half-sobbing, he crawled round and round, going in wider circles. Snow whipped into his face. Splinters of ice cut through his gloves and slashed at his knees, but he felt nothing. Nothing but a deadly, creeping fear.

Suddenly his leg bumped against a hard surface. He pounced on the object and brushed away the snow. Then relief swept over him, and he breathed a prayer of thanks. He had found the package, safe in its canvas cover.

This time, Kaasen tied the serum tightly on the sled. He wouldn't make the same mistake again. Ready at last, he took his place and gave the signal. Balto could just barely hear him above the wind. He barked, and the team lunged forward.

Head down . . . nose to the ground . . . track the scent . . . hold the trail . . . keep the lead line straight and taut . . .

Suddenly there was danger! Balto reared back and stood still, his legs rigid. The dogs piled up behind him, and began yelping in confusion. Kaasen was puzzled. Why did Balto stop? He set the brake and stumbled forward to investigate. One quick look gave him the answer. A racing creek had broken through its covering of ice. Freezing water was gushing out, just inches away from Balto's feet. If the dog hadn't stopped short, the team would have floundered into it. And Kaasen would have lost much time getting their paws dried out again.

The driver smiled and patted Balto gratefully.

He inched the team carefully to one side. They mushed upstream, and made a safe crossing where the ice was still solid. Then once more they worked back to the trail. Numbly they kept going, putting one foot in front of the other.

As the sled neared Port Safety, the storm began to ease. The gale died down enough so that Kaasen could see for a short distance. With relief, he picked out some familiar landmarks. Yes, Port Safety was just ahead.

Kaasen saw his goal — a small mail cabin perched on a hillside. And now he became confused. There were no lights showing in the cabin. The whole cluster of buildings was dark and quiet. And he heard no dogs barking.

The driver's mind raced with unanswered questions. Wasn't Ed Rohn supposed to be here, ready to relieve him? Had there been another change of plans? Was there some misunderstanding?

Half-frozen, Kaasen forced himself to think calmly, clearly. Maybe Ed Rohn was in the cabin, still asleep. If so, it would take time to wake him up. Time for him to get dressed, and harness his dogs. And valuable minutes would be lost. Rohn was a good racing driver, he knew. But the man and his team had no experience mushing through a bad storm. It would be risky for them. They might not be able to make it.

Kaasen's brain was spinning. Should he go find out what was wrong? But that would take a while. He looked at Balto and the other huskies. They were tired, but still running well. The storm had eased up, and Nome was only twenty miles away . . .

The mail cabin loomed above them on the hillside, dark and still. It seemed to send a wordless message. And Gunnar Kaasen suddenly made up his mind. There was no time to waste. Not a minute, not a second. He turned to his team and snapped the harness lines.

"Mush!" he shouted. "We're going to Nome!"

At first, the sled moved smoothly. The air cleared, and the huskies made good time. Then, a few miles outside of Port Safety, the blizzard thundered in again. The wind howled and the snow whirled around them. Ice dust slashed at Kaasen. Time after time, he had to brush a thick crust of frost from his bleeding face. Then Kaasen noticed, with a shock, that he could no longer see his wheel dogs. The snow was so heavy, he couldn't see past the end of his sled.

"Now it's up to you, Balto," he muttered through cracked, frozen lips.

Out in front, the big dog clung to the trail. The wind made it very hard to follow the spoor. Muzzle close to the ground, eyes half-closed, he fought with all his instincts. By now, Balto was limping. Splinters of ice were cutting painfully into his paws. He could tell, by the feel of the traces, that the other dogs were limping, too. But, pain or no pain, he didn't falter or slow the pace.

Another mile passed slowly. And another. And the gale raged with new fury. To Kaasen, it seemed as if the storm felt cheated. For hundreds of miles it had lashed at the relay teams, trying to destroy them. But the race had gone on. And now, with only a few miles left, the storm was making one last deadly try.

Weary, anxious, half-dead with cold, Gunnar Kaasen looked up at the thick, murky sky.

"We're not licked!" he shouted hoarsely. "We're going . . . to Nome! We're . . . going to make it!"

Balto heard his master raving at the wind. He didn't understand the words, but he sensed their meaning. A low growl rumbled deep in his throat — and he matched Kaasen's anger with a savage defiance of his own.

Head down, shoulders hunched, blind to the cold and the pain, Balto limped forward . . .

February 2, 1925
5:00 A.M.

Thump . . . thump . . . thump . . .

Dr. Welch sat up in bed. He listened, puzzled. Who was pounding on their front door at this strange hour? Or had he been dreaming?

Thump . . . thump . . .

There it was again. Yes, there *was* somebody at the door. Careful not to wake Lula, he climbed out of bed, pulled on his bathrobe and went unhappily downstairs. More trouble, he thought. Probably a neighbor, reporting a new diphtheria case. Or even another death. Maybe something had gone wrong with the serum relay, and they were coming to break the news.

The doctor opened the front door. Something staggered in and half-fell against him. Startled, Dr. Welch drew back. The figure looked like a weird snow-covered monster — a creature straight from the North Pole. Then he recognized the face under its mask of ice.

"Kaasen!" he shouted. Quickly, he helped the driver into a chair. He threw back Kaasen's hood, felt his pulse and examined his glazed eyes.

"You'll be all right, Gunnar," he said. "Sit here quietly. You're just totally exhausted." Then he asked an important question — but dreaded to hear the answer.

"What happened to the serum?"

Kaasen raised a weary arm and gestured toward the door.

"Serum . . ." he mumbled, "outside . . . on sled . . ."

Dr. Welch broke into a grin and patted Kaasen's shoulder.

"You did it!" he said. "You did the impossible!"

The fresh serum saved the people of Nome. No more people died, and the epidemic was brought under control. Later a bronze statue of Balto was created for New York City's Central Park honoring the men and dogs who won "the race against death."

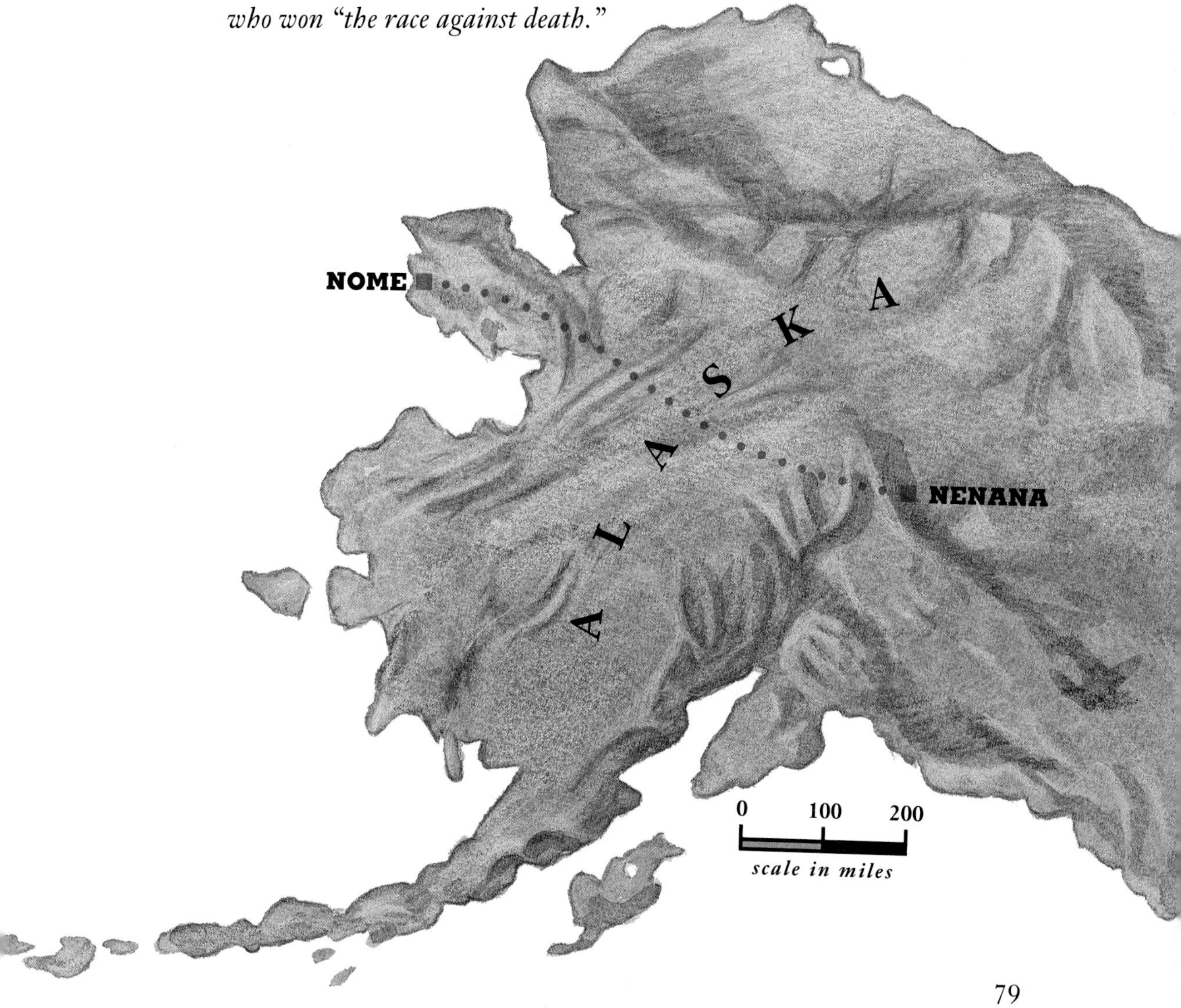

NOME

A L A S K A

NENANA

0   100   200

scale in miles

Thinking and Discussing

In what ways must the drivers rely on themselves to accomplish their mission? In what ways must they depend on others? What character traits do the drivers have in common?

Notice the author's use of short sentences, shifts in point of view, and dates and times. How does this help add suspense to "Race Against Death"?

Choosing a Creative Response

Creating a Poster   Design a survival poster for newcomers to Alaska. List safety rules for winter weather. Include information about required clothing for outdoor activities, such as ice fishing. On your poster, tell how friends can help each other in a dangerous climate. For example, you might explain how partners can warn each other about early signs of frostbite.

Conducting a Town Meeting   With a group of classmates, imagine that you are at a Nome town meeting. Discuss Nome's harsh climate, its isolation from railways, and any other problems you might think of. Offer suggestions for avoiding emergencies like the one described in the story.

Creating Your Own Activity Plan and create your own activity in response to "Race Against Death."

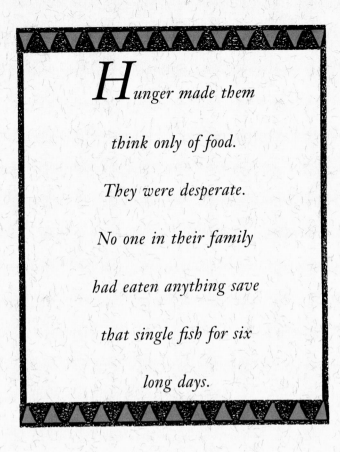

*H*unger made them

think only of food.

They were desperate.

No one in their family

had eaten anything save

that single fish for six

long days.

LONG CLAWS

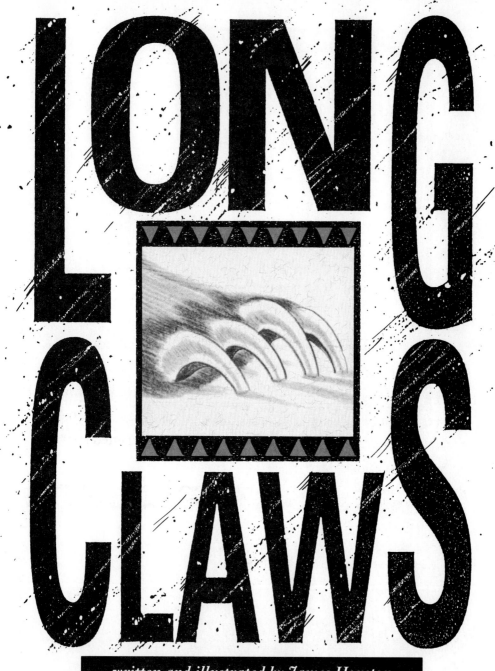

written and illustrated by James Houston

Pitohok and Upik hurried back into the igloo, shouting, "An owl helped us! Look! We found these fish where it scratched the snow. We dug them up. Four big ones!" Upik clutched the frozen lake trout in her arms, displaying them like precious silver toys. Someone had buried them outside to be eaten later.

Upik handed the largest trout to her mother, who held it over the small flame of her stone lamp until it softened slightly.

"I treasure my hunger before a feast," she whispered as she passed the fish and her sharp-curved ulu knife around to the other members of the family. She gazed at her four children — Pitohok and Upik, their small sister Kanajuk and the baby, who was peeking out from the hood of her parka. Then she looked at her old father. Would any of them survive now that her husband was no longer living?

Pitohok, her son, had a smooth brown face and quick, dark eyes. His teeth were square and strong. Like his sister, he wore a fur parka and pants and boots made of caribou skins. Bundled up like that, they both looked plump. Only the dark shadows below their broad cheekbones betrayed their hunger.

Upik's black shiny eyes, white teeth, and wide, clear face were a pleasure to see. When her parka hood was pushed back, her lustrous blue-black hair hung down in two braids thickened by willow sticks and bound stiff with beads.

When the grandfather sniffed the rich smell of thawing fish, he sat up slowly on the fur-covered sleeping platform that was made of snow. Quickly, they each ate their share of the fish.

"Grandfather," Pitohok said, "the fish will give us enough strength to travel. Tell me where the last caribou is buried so that I may go and find it."

"Oh, it is far from here," his grandfather answered. "Too great a distance for you to go alone."

Pitohok looked at his sister and wondered if she had enough strength to walk with him on such a journey.

"Tell me where it lies," Pitohok asked again.

"It is three days' hard walking west of here," his grandfather said, "near the short hill that stands before the Crooked River. Out on that plain last autumn a young male caribou fell before my rifle. A strong wind was blowing and it began to snow. A great feeling of weakness came over me. I had no way to carry home that last caribou and no time to build a proper cache[1] to hide it. I knew that the heavy snows would drift over its body, hiding all but its horns from sight. So I turned its antlers high hoping that someone might find it later." He looked at Pitohok. "It is too great a journey for one person without dogs."

"I will go with him," said Upik.

"Yes, she could help him," said their mother.

Their grandfather closed his eyes in pain. "It is our only chance. If you two make such a journey, you must first search for the Crooked River. Beyond it stands the pointed hill. If you find that hill, climb to its peak and carefully study the land. I believe that you will see that caribou's antlers standing wind-blown, clear of snow. It is bad that we had to break up the sled and burn its wood in the coldest days of winter. It is sad that the dogs are gone," he

---

[1] **cache** (kăsh): a hiding place for a supply of provisions and other items.

said. "But it is good that we are all alive! I will try hard to think of some way to make a sled for you."

"We will need to dig for that caribou," Pitohok said, "but we cannot find the shovel."

"Of course, you cannot find the snow shovel," their grandfather said. "I warned all of you that that shovel should have been left lying flat. Someone in this camp stood it upright in the snow. I saw it," the old man said. "It was standing like a human. That shovel has a soul like any one of us, like birds, like caribou, like fish, like every other thing. When someone left it standing, it did just what you or I would do. As soon as it grew dark, that shovel ran away. Why not? It doesn't like to stand out there in the cold waiting to be a slave to any one of us!"

Pitohok and his sister did not pause long to puzzle over their grandfather's old-fashioned ideas. Hunger made them think only of food. They were desperate. No one in their family had eaten anything save that single fish for six long days.

Upik looked into her mother's eyes. She could see hunger there and fear that the caribou herds, which were their main food, would not come again in time to save their lives.

"Sleep well," their mother told them. "Only tomorrow when your grandfather looks at the sky will it be decided whether you will go or stay."

"If you cannot find the shovel," their grandfather told Pitohok, "take the hand axe and my old snow knife. You can dig with them."

That night the grandfather asked Pitohok's mother to soak two caribou skins in water. When she had done this, he carefully folded each of them lengthwise six times and turned them up on the ends until they took on the rough appearance of a pair of sled runners. These he placed outside to freeze.

Upik's mother stayed awake sewing by her lamp throughout the night so that she could give her two older children each a pair of

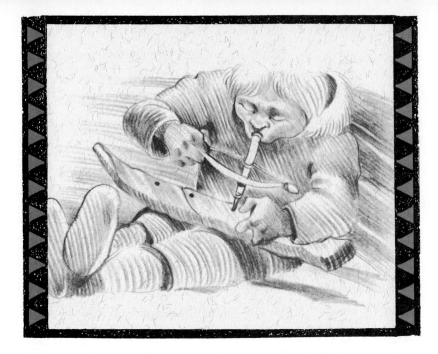

warm, new caribou-skin boots. In the morning the wind was down, but it was bitter cold.

"Bring in the frozen runners," said the grandfather. "If they are hard enough, I shall show you how to build a small sled, using only what we have."

The old man examined the two frozen skins that he had so carefully shaped into sled runners. They were straight and not much longer than his outstretched arms. They were frozen as hard as wood.

Taking an old-fashioned bowdrill, the grandfather placed between his teeth a small bone with a hole in it, shaped just large and deep enough to hold one end of the arrowlike drill shaft. He twisted the string of a short bow around this shaft. By drawing the short bow swiftly back and forth with his right hand in a sawing motion, he made the shaft whirl around so that the sharp nail in its lower end became a drill. Pressing hard, he drilled three holes near the top of each folded caribou-skin runner and forced strong braided caribou sinew through each of these holes.

"Hand me those last three frozen fish," the old man said.

Pitohok passed them to his grandfather.

The grandfather carefully lashed the three stiffly frozen trout on top of the runners so they would serve as cross bars. In this way he was able to bind together a sturdy makeshift sled.

"Now hand me those pulling straps," he said to Upik's mother.

He drilled two more holes in the runners and attached the long leather straps to the front of the sled. Pitohok stood before him while he adjusted this harness to fit Pitohok's shoulders.

"Now," said their grandfather, "here is my old rifle and the only two brass cartridges left to us. I have loaded these with the last two pinches of gunpowder we possess. We have no more lead to make bullets, so I have carved two bullets of stone to fit into these cartridge casings. Stone bullets are strong enough, but I must warn you that they sometimes break and fly apart. Go with strength." Their grandfather sighed. "If you can find that buried caribou, we may all live to see the summer come again."

Upik and Pitohok pulled on their warmest clothing and tied up a roll of caribou sleeping skins.

"We won't come back until we have the meat," Pitohok told his grandfather.

Upik and Pitohok bent low as they went out the long snow tunnel that protected their igloo from the Arctic winds. Their mother followed them outside, but they could find no words to say between them. She held Kanajuk's hand as she watched Upik and Pitohok trudge away, dragging the small frozen sled behind them. Tears filled her eyes, for she wondered whether she would ever see her children again.

Beyond the igloo, the vast flat white snow plain stretched all around them. Far to the east lay Hudson Bay, to the south frozen Kasba Lake. To the north and west the land continued endlessly toward distant, blue, snow-covered mountains and oceans that they had never seen.

Upik and Pitohok traveled steadily westward. The late winter sun faded and soon the whole sky was hidden by a heavy blanket of gray clouds that stretched to the far horizons of the enormous snow-covered land. Only the painful squeal of snow beneath their soft skin boots broke the silence that hung around them.

As it grew dark, the first snowflakes floated down from the western sky. Then gusts of wind swept moaning across the land, driving the fine snow upward into whirling, twisting forms that drifted toward them, then scurried away like ghosts across the lonely plain.

Pitohok stopped at once and drew the snow knife from beneath the lashings of the sled. He licked both sides of the long thin antler blade until it was glazed with ice and would slice smoothly into the hard snow beneath his feet. Carefully he cut out snow blocks and stood them around him in a small circle, cleverly piling them until they curved in at the top to form a dome. Upik stayed outside and packed dry snow into the chinks between the blocks. She could feel the cold wind's force increasing and knew that any weakness in their igloo might allow it to be broken and torn to pieces. Their house of snow was just big enough for the two of them. Upik wondered if it would stand firm.

She stuffed their caribou sleeping robes through the low entrance, and Pitohok yelled to her against the howling wind.

"Push the sled inside as well. We may have to eat it before this storm has ended."

He was right. The blizzard raged and screamed over their small shelter for three long, gloomy days and terrifying nights, leaving them weak with fear and hunger. Their igloo trembled like a frightened rabbit during the awful storm. But it held.

On the fourth morning the wind died out. Pitohok looked at the three frozen trout that formed their small sled. "Tomorrow we will have to eat one of the fish, or we will not have the strength to travel. Two fish will be just enough to hold the sled together."

That night Upik unlashed the lake trout that had been the sled's center crossbar and placed it between herself and the caribou robe beneath her. She slept on top of it all night. In the morning her body heat had thawed the fish enough for them to eat. They shared it with the eagerness of wild animals.

All that day they traveled, then built another igloo and slept again. When they crawled out at dawn, Pitohok pointed into the west. "Do you see something strange over there?"

He cupped his mittened hands together and boosted his sister high. She shaded her eyes and examined the flat horizon.

"It's the hill!" she cried. "And beyond it I can see a long windswept streak that looks like ice. That must be the Crooked River."

"Hurry," said Pitohok. "We must find that caribou while the light is strong."

It was almost evening when they reached the pointed hill. It was not much taller than two men standing one on the shoulders of the other, but in this dead-flat land it looked like an enormous mountain. Eagerly Pitohok climbed it. As he reached the top, he disturbed a snowy owl that took flight across the plain.

Upik, seeing it, crouched down and sang her secret song:

"White owl, I sing to you.

Softly I sing to you,

Owl, my helping spirit."

"Look! Look out there where she is flying," called Pitohok. "I can see the caribou antlers standing upright in the snow. But do you see something moving toward the antlers through the blue shadows of the snowdrift?"

"Yes, I see it," Upik called up to him. "It's dark brown and humped over like a dog."

"It's Kugvik, the wolverine!" said Pitohok. "Look at the way that one moves and digs. They're the worst meat robbers in the world. Quick! I need the rifle."

Upik untied their grandfather's old rifle from the sled and carried it up to her brother. Pitohok sat down on the snow. From his small leather bag, he took out the two precious brass cartridges and examined the stone bullets. He chose one, opened the rifle, and placed the cartridge in its breech.

He held his grandfather's heavy rifle steady by resting his elbows on his knees. With one eye closed, he took careful aim at the wolverine that was digging with its sharp claws through the hard-packed snow, trying to get at the caribou.

Upik jumped back as the heavy rifle boomed and echoed across the wide snow plain.

"I missed," said Pitohok, his voice full of disappointment.

"That's no wonder," Upik called to him. "The bullet that you fired broke into three small pieces. I saw the bits of stone fall onto the snow. But the noise of the rifle frightened the wolverine. He is running away!"

Pitohok came leaping down the hill and lashed the rifle onto the sled again. "Follow me!" he said, snatching up the long straps. "We must reach that caribou before night comes."

The first stars twinkled in the western sky as they came up to the caribou antlers that stood above the snow.

Pitohok stared in wonder at his sister. "Is that grandfather's shovel standing in the snow beside the antlers?" he whispered. "Are we seeing something magic?"

"Is it truly ours?" asked Upik.

"Yes, it's ours," said Pitohok, bending to look closely at its familiar wooden shape and its worn leather stitching. "I'd know that snow shovel anywhere. I've dug with it so many times."

"Grandfather must have left it here last autumn," Upik said, "when he was growing weak and it was dark and storming."

Pitohok drew the snow knife from beneath the lashings of the sled and paced out a circle for their igloo.

"I am going to build it right on top of the caribou, leaving only its horns outside," Pitohok said, "so that wolverines can't come back here in the night and steal the meat from us."

When their new igloo was completed, Upik looked up and saw the cold-faced winter moon rising in the eastern sky. As Pitohok crawled into the igloo, he sighed and said, "Perhaps we don't have to eat. My belly feels full just knowing that we're going to sleep on top of all this rich caribou meat." He patted their snow floor. "Imagine how glad our family will be when we return with such a treasure."

They rose early in the morning and tried again to forget their hunger as they broke the igloo's side walls. Using the snow knife and the shovel, they dug up the frozen caribou and lashed it onto the small sled.

Before they left, Pitohok carefully stood the shovel upright in the snow. He smiled and said, "If you can walk, please hurry home to our grandfather and tell him we are coming."

The snow shovel did not move or seem to hear his words.

Pitohok took up the long pulling straps and together they headed back toward their home. They hauled the welcome weight of meat behind them, following their own footprints eastward, hurrying until it was almost dark. Then they built a small igloo and slept exhausted.

Many times the following morning Upik looked back at the precious caribou lashed to the creaking sled. She tried to fight off her hunger by saying, "Just think of the wonderful smell that meat will make as it simmers in our mother's pot."

The morning sun had risen high above the plain when Pitohok stopped and pushed up his wooden goggles. He shaded his eyes, then pointed at a small dark speck far away. "Do you see it?"

"Yes, what is it?" Upik asked him as she watched it moving slowly toward them across the endless plain of snow.

"I don't know," said Pitohok as he pulled down his goggles to protect his eyes again. "It's not a caribou or a man. But it is certainly something that's alive."

"Let us hurry home," said Upik. "I don't like the look of that moving spot. It sways from side to side in a heavy way that frightens me."

By midafternoon the brown speck had grown much larger.

"It is moving faster than we can walk. What is it?" Upik asked her brother.

"I am not sure," he said, handing her one of the straps. "Let us run for a little while together, then walk, and run again. Perhaps it will turn and go away."

In the late afternoon they had to stop and rest because their legs were too tired to go on.

"Can you tell now what it is," Upik asked, "that thing that is coming closer to us?"

"Yes," Pitohok said. "It is Akla, a barren-ground grizzly bear. It is moving in our footprints, following our scent."

"I am afraid," said Upik. "I have never seen an akla, but I have heard terrible things about them. Hunters call them 'Long Claws.'"

"Let us walk fast again," said Pitohok.

When the sun started to sink into the west, Pitohok knew that they could not get away from the huge, hump-shouldered grizzly that came shambling after them, rolling its enormous hips, gaining on them with every step it took.

"We've got to do something," Pitohok gasped, and now his voice was full of fear. "That akla's going to catch us no matter how fast we walk. And if we run now, it may get excited and attack. Grizzlies are tireless in following their prey and can make short, fast bursts of speed. Grandfather has told me that strong aklas in their prime can sometimes catch a running caribou."

"What shall we do?" Upik asked him, and Pitohok could tell by her voice that she was almost crying.

Pitohok stopped and drew his grandfather's rifle out from under the sled lashings. He put their last stone-nosed cartridge inside its barrel. Looking at his sister, he said, "I hope we won't have to use it."

He stood the rifle upright in the snow. Then quickly he bent and unlashed the frozen caribou and rolled it off the sled. With his short, sharp knife he cut the bindings that held the sled together. As it fell apart, Pitohok grabbed one of the runners. Whirling it around his head, he threw it as far as he could along the trail toward the oncoming grizzly. The second runner he flung far to the right, hoping to draw the big bear away from their path.

The akla stopped, raised its massive head and stared at the two human creatures. Pitohok and Upik could hear its stomach rumbling with hunger as it ambled forward and sniffed the folded caribou skin. Placing one paw upon it, the grizzly tore it into pieces with its teeth and began devouring it.

Pitohok knelt down beside the frozen caribou and grasped it by its front and rear legs. "Quick!" he said to Upik. "Help me heave this meat onto my shoulders."

She did so, scarcely able to believe how heavy it was.

As soon as Pitohok rose to his feet, he started walking, hurrying once more along their own trail that would lead them home.

"You bring the rifle and the snow knife and the last two fish," he called back to his sister. "One sleeping robe will have to do us. Tie it around yourself. Leave the other one. Move!" Upik could hear a sound of horror creeping into his voice again. "Don't let that Long Claws near you!"

Upik's legs ached with tiredness, but she hurried after him, afraid to look back, afraid she would find the grizzly close behind her.

The evening sun turned red as it slid down and touched the long, flat white horizon. Pitohok looked back then and groaned beneath the heavy weight of caribou. "Long Claws is still coming after us. Give him a fish. Hurry and fling it back toward him."

Upik did as she was told. Pitohok looked again, then slowed his pace. "He's lying down," Pitohok gasped. "He's eaten the trout.

He looks now as if he's going to sleep." It was growing dark and Pitohok was staggering with weariness. "Hold onto me," he groaned. "Help me. I've got to make my feet carry me over that next snow ridge so the akla won't see us stop to build our igloo."

When they were beyond the huge bear's sight, Pitohok collapsed, letting the caribou fall to the snow. Upik helped him up, but Pitohok was so exhausted that he could scarcely rise. With the snow knife Upik cut a shallow gravelike hole and they slid the caribou in and carefully covered it with snow. They built their igloo on top of it.

Once inside, Pitohok wedged a snow block firmly into place, trying to jam the entrance. "Let us share our one last fish," he said. "I have never been so hungry or so tired in all my life."

Even while they were eating, they listened carefully. But they did not hear the akla. Upik could not finish her share of the fish, so exhausted was she from their terrible journey. They rolled themselves into the caribou robe and slept, not knowing if the akla would let them live to see the next day dawn.

When Pitohok awoke, he said, "The weather's changed. Can you not smell and feel spring's dampness in the air?"

Cautiously he cut away the entrance block and crawled outside. Upik followed him. The land was blanketed in lead-gray fog that hung heavily above the snow, hiding everything from view. The huge akla might have been very close to them or very far away.

Pitohok dug up the caribou and cutting a larger entrance in their igloo, shoved the frozen animal outside.

"There is Long Claws. He is waiting for us," Upik whispered with terror in her voice.

Pitohok looked up and saw the dark outline of the akla standing watching them. It was less than a stone's throw away, its wide back glistening with silver hoarfrost, which made the coarse hair on its massive shoulders bristle like countless needles.

"Shall I try to shoot him now?" Pitohok whispered to his sister.

"No," she said. "No! I'm afraid that last bullet will break and the noise will only anger him."

"Then hurry," he cried. "Help me get this caribou up onto my back. I don't know how far I can carry it today. My legs feel weak as water. But we've got to get it home."

Swaying its huge head back and forth, the grizzly let a low growl rumble in its throat. It was so close now that for the first time Upik could see the akla's long, sharp claws. They cut deep furrows in the snow when it came shambling toward them. Its beady black eyes watched every move they made.

"Leave our caribou sleeping skin in front of the igloo. That may fool him," Pitohok whispered. "If he goes inside, he will surely smell the place where the caribou lay last night. He may stay there digging long enough for us to lose him."

Together they hurried away, trying to hide themselves from Long Claws in the heavy ice fog. They walked and walked until they came to a riverbed that seemed familiar to them. Violent winds had blown one bank free of snow, but in the swirling fog they could not tell where it would lead them. Pitohok struggled up onto the stones that formed the bank of the frozen river. His sister had to help him by pushing at his back.

"Be careful not to leave a single track up here," Pitohok gasped. "Step from rock to rock," he warned her. "The wind is at our back. If the akla cannot see us or smell our footprints, we may lose him."

Together they traveled on the stony river bank until about midday, following a twisted course, leaving no path behind them.

"I hope we are far enough away from him," Pitohok gasped. "I can walk no farther."

He sank to his knees and let the heavy weight of the caribou sag down until it rested on the wind-cleared stones. He lay against it, his chest heaving as he tried to catch his breath. Although the air was stinging cold, Upik had to kneel and wipe the frost-white sweat from her brother's face.

"He's gone." Upik sighed, glad to rest the heavy rifle in the snow. She looked around in the still-thick fog. "Which way do we go now?"

Pitohok peered over his shoulder and felt cold sweat trickling down his spine. He could see no sign of the sun. Everything was hidden by a wall of fog.

"I . . . I don't know," he admitted. "I was trying so hard to get away from the akla that now . . . we're lost!"

Pitohok struggled painfully onto his knees and looked in all directions. He saw nothing but gray ice fog that drifted in phantom swirls along the frozen river.

"Oh, I wish someone would help us," Upik whispered aloud, and as if in answer to her words, the snowy owl came toward her, winging low out of the fog. Upik saw the owl turn its head as though it had seen the bear, then stare at her with its huge golden-yellow eyes. Suddenly the owl changed its wingbeat, hovering as if by magic at the very edge of the smokelike mists. It seemed to signal Upik. Then, turning sharply to the right, it flew off, cutting a dark trail through the ice-cold wall of fog.

Upik stood up, and, using all her strength, helped her brother heave the caribou onto his back. She struggled to ease the heavy burden as she stood upright.

"We should follow her," said Upik. "I think she knows the way."

Her brother's answer was a moan when the full weight of the frozen caribou settled on his tired, cramped shoulders. "Yes, follow the owl," he whispered.

Upik tried to steady Pitohok while they walked. She looked back only once at the zigzag trail they left in the snow as her brother's strength grew less and less. Both of them had lost all sense of distance and of time. Upik followed the owl's course through the dense fog, wondering if they would ever reach their home.

They had not gone far before Upik heard the sound of heavy breathing. She turned, then screamed in terror. The huge grizzly, its heavy head rolling, its tongue lolling out of its mouth, came padding after them. It was only a pace behind Pitohok. Upik saw Long Claws raise its head and sniff at the rich burden of caribou, which had softened a little because of the heat of Pitohok's body. The grizzly stretched out its neck and licked the frosted nostrils of the caribou.

"What's the matter?" Pitohok asked her. Then turning, he, too, saw the bear. His voice caught in his throat. "You've got to . . . to try and shoot him," Pitohok gasped. "I can't do it. My arms are too tired. My whole body is trembling from carrying this weight. Let him get close to you," he said, "then shoot him . . . in the head."

Upik stopped, raised the heavy rifle and tried to sight along its wavering barrel. "I can't," she said. "I am afraid . . . afraid this

last stone bullet will break." She was weeping. "Drop the caribou," Upik begged her brother. "Let Long Claws take it. We can walk away alive. It will stop and eat. Please drop the caribou. I am afraid that the akla is going to kill you for that meat."

Pitohok hunched his shoulders and struggled forward, as if he had not heard her plea. But now Upik could see that he held his short knife in his hand and that he would not give up their prize of meat without a fight.

Once more she heard an angry rumble in the grizzly's throat and saw it reach out with one terrible paw and rake the caribou along the whole length of its back. As its claws hooked against the caribou's antlers, Pitohok was thrown off balance and stumbled sideways, falling onto his knees. The big bear moved closer. Driven by fear and desperation, Pitohok rose and continued walking, his eyes narrowed, his mouth drawn down with strain.

The huge akla, with lips drawn back to show its enormous teeth, came after him again. Upik once more raised her grandfather's rifle and looked along its sights. The bear must have heard the safety catch click off, for it stopped, turned its head and stared straight up the gun barrel at her. At that moment, looking into its eyes, Upik realized that the bear was neither good nor evil. It was a hunter like themselves, desperate to feed itself and remain alive in the lonely, snow-filled wilderness. She lowered the rifle. She could not bring herself to try to kill the bear.

At that moment, Pitohok whispered hoarsely, "I see the owl again! She's sitting on our family's empty food cache. Can it be?" he sobbed. "Are we . . . almost home?"

The bear moved in again behind him and, raising up on its hind feet, struck out angrily at the caribou's plump haunches. Pitohok reeled from the heavy blow and staggered to his knees. He tried to rise, then sank back onto the snow.

"I can't go on," he said. "I'm finished." He had lost his knife. There were tears in his eyes, but his teeth were clenched in anger. He tightened his grip upon the caribou.

"Let go," Upik begged her brother. "Let him have the meat."

"No," Pitohok said. "If I lose this caribou to that bear and return home with nothing, none of us will live, and I, myself, would die of shame."

He turned away from the hot breath of the snarling grizzly whose great swaying head was not more than an arm's length from his face.

"Run!" Pitohok whispered to his sister. "Run for the igloo and save yourself."

Upik bent and grabbed her brother underneath the arms, trying to help him up, but he was too weak. Then she turned around so that she stood directly between him and the akla's gaping jaws.

"No — don't do that," Pitohok gasped. He was hunched over like an old man. "Put the rifle under the caribou to help me support this weight," he moaned, "or I . . . shall never rise. You run!" he begged his sister. Pitohok wept aloud as he whispered, "I can't do any more. All my strength has gone. It's going black . . . I'm going to . . ."

"You are coming with me, now!" cried Upik. "I can see our igloo. It's not far from us. Can you not see it through the fog?"

The big grizzly raked its claws through the snow. Upik put her left shoulder underneath the caribou and her arm around her brother's waist and strained with all her might. Together they rose from the snow and staggered off toward their family's house. Pitohok stumbled once again and fell onto one knee. He hung there gasping for breath.

The akla snarled and opened its mouth wide to take the caribou's leg and Pitohok's mitted hand between its crushing jaws.

"*Unalook! Kukikotak!*" Upik screamed at the bear. "We shared our fish with you. Don't you dare to harm my brother. He must take this food home to our family. They are starving . . . don't you understand?"

The huge bear let go of Pitohok's hand and the caribou's leg and stood there glaring back at her.

"Quick! Get back on your feet," Upik whispered. "We have only a little way to go."

The grizzly must have seen the snowhouse, too, for suddenly it shambled around in front of them, blocking Pitohok's way.

"I warned you not to hurt my brother," Upik screamed again.

As if ruled by magic, the huge bear stepped back and let them pass.

"Mother! Mother! Come and help us!" Upik wailed.

Long Claws turned its head and stared at her when Upik's mother burst out of their igloo entrance. She saw the great humped shoulders of the akla and, like her daughter, screamed at it, then turned and rushed inside again.

Upik tried to take half of the caribou's weight on her own shoulders while pulling Pitohok to his feet. Slowly he rose, but his knees would scarcely support him.

"Don't drop it now," Upik said in a stern voice. "We're almost there."

Together they staggered painfully toward the igloo.

"Everything is whirling around," cried Pitohok. "It's going black again . . . I'm falling. . . ."

Because she no longer had the strength to hold him, Upik and her brother collapsed together on the snow. She shook him, but Pitohok seemed to have lost the power to hear or move or speak. Upik tried to drag him toward the igloo, but his arms remained locked tight around their precious burden of meat.

Long Claws turned once more and shambled after them, snarling like a huge and angry dog. It grasped the caribou's neck in its powerful jaws and started backing away, dragging the carcass and Pitohok, pulling both of them into the swirling fog.

The snow knife, the rifle and Pitohok's short knife were gone. Upik had no weapons but her hands and teeth. She turned and saw her grandfather crawling out of the igloo on his hands and knees. In his left mitt he held his huge curved bow and in his mouth a pair of arrows. Right behind him came their mother, her parka hood puffed out with icy wind, screaming aloud, raging to protect her children, ready to do battle with the enormous bear. Her hands outstretched like claws, their mother raced forward to attack.

Upik heard her grandfather call out, "Stop, woman. Hold! If you help me, we can pierce him right from here."

The grandfather knelt unsteadily and notched an arrow to the braided string. His hands shook with strain when he tried to draw the powerful bow. But he could not. In desperation Upik's mother knelt and helped to draw the heavy weapon almost to full curve. The point of the arrow wavered wildly when the grandfather tried to aim.

"Don't!" Upik cried, spreading her arms and running between her grandfather's unsteady arrow and the bear. "You might hit Pitohok."

Looking back, she saw her brother still being dragged across the snow behind the bear. In sudden anger she whirled around and ran straight between her brother and the akla, screaming, *You let go of him! Let go!*"

Surprised, the huge grizzly released the caribou for a moment and raised its head.

"Here, this is for you," she yelled and reaching into her parka hood, she snatched out the last piece of frozen trout that she had saved and flung it beyond the bear.

The akla looked at her, grunted, then turned and moved away from Pitohok, who still clasped the caribou as fiercely as an Arctic crab. The grizzly snatched up the piece of fish. Then, with its hips and frosted shoulders rolling, it disappeared into the silver wall of icy fog.

Pitohok's mother and his grandfather knelt beside him, trying to unlock his arms from the caribou.

Pitohok opened his eyes and stared at them. "I thought that akla would surely snatch the caribou away from me," he whispered.

"I, too, believed that he would take it from you," his grandfather agreed. "But no human knows exactly what the animals will do."

"Upik was afraid of the akla. We were both afraid of him, and yet she ran and put her body between me and the grizzly's snarling jaws. Grandfather, did you believe my sister would do that?"

"No. I did not know what she would do. Nobody knows the strength or courage that humans possess until real danger comes to test them."

Thinking and Discussing

In what ways does the author of "Long Claws" describe nature as being threatening? As being helpful? What do you think the author may be suggesting about the relationship between the Inuit people and nature?

Choosing a Creative Response

Composing a Song or Poem To remember their dangerous adventure, Upik and Pitohok might have made up a song or poem. Write your favorite part of the story as they might have recited or sung it.

Carving an Animal Figure The Inuit people are famous for their carvings. Make an illustration of an animal, bird, or person that Upik or Pitohok might have carved. You might want to do the actual carving on your own later.

Renaming Animals The grizzly bear in the story was also known by the descriptive name Long Claws. Invent descriptive names for the owl, the wolverine, and other animals that Upik and Pitohok could have seen during their adventure.

Creating Your Own Activity Plan and complete your own activity in response to "Long Claws."

Thinking and Writing

At the end of the story, Grandfather says, "Nobody knows the strength or courage that humans possess until real danger comes to test them." Think about someone you have known or heard about who discovered great strength in the face of danger. Write a description of the way the person was tested, and tell how unexpected courage and strength led to safety.

THINKING ABOUT ADVENTURE

Presenting Awards for Courage Think about the characters that you have met in "Spirit of Survival." Which ones, do you think, showed the most courage? Whom would you most like to meet?

Create an award for courage in the face of extreme danger. Draw a picture of the award, or design a three-dimensional trophy. Decide which character in "Spirit of Survival" will receive it. Then plan and hold an award ceremony in which students can role-play all parts.

Delivering a Speech Imagine you are one of the characters in "Spirit of Survival" and must make a speech. Describe your feelings to the people who have come to see you speak about your adventure. Tell them what you were like before the adventure, and emphasize how the dangerous trial changed your understanding of life.

Inventing a Safety Device Create an invention that might have helped a character in "Spirit of Survival." For example, you might design a pocket safety device for anyone traveling by water or snow. Give the invention a name. Write an ad describing the product's safety features. Include a drawing of your design, and label the special features it contains. Then advertise it by telling how one of the characters in "Spirit of Survival" could have used your ingenious device.

James Houston was born in Canada in 1921. After studying art in Paris, he returned home looking for interesting subjects to draw. By chance he visited an Inuit settlement on the northeast coast of Hudson Bay. He stayed in the Arctic for fourteen years.

Houston used his knowledge of Eskimo life and legends to write books for young people.

He was awarded the Canadian Library Association Book of the Year Award for *Tikta'liktak* and *The White Archer*. He also received the American Library Association Notable Books Award for *The White Archer, Akavak*, and *The White Dawn*. Houston now lives in Rhode Island.

Ariane Randall, the daughter of two college professors, was a student at Hunter College High School when she wrote about her terrifying experience in the ocean off Haiti. Ariane had gone with her father Francis for a week's vacation in Haiti while her younger brother and mother stayed home in New York City. "Survival at Sea" is Ariane's account of her disastrous return journey.

Armstrong Sperry was born in Connecticut in 1897. He studied art at Yale, in New York, and in Paris. After working in an advertising agency, he traveled for two years among the islands of southern Polynesia. He learned to speak Tahitian and spent hours drawing the islands and their people. This experience inspired many of Sperry's books, among them *One Day with Manu*, *Lost Lagoon*, and the Newbery Award winner, *Call It Courage*.

Seymour Reit is a native of New York City. After attending New York University, he began his career working as an animation cartoonist. He is well known for his character "Casper the Friendly Ghost."

After World War II, Reit became a writer and an artist for animated films. He has written many books for young people, some of which include *Coins and Coin Collecting*, *Race Against Death*, and *Bugs Bunny Goes to the Dentist*.

Colin Thiele was born in Eudunda, South Australia, in 1920. He has won awards for his poetry, plays, and novels, and his short stories and poems appear in many anthologies. Several of his books have been made into movies in Australia. They include *The Hammerhead Light* and *Storm Boy*.

THE ADVENTURES CONTINUE

Courage at Indian Deep by Jane Resh Thomas (Clarion, 1984) ■ In the midst of a blizzard, Cass notices a distress call from a sinking ship on Lake Superior. He shows unusual courage as he and his dog and a former school rival help rescue people from the ship.

Wild Timothy by Gary L. Blackwood (Atheneum, 1987) ■ Timothy's father takes him deep into the woods on his first camping trip. When his father sends him out to chop firewood, Timothy becomes hopelessly lost. Alone in the woods, he tries to remember the survival tactics he's only read about.

Thor Heyerdahl, Viking Scientist by Wyatt Blassingame (Nelson, 1979) ■ Explorer Thor Heyerdahl became world-famous when he successfully sailed the raft *Kon-Tiki* across the Pacific. This action-packed biography tells about *Kon-Tiki* and Heyerdahl's equally exciting expeditions *Ra I* and *Ra II*.

Julie of the Wolves by Jean Craighead George (Harper, 1972) ■ Julie, a thirteen-year-old Inuit girl, runs away from home and becomes lost on the arctic tundra. She needs all her courage to get through the many adventures that await her. She finds help where she least expects it — from a pack of wolves.

Night of the Twisters *by Ivy Ruckman (Crowell, 1984)* ■ Dan is in charge of the house and his younger brother while his parents are away. He's managing well when suddenly he hears sirens shriek out a tornado alert. Dan rushes his brother and a visiting friend into the basement. They huddle in the shower stall while the twisters strike.

Island of the Blue Dolphins *by Scott O'Dell (Houghton, 1960)* ■ By a terrible mistake, Karana's tribe leave her behind when they have to evacuate their island off the California coast. This award-winning story tells how she not only stays alive for the next eighteen years, but also finds happiness.

SCIENCE

BOOK 2

EXPLORING THE OCEANS

Captain's Log,
Friday

Descended in our undersea exploration vehicle to a depth of 2,000 feet. We are resting at the edge of a gaping canyon in the ocean floor. Nearby, weird, glowing fish swim up to examine the craft and peer back at us.

The crew is eager to explore and observe.
Today we begin.

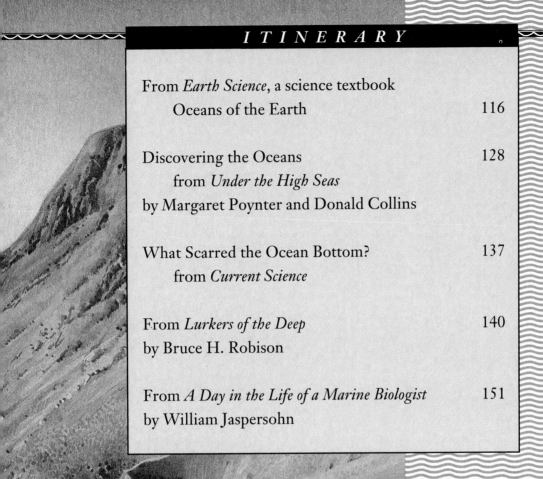

ITINERARY

From *Earth Science*, a science textbook

OCEANS *of the* EARTH

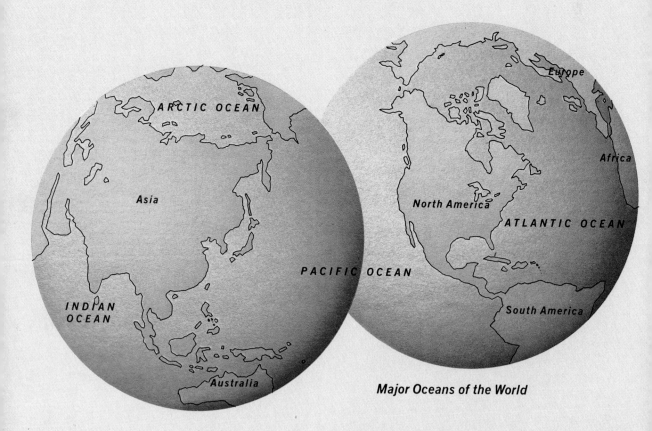

ARCTIC OCEAN

Asia

INDIAN OCEAN

PACIFIC OCEAN

Australia

Europe

Africa

North America

ATLANTIC OCEAN

South America

Major Oceans of the World

Illustrations by Joseph LeMonnier

f all the planets in our solar system, only earth is covered by vast oceans of liquid water. This water is like a thin soup. It teems with living things and is seasoned with salt and other minerals. As you read about the ocean, keep the following questions in mind:

a. How much of the world is covered by oceans?

b. What are the major oceans of the earth?

Oceans Cover Most of the Earth

Oceans cover more than 70 percent of the earth's surface. Astronauts looking at the Pacific Ocean from space see only cloud-covered water dotted with small islands and ringed with continents. The other side of the globe contains almost all the earth's land.

The oceans contain 97 percent of all the water on earth. Rivers, lakes, streams, and ponds hold less than 1 percent of the earth's water. The remaining 2 percent is frozen into ice in glaciers and around the North and South Poles. Water circulates among the oceans, the land, and the air by means of precipitation and evaporation in the water cycle.

Major Oceans of the World

The water of all the oceans circulates in one vast ocean. Geographers divide this great ocean into four separate bodies of water, as shown on the map. The Pacific is the largest and deepest ocean. It covers more than a third of the earth's surface. Next in size is the Atlantic. The third largest is the Indian Ocean. The Arctic is the smallest ocean. Much of the surface water in the Arctic is frozen most of the year.

Scientists who study the movements of the earth's crust find that the Pacific Ocean is getting smaller. Most of the crust beneath the Pacific is one huge plate. At its boundaries, the Pacific plate sinks under the surrounding continental plates. In the center of the Atlantic Ocean's floor, however, two plates are moving apart. The

Atlantic is slowly getting larger because new crust forms at the spreading boundary. The plates of the ocean floor move at about the same speed your fingernails grow.

Review It

1. How much of the earth's surface do oceans cover?
2. Name the four major oceans, from largest to smallest.

✳ WATERS OF THE OCEAN

A mouthful of seawater tastes saltier than a mouthful of potato chips. To understand why, you must know about the minerals in ocean water. Keep these questions in mind:

a. What is salinity?

b. How do the temperature and pressure of seawater vary?

Dissolved Salts Make Seawater Salty

Dissolved salts and minerals make ocean water salty. Notice in the table that sodium chloride — common table salt — is the most abundant salt in the ocean. Almost all elements found on earth are also found in seawater.

The ocean's crust is the main source of the minerals in seawater. Water seeps down through pores and tiny cracks in the ocean floor. Minerals in the crust dissolve in this water. The kinds of minerals and their ratio to each other are the same in seawater everywhere. An amount of water equal to the entire ocean filters into and out of the crust every eight million years.

The most abundant minerals in seawater

	Parts per thousand
Sodium chloride	27.2
Magnesium chloride	3.8
Magnesium sulfate	1.7
Calcium sulfate	1.3
Potassium sulfate	0.9
Calcium carbonate	0.1
Magnesium bromide	0.1

Salinity (sə lĭn′ĭ tē) is a measure of how salty seawater is. If you boil away all the water from 1,000 grams of seawater, about 35 grams of salt will remain. Only 965 grams is water. The average salinity of the oceans is 35 parts of salt in 1,000 parts of seawater.

118

In warm, dry climates, such as near the Mediterranean Sea, ocean water evaporates rapidly. The salts that remain make the water saltier than average. Salinity is low where rivers, melting ice, or heavy rains pour fresh water into the ocean.

Temperature and Pressure of Ocean Water

Temperature The sun warms the water on the ocean's surface. Wind and waves mix the heated surface water with cold water beneath it. Notice in the diagram that water temperature is almost the same throughout the top layer of water. The temperature of this layer — the **mixed layer** — is different in different parts of the ocean. At the poles, it is usually colder than 0° C. Near the equator, surface water can be as warm as 30° C. In the middle latitudes, the surface temperature changes with the seasons. The mixed layer is 100 to 300 meters deep.

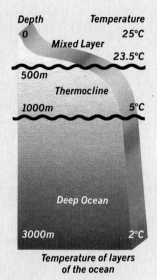

Temperature of layers
of the ocean

Beneath the mixed layer is the **thermocline (thûr′mə klīn′)** — a layer of water that rapidly gets colder with increasing depth. Seawater at the bottom of the thermocline is very cold. Even near the equator, the bottom of the thermocline is colder than 5° C. The thermocline can be as deep as 1,000 meters.

Below the thermocline, temperatures drop slowly. The freezing point of seawater of average salinity is -2° C. The temperature of deep ocean water is always near freezing.

Pressure Air above the earth presses on the earth's surface. The air pressure that results can be measured in "atmospheres." Average air pressure at sea level is one atmosphere. In the same way that air presses on the earth's surface, water presses on the ocean's bottom. Pressure becomes greater with depth. Water pressure on the sea floor increases by an amount equal to one atmosphere of pressure for every increase of 10 meters beneath the ocean's surface. Forty atmospheres of water press on objects 400 meters below the surface. Deeper in the ocean, pressures are even greater.

Review It

1. What is the average salinity of seawater?
2. What is the thermocline?
3. How many atmospheres of pressure would the ocean put on an object 6,000 meters beneath the surface?

EXPLORING THE OCEAN FLOOR

Most people know more about the surface of the near side of the moon than they know about the bottom of the ocean. Answer these questions as you read about the ocean floor:

    a. How do oceanographers measure the depth of the ocean?
    b. How is sediment brought up from the ocean bottom?
    c. What are the features of the sea floor?

Measuring the Water's Depth

Soundings are measurements of the depth of water. In the past, sailors took soundings by lowering ropes with weights. When the weight touched bottom, the length of wet rope showed the depth of the water. In deep water, a sounding was inaccurate because of the water's movement.

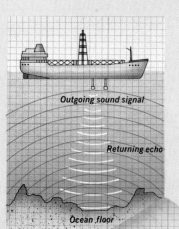

Outgoing sound signal

Returning echo

Ocean floor

Profile of the ocean floor

Today, scientists find the depth of water by using an **echo sounder**. This device measures depth by bouncing sound waves off the ocean floor. Notice in the diagram to the left that sound waves hit the ocean bottom and bounce back to the ship as an echo. The echo sounder measures how long a sound wave takes to reach the ocean bottom and return to the ship. Since the speed of sound in seawater is known, the sounder can calculate the ocean's depth at that spot. As the ship moves, the echo sounder makes a map.

Sediments on the Ocean Bottom

The layers of rock that make up the sea floor are covered with **sediments,** or material that has settled to the bottom of the ocean. Near the continents, most of these sediments were washed off the land as sand, clay, dust, or volcanic ash. Far from land, however, many sediments are the remains of organisms — or living things. As sea organisms die, their bodies fall to the ocean floor. Some parts of the ocean are so deep that bodies of organisms dissolve before they reach the bottom.

A core

The deepest sea floors are covered by tiny particles of clay carried from the continents by rivers. The particles slowly drift through the ocean until they sink to the bottom. It can take 1,000 years for two millimeters of sediment to accumulate on the bottom of the sea floor.

Scientists use several devices to gather samples from the ocean bottom. A grab sampler has jaws that close when they reach bottom. It takes bites out of the sediment beneath shallow water. A dredge is like a bag made of steel links. A ship drags the dredge along the ocean bottom. Dredges pick up large objects, such as loose rocks.

A corer works like a huge hollow drill. It brings long cylinders of sediment — **cores** — up to the surface in metal tubes. Special research ships bring up cores from beneath the water along the edges of continents. Scientists learn about the history of the sea floor by studying the layers of sediments in cores.

The Features of the Sea Floor

The drawing below shows a side view of the ocean's floor. At the far left is the **continental shelf** — a broad, gently sloping plain near the shoreline. Its width ranges from less than 3 kilometers off the west coast of Peru and Chile to more than 1,000 kilometers off the northeastern coast of Siberia. In most places, the shelf extends about 75 kilometers from the shoreline. The ocean averages 135 meters deep on the shelf. Scientists believe that fast-flowing currents containing mud or sand erode deep valleys — or submarine canyons — into the continental shelf. The Hudson River Canyon, for example, is a deep cut in the continental shelf off New York City.

The slightly steeper **continental slope** begins beyond the continental shelf. It drops to a depth of about 4,000 meters. Sand or mud washed down from the slope may form a gentle **continental rise** at the base of the slope.

The **ocean basin** extends hundreds of kilometers beyond the continental slope. Its depth averages more than 4,000 meters. Low hills, called **abyssal** (ə **bĭs′**əl) hills, cover parts of the ocean basin. If a hill is more than 900 meters high, it is called a **seamount.** The ocean floor is flat where sediment collects and covers the hills. These large flat regions are abyssal plains.

Sea Level

Shoreline

Land

Abyssal Hills

Continental Shelf

Continental Slope

Abyssal Plain

Volcanoes rise from the ocean basin in many areas. Some reach above the ocean's surface to form volcanic islands, such as the Hawaiian Islands. A volcano with a flat top is called a **guyot** (gē′ō). Oceanographers believe guyots are volcanoes that rose above the ocean's surface until waves eroded and leveled their tops.

Underwater earthquakes and volcanoes often occur at mid-ocean **trenches** and **ridges.** Trenches are deep cracks in the ocean floor where two plates are colliding. Trenches are the deepest places in the ocean. Most trenches cut 2 to 4 kilometers down into the ocean floor. They may be thousands of kilometers long, but only about 100 kilometers wide. Deep ocean trenches run around the edges of the Pacific Ocean.

Mid-ocean ridges are mountain ranges that zigzag along the ocean floor. Ridges form where plates are spreading apart. Magma is the molten material under the earth's crust. It pushes up into rifts — or valleys — that cut through the center of the ridges. This magma forms new sea floor. The Mid-Atlantic Ridge runs along the center of the Atlantic Ocean. Spreading boundaries with lower, less rugged mountains are called rises.

REVIEW IT

1. How do oceanographers use sound waves to measure the depth of the ocean?
2. What is a source of sediment found in the deepest part of the ocean?
3. Name three types of features on the ocean floor.

Volcano

Mid-Ocean Ridge

Guyot

Trench

OCEANS OF THE EARTH

Thinking and Discussing

According to the text, the Pacific Ocean is getting smaller, and the Atlantic Ocean is growing larger. What is causing these changes?

What are the three main characteristics of ocean water discussed in the text?

What terms have you learned to describe features of the ocean floor? Which explanations of the causes of these features do you find most interesting? Why?

Applying Science Concepts

Performing a Salt-Water Experiment Leave a container of salt water on a sunny windowsill for a few days. Observe the water daily and record your observations. When all the water has evaporated, observe and record the results. What has happened to the water? What has happened to the salt? What conclusions can you draw from the experiment to explain why the ocean stays salty?

Creating a Graphic Look at the graphics — maps, charts, and graphs—in this textbook chapter. They all help you understand important facts about the ocean. Alone or with a group of classmates, create another graphic that presents information about the ocean in a clear and organized way. You could, for example, make a chart that shows the pressure of the water beneath the ocean's surface or, with a little research, a map of ocean currents. You might want to explain your graphic to the class and display it in the classroom.

DIVING BELL

The diving bell was first suggested by the ancient Greek philosopher Aristotle. It finally came into being in the seventeenth century. Made of metal, the bell could be the size of a helmet, or it could be large enough to hold two people. The bell was lowered into the water with the open end downward so that the inside remained filled with air.

Writing

A REPORT OF INFORMATION

Scientists gather information about the ocean in many ways, including testing, exploration, observation, and photography. For the information to be useful, scientists must also present it in reports. The purpose of a report of information is to arrange and express facts clearly, in a way that enables a reader to understand the information quickly and easily.

For what subjects have you gathered information? Many people have a favorite topic or a hobby that they know a lot about. Perhaps you are an expert about the habits of cats, or how auto engines work, or what kinds of fish live in nearby lakes or streams. Pick a topic that interests you and that you know something about. Use the following steps to guide you in writing a report of information so that you can share your knowledge with others.

1. Prewriting Before you begin, think about your topic. What is the viewpoint you wish to present? What facts will you include to express that viewpoint in an interesting, informative way? Which facts may not be necessary? Plan an outline that will enable you to present the information in a clear, organized manner. Your outline should include all the important points about the subject that you want to cover in your report. If you need to, go to the library and research your topic. Select the most up-to-date reference books. Take notes, writing the information on note cards. Make sure you gather facts dealing with all the points on your outline. Finally, arrange your notes so that you have one stack of cards for each point. Then arrange the cards in each stack to fit the order of your outline.

2. *Write a First Draft* As you write, think about your audience and your purpose for writing. Remember that you want to inform your readers while holding their interest. Follow the organization that you planned in your outline, but also remember that you may improve your report as you go along.

3. *Revise* Read your first draft and make any needed changes. Does your report present your viewpoint and the important points in a clear, organized way? Is it interesting as well as informative?

4. *Proofread* Check your report for correct spelling, capitalization, and punctuation.

5. *Publish* Make a neat copy of your report. You may want to illustrate it with drawings or pictures from magazines.

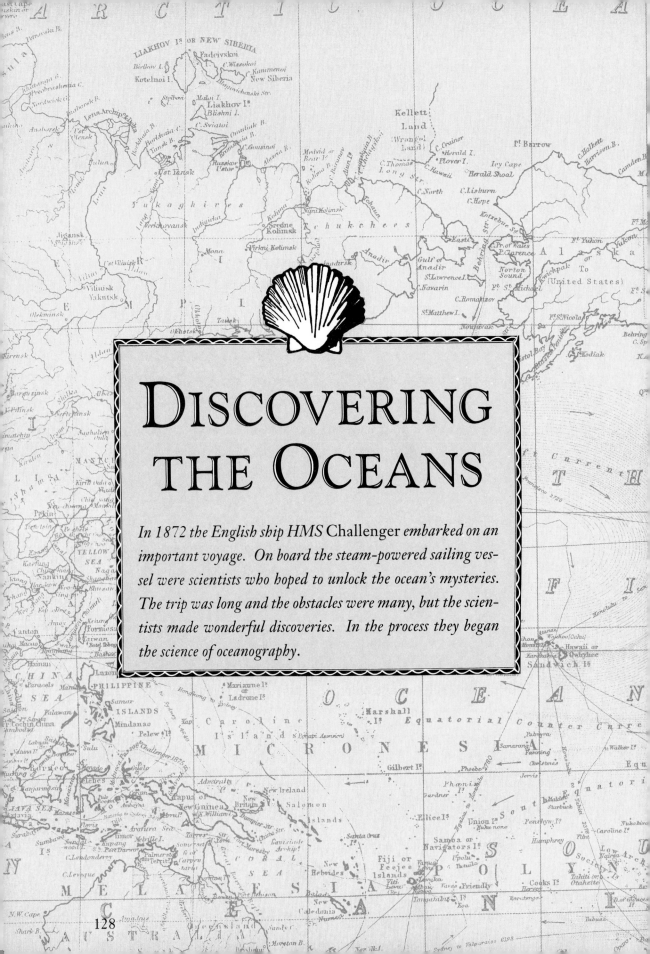

DISCOVERING THE OCEANS

In 1872 the English ship HMS Challenger embarked on an important voyage. On board the steam-powered sailing vessel were scientists who hoped to unlock the ocean's mysteries. The trip was long and the obstacles were many, but the scientists made wonderful discoveries. In the process they began the science of oceanography.

From *Under the High Seas*
by Margaret Poynter and Donald Collins

A giant step in the study of the world ocean was taken after the telegraph was invented in 1837. European and American businessmen were eager to use this speedy method of communication, so they enthusiastically supported the plans to lay a transatlantic cable. The success of the project depended upon finding the answers to some questions about the proposed cable route. What sort of water movement exists there? How is the ocean floor contoured? Are there any animals inhabiting the region, and if so, what kind? Will they chew the cable's covering? Or will they deposit their wastes upon it, thus causing it to rot?

Biologists, botanists, zoologists and oceanographers went to work to find the answers to these and other questions. They took soundings at regular intervals all along the route. They analyzed sediments from the sea floor. They made charts of the currents.

One weight that had been left on the sea floor for an hour came back to the surface with thirteen starfish clinging to it. The captain was delighted at what he considered proof that abundant life existed at great depths.

"The sea has sent forth its long coveted[1] message," he wrote in his log that night.

Some of the scientists weren't certain that the starfish had actually lived on the sea floor. "Couldn't they have clung to the weight as it passed through the water at a much higher level?" they asked.

---

[1]**coveted** (kŭv′ it əd): something desired or craved.

In 1860, their doubts were partially resolved. At that time, a submerged cable broke and was brought up for repair. Several sea creatures were clinging to it, one of which was a coral which could only have grown into place as the cable lay on the ocean bottom.

By the time the Atlantic cable project was completed, this particular section of the sea floor had been mapped in a detail that had never before been attempted. A vague picture of deep coastal trenches and a central plateau began to emerge. Until that time, it had been assumed that the sea floor sloped gradually down to its lowest point about halfway between the two continents, then climbed back up to meet the opposite shore. It now appeared that the middle of the ocean floor wasn't its lowest point, but perhaps its highest.

As usually happens in a scientific investigation, these discoveries led to a host of questions that cried out to be answered. What does the presence of these undersea mountains and valleys mean? Are they part of the lost continent of Atlantis?[2] Or are they part of a newly emerging landform, one which will appear above the surface of the sea millions of years hence?

To solve these and other mysteries, the world's major seafaring countries joined in the search for more facts. The "space race" of the nineteenth century began, but instead of competing, the participants cooperated with each other.

In 1872, England launched the HMS *Challenger*, which was to "investigate the condition of the Deep Sea throughout the entire Oceanic Basin." An old naval sailing ship with auxiliary steam power, it was an unlikely vessel to perform such a monumental task.

---

[2]**Atlantis**: a fabled island or continent of ancient times, said to have sunk beneath the sea during an earthquake.

Besides being clumsy and slow, it had an alarming tendency to pitch and roll much more than most ships.

As the *Challenger* groped its way across unknown seas using inaccurate and partially blank maps, the members of its crew often had to call upon all of their skills of seamanship. In the Antarctic, the ship was caught amid icebergs that were drifting in the gale force wind. By artfully navigating between two icebergs that were used as a windbreak, the sailors were able to escape the precarious situation.

Each time the *Challenger* had to "take a station" to make a depth sound, the sails had to be shortened, and the ship brought into the wind. Twin propellers, which were driven by the steam engines, were used to keep the craft steady in the water. Steam-powered winches creaked and groaned as the lines went slowly over the sides.

Each line could hold a variety of primitive gear. The nets that gathered the plankton and other forms of small marine life were muslin or silk bags attached to iron rings one foot in diameter. Water samples were collected in glass bottles that could be opened underwater by the men on the ship. Mercury recording thermometers measured the water temperature. These readings were far from accurate, and the instruments were often broken when they struck the side of the ship.

From the time the *Challenger* furled its sails to take a station to the time when the last foot of line was wound laboriously back onto the reel, two days sometimes passed. Stations were often held in the fury of a raging blizzard and in below-freezing temperatures. As the scientists waited for the dredging to be completed, they suffered agonies of frustration and uncertainty. Would the steam engine break down at a crucial moment? Or would the winches jam? What if the nets came up empty? Even the ship's parrot seemed uneasy. "What?" he echoed. "Two thousand fathoms and no bottom?"

The *Challenger*'s ordinary seamen had little understanding of the reasons behind the grueling search for bits of coral and shell and mud and clay. They knew only that they had to work long hours under the worst of conditions and that they were often on the receiving end of the scientists' anger when something went wrong. It was hard for them to understand how a man's happiness could depend to such a great extent on some slimy bit of muck, or a particularly unattractive sea worm.

The HMS *Challenger* returned to England in May of 1876. During the three and one-half years of its voyage, it had logged almost sixty-nine thousand miles and had taken over 360 stations, having stopped on the average every 200 miles.

The scientists were jubilant. They had measured the structure of the ocean all around the world and had found it to be marvelously complicated. They had analyzed the chemical composition of hundreds of water samples and saw that the sea contained many of the earth's minerals in solution. They had dredged up thousands of species of animal life that were new to the scientific world. Their findings had indicated that life exists in a myriad[3] of forms in all of the measured depths of the sea.   They had dredged

[3]myriad (mîr′ē əd): a very large, indefinite number.

up strange, charred-looking rocks that ranged in size from cinders to potatoes. These were put on display in the British Museum, but otherwise received little attention.

The *Challenger*'s scientists had felt the thrill of handling ooze that had lain hidden under thousands of fathoms of water for millions of years. This sediment was composed largely of the corpses of microscopic creatures that constantly filter like an endless snowfall to the ocean floor.

One of the most awesome results of the *Challenger*'s voyage was the partial uncovering of the hidden world of the ocean floor. This world contained a tantalizing mixture of tall mountain ranges, wide plateaus, and deep, plunging trenches. Far from being flat and uninteresting, the sea floor apparently rivaled the continents in the majesty of its landforms.

The *Challenger* had collected so much information that it took scores of experts twenty years to sort it out. The data eventually filled fifty thick volumes, and the study of the material kept the oceanographers of the world busy for many decades.

"Never did one expedition cost so little and produce such momentous results for human knowledge," wrote a scientist. "Indeed, the science of oceanography began the day the *Challenger* was launched."

Despite such words of praise, the *Challenger*'s voyage was only the beginning. The experts who had been on the vessel readily admitted that they had been "like blind men, groping about in the water with white sticks three-and-a-half miles long." Many of the mysteries that were found to exist at that time remain unsolved today.

DISCOVERING THE OCEANS

Thinking and Discussing

Evaluate the methods of collecting data used by the scientists aboard the *Challenger*. Were they impressive, or surprising, or were they what you would expect? Support your answers with examples.

The selection is divided into two parts. The first part tells mainly about the *Challenger* scientists and the ways in which they conducted research on their voyage. What do you read about in the second part? Why do you think the author arranged the selection in this way?

A biologist studies living things, a botanist studies plants, and a zoologist studies animals. Why are these scientists — as well as oceanographers — concerned with ocean study?

Applying Science Concepts

Identifying Scientific Accomplishments   The text discusses the accomplishments of the scientists aboard the *Challenger*. Make a list of these discoveries and accomplishments. Present your list to the class. Discuss the accomplishments you think are the most important or interesting.

135

DIVING SUITS

Early diving suits were bulky, and the diver depended on getting air from the surface through a hose or tube. In 1943, the famous French sea pioneer Jacques Cousteau made it possible for divers to carry their own air supply. Cousteau invented the **s**elf-**c**ontained **u**nderwater **b**reathing apparatus, or *scuba*. Today, for exploring deeper parts of the ocean, divers sometimes still use suits and helmets with air supplied through a hose.

WHAT SCARRED THE OCEAN BOTTOM?

Illustrations by James E. Taylor

Map by Pat Rossi

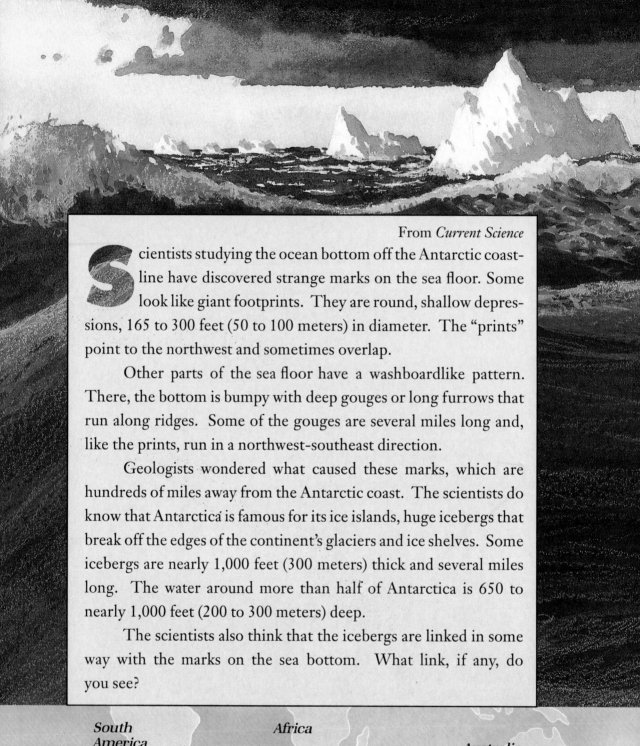

From *Current Science*

Scientists studying the ocean bottom off the Antarctic coastline have discovered strange marks on the sea floor. Some look like giant footprints. They are round, shallow depressions, 165 to 300 feet (50 to 100 meters) in diameter. The "prints" point to the northwest and sometimes overlap.

Other parts of the sea floor have a washboardlike pattern. There, the bottom is bumpy with deep gouges or long furrows that run along ridges. Some of the gouges are several miles long and, like the prints, run in a northwest-southeast direction.

Geologists wondered what caused these marks, which are hundreds of miles away from the Antarctic coast. The scientists do know that Antarctica is famous for its ice islands, huge icebergs that break off the edges of the continent's glaciers and ice shelves. Some icebergs are nearly 1,000 feet (300 meters) thick and several miles long. The water around more than half of Antarctica is 650 to nearly 1,000 feet (200 to 300 meters) deep.

The scientists also think that the icebergs are linked in some way with the marks on the sea bottom. What link, if any, do you see?

South America

Africa

Australia

Rio de Janeiro

SOUTH

ATLANTIC

OCEAN

Capetown

INDIAN

OCEAN

Sydney

iceberg lines

ANTARCTICA

WHAT SCARRED THE OCEAN BOTTOM?

Thinking and Discussing

What are the two types of marks on the sea floor? Which type tends to be bigger? In what direction do the marks run?

Why do you think scientists want to know the cause of the marks on the sea floor?

Applying Science Concepts

Planning a Scientific Study Imagine you are a scientist trying to explain the marks on the ocean floor. You believe that icebergs have floated over the spot and gouged the marks into the sea floor. What event would you have to observe to test your theory? What equipment would you need? What might be some of the difficulties in making your observations? Write a brief statement outlining your plan to test your idea and the difficulties you anticipate.

LURKERS OF THE DEEP

People have always been curious about the depths of the ocean: what is the bottom like, what — if anything — lives there? Technology has allowed us to probe ever deeper, to satisfy our curiosity and add to our store of knowledge. We know that the bottom is not a level, sloping plain but is rather a rugged terrain made up of features like those found on land. We have also learned much about the fish that dwell in the deepest parts of the ocean. In their way, they are as strange and fantastic as the legendary sea monsters of human imagination.

Photograph by Bruce Robison

Illustrations by Robert Hynes

From *Lurkers of the Deep*
by Bruce H. Robison

Gulper

Lurking in the still, dark waters of the deep sea are some of the strangest creatures on our planet. Fishes with huge teeth and glowing lights cruise through a cold blackness that is studded with small blue lights like the galaxies of space. Bright red shrimp, oddly shaped squid, and transparent animals made of jelly also live at these depths. To those of us who live on the land, the deep ocean is an alien environment, almost as harsh as that of the moon or Mars.

Only a few people have ever seen the creatures of the deep sea with their own eyes. Oceanographers, riding in tiny submarines, are some of the lucky explorers who have seen these animals. In these pages we will discover what deep-sea scientists have learned about the fishes and other animals they study. In many ways it will seem like a report on the exploration of another world.

Lanternfish

Let's start with the sun. Sunlight is radiant energy that travels 150 million kilometers (93 million miles) from the sun to the earth. We know the energy in sunshine as light and heat. Sunlight is the basic source of energy for all of the plants on our planet. Plants receive the energy of sunshine, and through a series of chemical reactions called *photosynthesis* (fō′tō **sǐn′**thǐ sǐs), they use the energy to make food from chemicals in their surroundings.

Sunshine and plants may seem an odd place to begin a discussion of deep-sea fishes, who live where there are no plants and where there is no sunlight. But the food that plants make with sunshine is important to every animal on earth, even those living deep in the ocean.

When sunlight reaches the surface of the earth it falls on grasses, trees, and other land plants and on plants that live in the ocean. Most of the oceanic plants are very small, no bigger than the period at the end of this sentence. These tiny plants are made up of only one cell, but each of them can perform the magic of photosynthesis. They are called *phytoplankton* (fī′tō **plăngk′**tən). There are so many of them in the ocean that counting them would be like trying to count the grains of sand on a beach.

Phytoplankton are usually found near the surface of the ocean. The surface waters have the most sunlight, and in order to produce food, the phytoplankton need to be in the light. Sunlight strong enough for photosynthesis reaches down only about 150 meters (nearly 500 feet) in clear oceanic water. Below this depth the dim light gradually fades to nothing. At depths of 600 meters (about 2000 feet) the water is as dark as the blackest night.

Because the oceans of the world occupy so much of its surface, more than half of the sunlight that falls on our planet lights up the waters where phytoplankton live. These billions of one-celled plants produce most of the food energy used by all of the animals of the ocean — from shrimp to whales.

But there is a lot more to the ocean than just the layer near the surface where plants can live. Down in the dim, dark waters below the plant layer lives a strange and wonderful group of animals: the creatures of the deep sea.

Most people see only the edges of the ocean. We see beaches where the ocean meets the land; in boats we can sail along the ocean's upper edge where it meets the air. In shallow water near the shore we can swim or wade; and by using scuba gear, it is possible to swim down to depths of 50 meters (more than 150 feet). But out beyond the shore the ocean gets very deep, going down about 4000 meters (more than 2 miles) in most places.

Hatchetfish

It is almost as difficult for people to explore the deep ocean as it is for them to explore the moon. One of the main reasons for this

is that the deep ocean is always dark. Sunlight reaches only a short way down, and the long stretch of water between the sunlit part and the bottom is dark except for the lights produced by the animals that live there.

Another important thing about the deep sea is its coldness. With no sunlight to heat it, the temperature of the water is usually between 3° and 10° centigrade (40° to 50° Fahrenheit). Just as the light gets dimmer as depth increases, so does the temperature get colder.

Gravity, the force that gives us weight by pulling us toward the center of the earth, also affects the animals that live in the deep sea. The deeper we go in the ocean the more the water above us weighs. The weight of the water is felt as pressure.

Hunter

Creatures on the land have only the weight of the air above pressing on them. At sea level the weight is described as one atmosphere of pressure. High in the mountains or flying in an airplane at great altitude, the pressure is less. Because water is thicker, or denser, than air, pressure increases very quickly with greater depth in the ocean. At a depth of 10 meters (about 33 feet) the weight of the water above is equal to one atmosphere. At 100 meters (330 feet) the pressure is 10 atmospheres plus the weight of the air above the ocean — a total of 11 atmospheres. One atmosphere of pressure weighs about one kilogram per square centimeter (15 pounds per square inch), so a fish living at a depth of 1000 meters in the ocean has a pressure of 101 atmospheres (1650 pounds per square inch) on it.

All of these things — the darkness, the cold, and the pressure — make it difficult for scientists to study the animals of the deep sea. They also make the deep sea a difficult place for most animals to live in. The result is that we don't know a great deal about deep-sea creatures but what we do know shows us that they are very unusual animals.

Lanternfish, like many deep-sea fishes, have light-producing spots on their bodies. Some lanternfish have large lights on their heads between their eyes, lighting the dark water in front of them much like the headlights on a car.

Hatchetfish share the deep-sea living space with the lanternfish. Their bodies are shaped like hatchet blades, and their small tails look like handles. Hatchetfish spend most of their time at depths of about 400 to 800 meters (1300 to 2500 feet).

The eyes of some species of hatchetfish point straight up. Their eyes help the fish to see well in dim light and to judge distances accurately.

Bristlemouth fishes are found in nearly all oceans. Most are quite small — about 5 centimeters (or 2 inches) long. When two similar species inhabit the same area, they generally divide the living space into two layers. The darker species lives in the lower, more dimly lit layer, and the lighter species lives above. In this way, the fishes match the light levels of their environment.

Dragonfish get their name from their ferocious appearance. They seldom grow longer than 60 or 70 centimeters (about two feet). The long, flexible projections called *barbels* (**bär′**bəlz) that hang from their lower jaws end in light-producing bulbs. The light seems to attract other fish that the dragonfish eat.

Most species of dragonfish have mouths filled with jagged rows of long, sharp teeth. In some species, the teeth are hinged so that they will fold inward toward the throat but not forward to allow escape. Anything that finds itself in such a mouth is trapped.

Anglerfish are ambushers. They have long projections, like

Anglerfish

147

fishing rods, growing from their heads. At the tip of the rods are glowing baits. Anglers have large mouths filled with long, sharp teeth. They quickly gobble up anything that is attracted to their bait.

Anglerfish live in depths below 1000 meters (3300 feet), where the water is inky black. Like most fish that live in the cold depths, anglerfish swim rather slowly. While awaiting their prey, they probably stay motionless in the dark water with only the lights of their lures to indicate their presence. But they spring into action when their lures are touched.

In some species of anglerfish, the female is much larger than the male. Once the tiny male anglerfish has found his mate, he attaches himself to her body with his teeth. For some species, this is the end of the male's life as a separate fish. The male is a permanent attachment to the female, its body shrinking until it is only a tiny lump nourished by the female's blood supply. Female anglers have been caught with as many as eleven attached males. However, in some species, the male lets go and swims away after mating.

Hunters are deep-sea predators. They actively seek out and chase their prey through a range of depths, from black depths below 1000 meters (3300 feet) to twilight depths above 600 meters (about 2000 feet). They go through greater changes in temperature and pressure than most other deep-sea fishes. Because they are fast-moving, they are harder to catch than most other deep-water fishes. Fewer of them have been captured for scientific study. Most of what is known about them is based on the smaller varieties of hunter.

Gulpers are fishes with huge mouths, tiny eyes, and long, slender bodies that seem to be at least half stomach. Some species have luminous organs at the tip of a long tail, used to attract prey fishes. Like many other deep-sea predators, the gulpers have stomachs with black walls. Thus, the lights of an eaten fish do not shine through the stomach wall to reveal the gulper's location.

Dragonfish

LURKERS OF THE DEEP

Thinking and Discussing

The selection discusses two layers of the ocean. What are the different layers? What kinds of life are to be found in each layer?

The text points out that many deep-sea fish have light-producing spots on their bodies. In terms of survival, why are the lights a good thing for some fish, but not such a good thing for others?

Applying Science Concepts

Diagramming the Food Chain Imagine that you have just eaten an ocean fish for dinner. Draw a diagram that shows how energy was transferred from the sun to your body through the food chain of the ocean.

Charting Deep-Sea Life Make a chart that compares and contrasts how the fishes discussed in the selection have adapted to life in the deep ocean. Include such categories as the food the fish eats, how it swims, where it lives, and what it looks like. Research any categories you cannot complete with information from the selection. Give your chart a title such as "Deep-Sea Fish Adaptation" and display it in the classroom.

The Johnson Sea Link, first launched in 1971, is a modern vessel for deep-sea exploration. The Sea Link can dive to a depth of 3000 feet. Its acrylic sphere gives explorers a total view of their underwater environment.

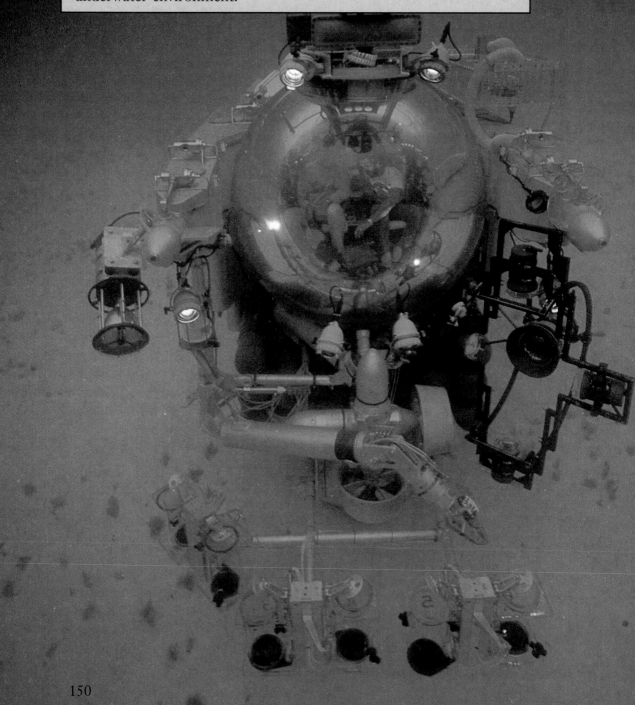

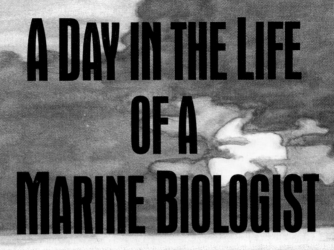

A Day in the Life of a Marine Biologist

Arthur Humes enjoyed collecting shells on the seashore of Cape Cod, Massachusetts, when he was a young child. As his interest in collecting grew, he used books to learn the Latin and Greek scientific names of the shells he was finding. That was only the beginning of a lifelong interest in the sea, for Dr. Arthur Humes became a marine biologist. For decades, he has studied ocean life, specializing in taxonomy — the classification of living things.

Dr. Humes is now the director of a program for college graduates who are learning to be marine biologists. The program is called BUMP (Boston University Marine Program) and is based at the Marine Biological Laboratory in Woods Hole, Massachusetts, a world-famous center for ocean research.

The following is the description of a field trip to an offshore island that Dr. Humes takes with his students. Before setting off for the island, the students attend a lecture about invertebrate marine animals (sea animals without backbones), the kinds of creatures they will collect on the island.

Illustrated by Robert Brooks and George Ulrich

Photographs by William Jaspersohn

From *A Day in the Life of a Marine Biologist*
by William Jaspersohn

Arthur begins his lecture. His enthusiasm is real. Many invertebrate marine animals, he explains, live in *intertidal zones*, which are areas of the seashore covered with water at high tide but exposed at low tide. There are five major kinds of intertidal zones, he continues. They include:

1) rocky intertidal zones,
2) marshes,
3) mud flats,
4) sandy intertidal zones, or beaches, and
5) salt ponds.

"Now, on today's field trip to the island," says Arthur, "we will sample zones one through four on this list." He then describes the kinds of animals found in each zone. Burrowing animals, for example, such as worms, tend to live on sandy or muddy shores, he explains, while animals that need something to attach themselves to, such as mussels, tend to live on rocks. But, he emphasizes, all shore invertebrates are affected by:

1) temperature changes,
2) exposure to sunlight,
3) food availability,
4) water loss, or desiccation,
5) the saltiness, or *salinity*, of the water,
6) the amount of living space in the zone, and
7) man.

"Number seven should come as no surprise," says Arthur. "Man's the worst enemy these animals have. Let's remember to exercise restraint as we do our collecting today. We don't need fifty thousand specimens. Please be good scientists and take only one or two of each animal you find."

The class members nod that they will. Arthur smiles. Then he glances at the clock and says, "Our ship leaves for the island in forty-five minutes. Any questions?" Nobody raises a hand. "Okay then," says Arthur, "let's get ready for the field trip."

The ship they will be taking is the R.V. (which stands for "Research Vessel") *Ciona*, owned by the Marine Biological Laboratory and rented to Arthur and his students for field trips. She's a sturdy vessel, forty feet long, and she's docked now in Eel Pond, fueled and ready for the island trip.

Meanwhile, out behind the BUMP offices, Mas and Tom[1] supervise distribution of the collecting gear. They hand the students dipnets. They hand them buckets. They hand them box sieves, shovels, forks, jars, bait seines, bottles, spades, clamforks — everything they'll need for collecting specimens in the field.

A few minutes before departure students and teachers assemble at the dock. The students are quiet. They wait to be told

---

[1] **Mas and Tom:** Mas Dojiri and Tom Duncan are more advanced students who assist Dr. Humes.

what to do. Some decide to pull on their boots now. Others simply stand. Many sport colorful nylon packs containing food, and yellow slickers in case of storms. Finally a signal is given and everyone boards the ship. Talk comes easier now. Tension about leaving turns to relief. The collecting gear is stowed behind the wheelhouse. The captain at the helm, "Brud" Lane, twists the ignition key in its lock and with a soft rumble the *Ciona*'s big diesel engine thrums to life. Tight fists of blue smoke pump from the white stack. Nobody moves. Captain Lane reverses the ship until the snapline goes slack and Tom Duncan can lift it off its mooring. "Line clear!" shouts Tom. Captain Lane nods and shifts the *Ciona*'s gears into forward. The ship gives a lurch. "Here we go!" somebody whispers, and the ship glides smoothly from the dock.

Since it's almost noon now, Arthur and his students eat their lunches on the *Ciona*'s main deck. The seas are calm. Woods Hole slips quickly from view.

A half hour later a student points off the port rail and asks, "Is that it?"

On the horizon an island has popped into view.

"That's it," says Arthur. The sight of the island stirs him deeply.

"Okay, if I can have your attention," he says to the students as the *Ciona* glides quietly into the island's harbor. "As some of you may know, this island is privately owned. Now, its owner has asked that we not smoke or start fires or light matches while we're here for the simple reason that there's no firefighting equipment on the island. Aside from that let's, as always, do our work well and not abuse the privilege of being here."

With that the *Ciona* docks at the island pier and everyone disembarks. Minutes later, equipment in hand, the group hikes up a wooded road that runs through the heart of the island and leads to the collection site.

The site is a sheltered cove, which, as Arthur says, contains so many different intertidal zones — mud, rock, sand, marsh — that it's perfect for finding specimens.

The site is reached by crossing a fine old stone bridge at the cove's narrowest end, then clambering down a rocky embankment.

Since collecting specimens is a wet and sometimes dirty business, Arthur recommends that students wear a good pair of hip waders when they go into intertidal zones.

Now he divides the classes into teams of three and four, and the teams divide the tools, and everyone fans out along the shore and goes to work.

The first zone the classes sample is an area of the cove where the bottom is pebbly mud. The best way of sampling such a zone is with a spade and simple sifting device called a *box sieve*. Arthur says that anyone can construct a box sieve by knocking the bottom off a wooden bottle crate and replacing it with a piece of medium- or fine-gauge wire mesh. The students use box sieves that Arthur built.

When a spadeful of mud from the cove bottom is dropped onto the mesh and the box is shaken in the water, the sediment drops through the mesh, leaving the animals.

And the first spadefuls of mud bring up some fine specimens. There is a clam. But what kind of clam, specifically? New Englanders would say it's a quahog (**kwô′hôg′**), while Southerners would call it either a round or a hard-shelled clam. And fish market people would say it's a littleneck, cherrystone, or chowder clam depending on its size. These are a clam's *common names*. Which one does a marine biologist use? Answer: none of them.

Instead, scientists worldwide have a system of classifying animals and plants that avoids this confusion of names. Using words from Latin and Greek, the system classifies animals within seven categories: *kingdom, phylum, class, order, family, genus,* and *species.* The categories "kingdom" through "family" serve to place animals into smaller and more closely related groups until finally "genus" and "species" describe only one particular type animal. Together, "genus" and "species" form an animal's *scientific name,* and it is this name that marine biologists use instead of common ones.

Most scientific names have a story behind them. For example, because quahog shells were once used by Indians as money, or wampum, the scientist who named this clam called it *Mercenaria mercenaria*, which in Latin means "one who uses itself for money." And this lugworm is scientifically known as *Arenicola cristata*, or "crested one that burrows in sand." Good marine biologists should always use scientific names, says Arthur. Not to use the scientific name, he says, "reflects badly on you as a scientist."

The next spadeful of mud produces two of Arthur's favorite invertebrates, *Pagurus longicarpus*, the hermit crab, and *Pectinaria gouldi*, the trumpet worm. Each lacks protective armor, so each has found its own ingenious way of protecting itself. The hermit crab, *Pagurus*, lives in empty snail shells and holds itself in place by means of rough spots on its tail and rear legs. In fact, its name, *Pagurus longicarpus*, literally means "that which fastens itself by its long legs."

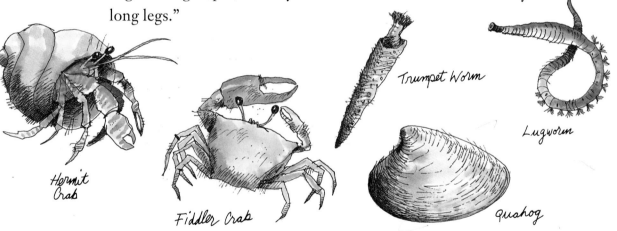

Hermit Crab

Fiddler Crab

Trumpet Worm

Lugworm

Quahog

By contrast, *Pectinaria*, or trumpet worm, lives in the mud in a tube which it cements for itself using thousands of tiny sand grains. Both these animals are common in muddy areas, but, as Arthur says, they're always delightful to find.

While Arthur and his group search the water, Tom Duncan and some others explore a patch of drier mud riddled with strange nickel-sized holes. What made the holes? Using a clamrake Tom

gently scrapes the mud, and suddenly, snapping and scrambling sideways from one of the holes, comes a *Uca*, or fiddler crab.

There are three species of *Ucas*, Tom tells the students: *Uca pugilator*, which tends to live in sandy areas; *Uca minax*, which burrows in ground above water; and *Uca pugnax*, like this one, which burrows in intertidal mud. Tom knows this one's a male because one claw is bigger than the other. Tom says not to worry about their claws — they don't hurt when they pinch. But making a *Uca* stand still in your hands can be a problem.

Up along the marshy part of the cove Arthur finds some old boards washed there by storms and high tides. They're easy places to miss but if you overturn some you're likely to find a few marsh snails, *Melampus bidentatus*.

Melampus lives under such debris for moisture and protection from the sun. But in addition, the boards crush the marsh grass underneath them, causing it to decay, and decaying marsh grass, as Arthur explains, is *Melampus*'s favorite food.

Field trips like this one are scheduled for low tide because that is when the intertidal zones are exposed. Arthur has timed this field trip perfectly. While the class has been working along shore, the water in the cove has been draining into the sea. The tide finally reaches dead low. Now the class can cross the mud to the cove's sandy intertidal zone.

And there, you just sink a spade into the wet sand, and all kinds of wonderful creatures pop forth.

Soon it is time to leave. The tide is beginning to rise and in an hour the little cove will again be submerged in water. Smiles warm the air. The collecting buckets are full. Altogether the class has found some sixty different species of marine invertebrates.

"How was the cove?" Captain Lane asks when the group arrives at the pier.

"Nice," smiles one of the female students.

"Muddy!" shouts a male student.

"Well, come aboard anyway," says Captain Lane. And the students all clamber aboard the ship.

As the *Ciona* quits the harbor and the island shrinks from view, Arthur glances at his students, most of them quiet, and thinks, They were good. They worked hard.

A DAY IN THE LIFE OF A MARINE BIOLOGIST

Thinking and Discussing

Why do you think the author chose to follow the activities of Arthur Humes and his students on their trip to the island, rather than simply describing the work of a marine biologist?

Why do you think Arthur Humes says that man is the main enemy of the sea life the students are studying?

Why is the sheltered cove a good place for finding marine life specimens?

Applying Science Concepts

Creating a Manual for Collectors Write a manual intended for people who are going on a collecting trip alone, without the guidance of someone like Arthur Humes. The manual should cover one or two intertidal zones and the marine life to be found in them. Include instructions on the proper clothes, as well as the required tools and their uses. Give each section a chapter name, and give the manual a title.

THINKING ABOUT SCIENCE

With your classmates, create a large ocean mural that you can hang on the classroom wall. Depict on the mural some of the scenes you have read about, from scientists and students exploring intertidal zones to underwater research vessels exploring the deepest parts of the ocean. Include the shoreline, land features of the deep sea, and plant life. Illustrate the inhabitants, from the common fish most people know about to the unusual ones you have studied in "Lurkers of the Deep."

GIVING A REPORT

With a group of classmates, select a state or country that is on the ocean and to which the ocean is important. You might pick Florida, Maine, Japan, England, Hawaii, or any other ocean state or country on the globe. Gather facts about the place you choose. How does the ocean affect the lives of the people there? What is the ocean itself like?

With your group, give a presentation to the class about the state or country. If you wish, use charts, maps, diagrams, or other graphics. Encourage questions from the class.

Donald Collins received his Ph.D. from the California Institute of Technology in 1969. He currently works at the Jet Propulsion Laboratory at the California Institute of Technology and lives in Altadena, California, with his wife and two sons. In his spare time, Dr. Collins is active in Scouting.

William Jaspersohn was born in New Haven, Connecticut, in 1947. He received his bachelor's degree from Dartmouth College in 1969 and taught English for two years before becoming a free-lance writer. Jaspersohn's books include *How the Forest Grew*, which won the *Boston Globe–Horn Book* Honor Award in 1980, and several photodocumentaries, including *A Day in the Life of a Veterinarian*, *The Ballpark: One Day Behind the Scenes at a Major League Game*, and *A Day in the Life of a Television News Reporter*.

Margaret Poynter was born in Long Beach, California, in 1927. She became a free-lance writer in 1972 and joined the staff of the *Pasadena/Altadena Weekly* in 1979. Her first book, *Frisbee Fun*, was published in 1977. She has since published more than twenty books, including *The Zoo Lady, Search and Rescue, Volcanoes: The Fiery Mountains* (named an outstanding science book for children by the National Science Teachers Association in 1980), *Voyager: The Story of a Space Mission* (named an outstanding science book in 1981), and *Cosmic Quest*.

Bruce H. Robison works as a research biologist at the Marine Science Institute of the University of California at Santa Barbara. He has spent several years aboard research vessels, conducting hundreds of deep-sea trawl hauls to study the fish that live at great depths. One of his most exciting experiences was a dive in the three-man submersible *Alvin*, in which he descended to a depth of over a mile in the Atlantic Ocean.

The Great Barrier Reef:
A Treasure in the Sea
by Alice Gilbreath
(Houghton, 1991; Dillon, 1986)

Off the coast of Australia lies the Great Barrier Reef, one of the natural wonders of the world. This informative book explains how the reef was formed, focuses on creatures living on the reef, and presents current environmental problems.

The Black Pearl
by Scott O'Dell
(Houghton, 1967)

Ramón Salazar realizes his dream of diving for pearls when he finds the great pearl — the magnificent, dusky Pearl of Heaven — in a sea creature's cave. The Manta Diablo, whose pearl it is, and Sevillano, the finest diver in the Salazars' fleet, both want the pearl, and Ramón knows no peace as long as he possesses the gem.

How Did We Find Out About
Life in the Deep Sea?
by Isaac Asimov
(Walker, 1981; Avon, 1982)

The popular author describes the discovery of life beneath the ocean — how it came about and what exists there.

Incredible Facts About the Ocean:
The Land Below, the Life Within
by W. Wright Robinson
(Dillon, 1987)

Excellent photographs, many taken from outer space, illustrate the fascinating world of the sea. Discover how the oceans create deltas, islands, and sandbars, and how land below sea level shapes bays, gulfs, and seas.

Exploring the Sea:
Oceanography Today
by Carvel Hall Blair
(Random, 1986)

Colorful illustrations and diagrams help to give a broad overview of the oceans of the world, unlocking the mysteries of their origin. Dr. Blair includes fascinating discussions of undersea equipment such as the research submarine *Alvin* and the robots used to explore the sunken *Titanic*.

The Mysterious Undersea World
by Jan Leslie Cook
(National Geographic Society, 1980)

Striking color photographs help the reader investigate the sea, its plants and animals, and coral reefs. Submersibles, ocean pets, and aquariums are also explained briefly.

REALISM

BECOMING

C O N T E N T S

The turning point in the process of growing up is when you discover the core of strength within you that survives all hurt.

— *Max Lerner*

Taller Than Bandai Mountain

BY

Dan D'Amelio

Life has never been easy for Hideyo. He works hard in a small rice field that provides barely enough food for his mother, his sister, and himself. He studies long hours at school with perhaps only a handful of rice for lunch. Hardest for him, though, is the constant teasing and tormenting by his schoolmates, who ridicule him because of his left hand, useless since it was horribly burned when he was a baby. Until recently, Hideyo has felt that not only is his hand damaged, but his whole future as well. Then one day his teacher's wife, Takike, tells him that his mind and spirit are whole, and he can use them to help others. She also gives him hope by telling him of a wonderful doctor, Watanabe, who lives in a nearby village and might be able to help him.

Watanabe-san held Hideyo's wrist. The early-morning sunlight lit the table on which Hideyo rested his arm. He stared at the doctor's silver instrument as it probed the stumps of his fingers. No matter how much it hurt, he would not — must not — show pain.

Watanabe-san looked at him. "Your hand is too tense," he said. "Do not look at it." Hideyo shifted his gaze to the sunlight coming through the partially curtained window.

Suddenly the sunlight turned to sparks that pierced his brain. He swallowed, then glanced at the doctor. Had he shown any sign of pain? He looked at the wall. Above the desk, on a shelf, was a row of books. He tried to make out the titles. Suddenly the books seemed to explode into fragments. He gasped.

The doctor put the instrument aside, then bandaged the hand. "That is all for now," he said. He went to a wash basin, pushed up his sleeves, and washed his hands. Then he reached for a towel. He looked at Hideyo as he dried his hands.

The doctor had dark eyes and his straight hair was streaked with gray. He tossed the towel aside.

"Did a doctor ever look at your hand?"

"When I was a baby."

"Was it that fool — the doctor in Inawashiro? Of course, it was; you do not have a doctor in your village." Watanabe-san picked up a cigar and lit it. He puffed on it rapidly and turned his eyes away. "Why did you not come to me sooner?"

"We are peasants, Watanabe-san," said Hideyo.

"What? What did you say?"

"We are peasants," Hideyo repeated softly.

"There are no more peasants. Don't you know that?" The doctor's voice was hoarse. He shoved the cigar into his mouth.

Hideyo smiled to himself. Feudalism had been abolished in 1871, eighteen years ago. Everyone knew that. But his mother still thought of herself as a peasant, for her life had not changed. She worked just as hard as she had when she was a girl.

Watanabe-san clamped down with his teeth on the cigar. "Times are better now," he said. "A man can make of himself anything he wishes — if he has the ability." He walked to the door and stepped out. Hideyo followed him.

The sun's rays seemed to pierce the hilltops. "Have you ever seen a hospital?" said Watanabe-san.

"No, sir."

"Come with me," said Watanabe-san.

Hideyo followed the doctor to a hut at the edge of the clearing behind the house. It was dark inside the hut and there was a heavy odor of sweat and vomit. The doctor stepped around a small bamboo partition.

"Good morning, Watanabe-san," said a young girl's voice. Her head was raised from the mat where she lay. She was smiling weakly.

The doctor knelt down beside her. "How is my little princess today?"

"Better," she said.

Watanabe-san placed his hand on her forehead, then pressed back her eyelids.

"When can I go home, Watanabe-san?"

"Maybe soon," he said. The girl glanced at Hideyo. "This is Hideyo Noguchi." Hideyo smiled. Watanabe-san blew a kiss to the little girl, then walked further into the hut.

An old woman lay in the semidarkness, motionless as a mummy. Watanabe-san knelt down and drew the blanket up around her shoulders. The woman's eyes, glazed and expressionless, stared vacantly. Watanabe-san placed his hand on hers for a moment, then slowly came to his feet.

There were voices coming from the end of the hut. Hideyo followed Watanabe-san. A man with thick hair and a bony chest was sitting up, arguing with a young attendant.

"What is wrong?" said Watanabe-san.

The attendant, a boy a little older than Hideyo with a heavy lower lip, motioned to the man. "He wishes to leave, Watanabe-san."

The man leaned back on his elbows and turned his gaze away from Watanabe-san. "I must leave," said the man. "My family needs me."

"Your family has enough to do without taking care of you," said Watanabe-san.

"I am no longer sick."

"Lie down. Be quiet."

The man lay back. Then he raised his arms toward Watanabe-san. "It is not right that I should stay here, leaving my family to struggle without me."

"Your wife is a good woman; your children are able," said Watanabe-san. "When you are ready, you will go back to them. Now rest."

Outside, Hideyo blinked in the sunlight. Watanabe-san relit his cigar. He puffed on it for a moment. Then he took it out of his mouth and stared at its burning end. There were dark rings under his eyes. He turned now, his shoulders stooped, and walked toward the house. On the steps he paused and looked back at Hideyo. "You will come again next week," he said, and started to go in.

"Wait," Hideyo almost shouted. "I forgot." He reached into his pocket and took out a knotted handkerchief. He untied the knot with his teeth and right hand, took out several coins, and held them up to Watanabe-san.

The doctor looked at Hideyo, then rubbed his cheek with his thumb. "How did you get this money?"

"My mother and sister and I worked in a neighbor's paddy[1] at night, after our own work was done, for the past year," said Hideyo.

Watanabe-san bit on the cigar, then took the coins and put them back in the handkerchief. He tied the ends together and placed the handkerchief in Hideyo's pocket.

"Next week," he said, and turned away.

Hideyo walked along the dirt road that led to Inawashiro. When he could see the Great Stone near the peak of Bandai clearly, he would know that he was halfway home. Several miles before Inawashiro he would turn off onto a narrower road that led to Okinajima. From Wakamatsu to his village it was twenty miles. He would be home in about five hours.

That morning he had left for Wakamatsu early, when it was still dark. His mother had wanted to go with him, but he had insisted that he go alone. If the news was bad, he wanted to be the one to tell her — to lie a little, if need be, so that she would not be disappointed.

---

[1]**paddy:** a marshy, flooded, or specially watered field in which rice is grown.

176

But, he knew now, the news was good. Watanabe-san had not taken payment for his services. The money could be used for winter clothing. Of course, they would have to repay Watanabe-san in some other way. A debt was a debt; it was a matter of honor.

The best news, of course, was that Watanabe-san wanted him to come again. This could only mean there was a chance that something could be done for his hand.

He looked at the hand now. He had never been able to pick up anything with it. The stumps of his fingers were rigid and unbending. He would endure any amount of pain if Watanabe-san could bring life to his hand.

He stopped and picked up two stones. With his right hand he threw the first stone beyond the distant pines. He glanced at the stone in his left hand. He knew that even without the bandage he would not be able to throw it beyond the bend in the road. He let the stone drop to the ground.

He gazed at the road ahead. At least he was going home. He had never thought of the suffering of others until this day. The little girl, did she cry herself to sleep? The old woman would die alone, away from her loved ones. And the man with the bony chest who worried about his family . . .

If only a doctor could be a magician — could cure people quickly. But, of course, a doctor was only a man, although a special kind of man — one who could call a sick girl "princess" and place a comforting hand on a lonely old woman.

Watanabe-san was only a man — a special kind of man.

Hideyo was almost used to the odor of sweat and vomit. The first day he had worked at the hospital the odor had made him ill. Azu, the other attendant, had laughed when he had rushed out to be sick after the first morning. That was at the start of the summer vacation, two weeks ago. Now the only thing that had not changed was Azu himself. He still did all he could to make Hideyo's work difficult.

Hideyo scrubbed the basin hard. He knew that in a moment Azu would come out to inspect his work. Perhaps this time Azu would be satisfied, would not find fault. It was curious. Azu had never said anything about his hand. For that Hideyo was grateful. He knew that Azu wanted to be a doctor some day. He was several years older than Hideyo and smart; Watanabe-san had only to tell Azu something once and he understood immediately. Of course, he had been at the hospital a good deal longer than Hideyo. It was too bad that the two of them could not be friends. Perhaps Azu was right; he was clumsy and careless. But today he would clean the basins, scrub the hospital floor, and burn the old bandages, and Azu would not find a single fault with his work. He would do his tasks carefully, very carefully, and everything he did would be perfect.

He held up the basin now and looked at it closely. It was spotless and shone clean and bright. He could see his face clearly in it. He smiled and his image smiled back at him.

"What are you doing?" It was Azu.

"I — I . . ."

"Are you finished with the basins, yet?"

"This is the last one, Azu."

Azu took the basin and scrutinized[2] it. He turned it over. Then he went into the hospital, took a sheet of paper from a small table near the doorway, and ran the edge of the paper along the bottom of the basin, where the lip ended. He held the paper up and smiled. Then he shoved the paper at Hideyo.

"Look at that dirt," he said. "The basin is filthy. You can't even clean a basin properly." He threw the basin into the bucket of suds. "Do it over again." He walked back into the hut.

Hideyo knelt down beside the bucket, reached in and pulled out the basin, and picked up the brush. He gripped the brush hard. For a moment he pictured himself rushing in and throwing the

---

[2]**scrutinized** (skrōōt′n īzd′): observed or examined with great care.

contents of the bucket at Azu. How foolish Azu would look, dripping from head to foot, suds running down his face, over his heavy lower lip. But only in his imagination could Hideyo commit such an act, because of Watanabe-san.

Hideyo looked at his left hand. He had picked up the basin with that hand, something he could never have done until a few days ago. He let the basin slide back into the water, then reached in with his left hand and picked it up again. The stumps bent enough for him to grip the basin's side. Watanabe-san was bringing life to what were left of his fingers. Each time the doctor worked on the hand the rigid stumps yielded a bit. All his life Hideyo would be grateful to Watanabe-san. And he was willing to work there for the rest of his life to repay him, no matter what Azu did.

Someone inside was crying. It sounded like Aki, the "little princess." Had Azu gone to her side? The crying continued. Azu came out. From the grim line of Azu's mouth Hideyo knew he was going to get Watanabe-san. The crying grew louder, and Hideyo stepped inside.

Aki was doubled over on the bed, her face buried in her hands.

"Aki," he called softly. "Aki."

She looked at him, her eyes filled with tears.

Hideyo smiled. "What is wrong, Aki?"

"I saw lightning and heard thunder," she said.

"There is no storm," said Hideyo. "The sun is out. You must have been dreaming."

"No. No, I was not dreaming. I was awake. There was lightning and thunder that roared. The lightning struck at me and I tried to cry out but the thunder covered my voice. I was not dreaming, Hideyo."

"You are safe now, Aki. The lightning and thunder are gone."

"Why did it come, Hideyo? Why?"

Hideyo patted her hand. "Lie still, Aki." Watanabe-san and Azu came in.

"Hello, little princess," said Watanabe-san. He knelt down by her side.

"Get back to your work," Azu ordered. Hideyo left them. In a moment Azu rushed past him toward the house. He came back with a small bottle of medicine.

After several moments, Watanabe-san left the hospital. His face was pale. The rings under his eyes were very dark.

It was quiet in the hut now. Hideyo walked slowly to the doorway and stepped inside. Aki lay on her back, her eyes open, her breathing heavy. Hideyo looked at Azu. "Will she be all right?" he whispered.

Azu shrugged. "She has tuberculosis."

"Is there nothing more that can be done?"

"We could use moxa,[3] like the older doctors do, but Watanabe-san says that is a waste of time. He knows the modern treatments. Have you finished your work outside?"

"Yes, Azu."

"Well, I will inspect it later," said Azu. "It would be best not to scrub the floor now. Instead you can get rid of the bandages. Be sure the wind is blowing in the right direction."

"Yes, Azu."

Behind the hospital was a wooden barrel with a wooden top. Beside the barrel was a flat wheelbarrow. Hideyo picked up the barrel and placed it on the wheelbarrow, then pushed the wheelbarrow down the slope behind the hospital. He had to grip the handles of the barrow hard, because the slope became steep near the bottom. He almost lost his grip with his left hand.

At the bottom of the slope was a narrow path that wound around some low bushes. Then the ground was clear. In the center of the clearing was a deep pit.

---

[3]**moxa:** a soft woolly substance made from tree leaves and used in Japan as a medicine.

Hideyo stopped near the pit and rolled the barrel onto the ground. He untied the cover, then tipped the barrel so that its open end was just over the edge of the pit. The blood-specked bandages, soiled dressings, and stained wads of cotton emptied into the ash-strewn pit. With a small tinderbox[4] Hideyo struck a spark which he blew into a flame. The flame leaped up. Smoke, thick and black, curled skyward.

Hideyo stared at the fire. It was good to see the flames destroy the refuse. Lighting the fire and seeing it burn through the pit was always strangely enjoyable. He watched in fascination as the fire hungrily consumed the pile.

When there were only ashes left, he sat by the edge of the pit and looked at the smoldering heap. A thin wisp of smoke drifted upward. The fire had done its work quickly.

Suddenly something darted overhead. It was a small bird. It flitted through the trees, then flew high toward the sun and slowly, in the sun's bright rays, disappeared from view.

The fields, trees, and sun fitted together, it seemed, into a single large-canvassed painting. Everything was still and perfect. But slowly Hideyo became aware of the stench from the pit. He came to his feet. As he did so he heard a voice within him say, "I will become a doctor." He stood still and listened to the voice in quiet reverie.

In the months and years that follow, Hideyo clings to his dream despite many obstacles. Eventually Hideyo's search for knowledge takes him to North America, Europe, South America, and Africa. Through all his work, he displays the strength he had learned so long ago in the muddy waters of a Japanese rice paddy.

---

[4]**tinderbox:** a metal box for holding fire-starting materials.

Responding to *Taller Than Bandai Mountain*

Thinking and Discussing

Although Hideyo is in great pain as the doctor examines his hand, he still appreciates the beauty of the early morning sunlight. Why do you think the author puts these opposite feelings together? What is being suggested about Hideyo's character?

Hideyo tries hard to please Watanabe-san's attendant, Azu, but nothing he does is good enough. Reread the dialogue between them. What does the dialogue suggest about Hideyo and Azu?

Why do you think the author chooses specific incidents to portray Hideyo's motivation to become a doctor? How does his portrayal of these events make Hideyo's decision seem real?

Choosing a Creative Response

Holding a Discussion If Watanabe-san called a meeting to discuss hospital conditions, what might Hideyo, Azu, and the hospital patients say? Act out the discussion with your classmates.

Creating Your Own Activity Plan and complete your own activity in response to *Taller Than Bandai Mountain*.

Thinking and Writing

The author of a biography may choose to add fictional details to make the story livelier. For example, dialogue may be added to reveal characters. Imagine that you are writing a fictionalized biography of Watanabe. Write a conversation between Watanabe and another character, giving the reader an idea of his personality.

Writing an Autobiographical Incident

Taller Than Bandai Mountain describes incidents that helped Hideyo Noguchi learn about himself and the world around him. Such experiences are part of everyone's life while growing up. Sometimes these incidents are difficult or sad. Sometimes they are funny. Think about a memorable moment in your own life. How did this incident lead to a better understanding of life and of others? Write about your experience in an autobiographical incident. If these selections give you a different idea, write about that.

1. Prewriting

Before you begin writing, choose a personal experience that you would like to share with others. Why is the experience memorable? Which details are important to tell about? Who was involved? Can you remember any conversations from the experience? Jot down some notes as memories of your experience come back to you.

2. Write a First Draft

Based on your prewriting notes, write a first draft. Do not worry too much about punctuation, spelling, or grammar at this point. Concentrate on the plot, the setting, and the characters of your autobiographical incident. Try to recreate the incident for your readers as you first experienced it. Include what you felt then and what you feel now about your experience.

3. Revise

Share your first draft with a partner. Ask whether your autobiographical incident is believable and vivid. Does the experience you want to recreate come alive on paper? Can your partner suggest ways to improve it? Make any changes you think will improve the story.

4. Proofread

Check your autobiographical incident for correct spelling, punctuation, and grammar. Use proofreading marks to make any needed corrections.

5. Publish

Make a clean copy of your autobiographical incident, and create an exciting cover for it. Read it aloud to the class, or design a bulletin board display in which you share your experience with the class.

BARRIO BOY

BY ERNESTO GALARZA

From Jalcocotán, a mountain village in Mexico, Ernesto's family moves many times, seeking work and safety from the Mexican Revolution. Ernesto and his mother, Doña Henriqueta, finally settle in a barrio, a Spanish-speaking neighborhood, in Sacramento, California. The ways of Americans, or gringos, seem strange to the new immigrants. But this land offers many new possibilities for Ernesto, possibilities that could brighten his future.

We found the Americans as strange in their customs as they probably found us. Immediately we discovered that there were no *mercados* and that when shopping you did not put the groceries in a *chiquihuite*. Instead everything was in cans or in cardboard boxes or each item was put in a brown paper bag. There were neighborhood grocery stores at the corners and some big ones uptown, but no *mercado*. The grocers did not give children a *pilón*, they did not stand at the door and coax you to come in and buy, as they did in Mazatlán. The fruits and vegetables were displayed on counters instead of being piled up on the floor. The stores smelled of fly spray and oiled floors, not of fresh pineapple and limes.

Neither was there a plaza, only parks which had no bandstands, no concerts every Thursday, and no promenades of boys going one way and girls the other. There were no parks in the *barrio*; and the ones uptown were cold and rainy in winter, and in summer

there was no place to sit except on the grass. When there were cele-brations nobody set off rockets in the parks, much less on the street in front of your house to announce to the neighborhood that a wed-ding or a baptism was taking place. Sacramento did not have a *mercado* and a plaza with the cathedral to one side and the Palacio de Gobierno[1] on another to make it obvious that there and nowhere else was the center of the town.

It was just as puzzling that the Americans did not live in *vecindades,*[2] like our block on Leandro Valle. Even in the alleys, where people knew one another better, the houses were fenced apart, without central courts to wash clothes, talk and play with the other children. Like the city, the Sacramento *barrio* did not have a place which was the middle of things for everyone.

In more personal ways we had to get used to the Americans. They did not listen if you did not speak loudly, as they always did. In the Mexican style, people would know that you were enjoying their jokes tremendously if you merely smiled and shook a little, as if you were trying to swallow your mirth. In the American style there was little difference between a laugh and a roar, and until you got used to them, you could hardly tell whether the boisterous Americans were roaring mad or roaring happy.

It was Doña[3] Henriqueta more than Gustavo or José [my cousins] who talked of these oddities and classified them as agree-able or deplorable. It was she also who pointed out the pleasant sur-prises of the American way. When a box of rolled oats with a picture of red carnations on the side was emptied, there was a plate or a bowl or a cup with blue designs. We ate the strange stuff regu-larly for breakfast and we soon had a set of the beautiful dishes. Rice and beans we bought in cotton bags of colored prints. The

---

[1]**Palacio de Gobierno:** a government office building; City Hall.

[2]**vecindades:** neighborhoods; communities.

[3]**Doña:** a title of respect before a woman's given name.

bags were unsewed, washed, ironed, and made into gaily designed towels, napkins, and handkerchiefs. The American stores also gave small green stamps which were pasted in a book to exchange for prizes. We didn't have to run to the corner with the garbage; a collector came for it.

With remarkable fairness and never-ending wonder we kept adding to our list the pleasant and the repulsive in the ways of the Americans. It was my second acculturation.[4]

The older people of the *barrio*, except in those things which they had to do like the Americans because they had no choice, remained Mexican. Their language at home was Spanish. They were continuously taking up collections to pay somebody's funeral expenses or to help someone who had had a serious accident. Cards were sent to you to attend a burial where you would throw a handful of dirt on top of the coffin and listen to tearful speeches at the graveside. At every baptism a new *compadre*[5] and a new *comadre*[6] joined the family circle. New Year greeting cards were exchanged, showing angels and cherubs in bright colors sprinkled with grains of mica so that they glistened like gold dust. At the family parties the huge pot of steaming tamales was still the center of attention, the *atole* served on the side with chunks of brown sugar for sucking and crunching. If the party lasted long enough, someone produced a guitar, the men took over and the singing of *corridos* began.

In the *barrio* there were no individuals who had official titles or who were otherwise recognized by everybody as important people. The reason must have been that there was no place in the public business of the city of Sacramento for the Mexican immigrants. We only rented a corner of the city and as long as we paid the rent on time everything else was decided at City Hall or the County

---

[4]**acculturation:** the process by which someone becomes part of the culture of a particular society.

[5]**compadre:** godfather.

[6]**comadre:** godmother.

Court House, where Mexicans went only when they were in trouble. Nobody from the *barrio* ever ran for mayor or city councilman. For us the most important public officials were the policemen who walked their beats, stopped fights, and hauled drunks to jail in a paddy wagon we called *La Julia*.

The one institution we had that gave the *colonia* some kind of image was the *Comisión Honorífica*, a committee picked by the Mexican Consul in San Francisco to organize the celebration of the *Cinco de Mayo*[7] and the Sixteenth of September, the anniversaries of the battle of Puebla and the beginning of our War of Independence. These were the two events which stirred everyone in the *barrio*, for what we were celebrating was not only the heroes of Mexico but also the feeling that we were still Mexicans ourselves. On these occasions there was a dance preceded by speeches and a concert. For both the *cinco* and the sixteenth queens were elected to preside over the ceremonies.

Between celebrations neither the politicians uptown nor the *Comisión Honorífica* attended to the daily needs of the *barrio*. This was done by volunteers — the ones who knew enough English to interpret in court, on a visit to the doctor, a call at the county hospital, and who could help make out a postal money order. By the time I had finished the third grade at the Lincoln School I was one of these volunteers. My services were not professional but they were free, except for the IOU's I accumulated from families who always thanked me with "God will pay you for it."

My clients were not *pochos*, Mexicans who had grown up in California, probably had even been born in the United States. They had learned to speak English of sorts and could still speak Spanish, also of sorts. They knew much more about the Americans than we did, and much less about us. The *chicanos* and the *pochos* had certain feelings about one another. Concerning the *pochos*, the

---

[7]**Cinco de Mayo:** Fifth of May.

chicanos suspected that they considered themselves too good for the *barrio* but were not, for some reason, good enough for the Americans. Toward the *chicanos*, the *pochos* acted superior, amused at our confusions but not especially interested in explaining them to us. In our family when I forgot my manners, my mother would ask me if I was turning *pochito*.

Turning *pocho* was a half-step toward turning American. And America was all around us, in and out of the *barrio*. Abruptly we had to forget the ways of shopping in a *mercado* and learn those of shopping in a corner grocery or in a department store. The Americans paid no attention to the Sixteenth of September, but they made a great commotion about the Fourth of July. In Mazatlán Don Salvador had told us, saluting and marching as he talked to our class, that the *Cinco de Mayo* was the most glorious date in human history. The Americans had not even heard about it.

In Tucson, when I had asked my mother again if the Americans were having a revolution, the answer was: "No, but they have good schools, and you are going to one of them." We were by now settled at 418 L Street and the time had come for me to exchange a revolution for an American education.

The two of us walked south on Fifth Street one morning to the corner of Q Street and turned right. Half of the block was occupied by the Lincoln School. It was a three-story wooden building, with two wings that gave it the shape of a double-T connected by a central hall. It was a new building, painted yellow, with a shingled roof that was not like the red tile of the school in Mazatlán. I noticed other differences, none of them very reassuring.

We walked up the wide staircase hand in hand and through the door, which closed by itself. A mechanical contraption screwed to the top shut it behind us quietly.

Up to this point the adventure of enrolling me in the school had been carefully rehearsed. Mrs. Dodson [our friend] had told us

how to find it and we had circled it several times on our walks. Friends in the *barrio* explained that the director was called a principal, and that it was a lady and not a man. They assured us that there was always a person at the school who could speak Spanish.

Exactly as we had been told, there was a sign on the door in both Spanish and English: "Principal." We crossed the hall and entered the office of Miss Nettie Hopley.

Miss Hopley was at a roll-top desk to one side, sitting in a swivel chair that moved on wheels. There was a sofa against the opposite wall, flanked by two windows and a door that opened on a small balcony. Chairs were set around a table and framed pictures hung on the walls of a man with long white hair and another with a sad face and a black beard.

The principal half turned in the swivel chair to look at us over the pinch glasses crossed on the ridge of her nose. To do this she had to duck her head slightly as if she were about to step through a low doorway.

What Miss Hopley said to us we did not know but we saw in her eyes a warm welcome and when she took off her glasses and straightened up she smiled wholeheartedly, like Mrs. Dodson. We were, of course, saying nothing, only catching the friendliness of her voice and the sparkle in her eyes while she said words we did not understand. She signaled us to the table. Almost tiptoeing across the office, I maneuvered myself to keep my mother between me and the gringo lady. In a matter of seconds I had to decide whether she was a possible friend or a menace. We sat down.

Then Miss Hopley did a formidable[8] thing. She stood up. Had she been standing when we entered she would have seemed tall. But rising from her chair she soared. And what she carried up and up with her was a buxom superstructure, firm shoulders, a straight sharp nose, full cheeks slightly molded by a curved line along the nostrils, thin lips that moved like steel springs, and a high forehead topped by hair gathered in a bun. Miss Hopley was not a giant in body but when she mobilized it to a standing position she seemed a match for giants. I decided I liked her.

She strode to a door in the far corner of the office, opened it and called a name. A boy of about ten years appeared in the doorway. He sat down at one end of the table. He was brown like us, a plump kid with shiny black hair combed straight back, neat, cool, and faintly obnoxious.[9]

Miss Hopley joined us with a large book and some papers in her hand. She, too, sat down and the questions and answers began by way of our interpreter. My name was Ernesto. My mother's name was Henriqueta. My birth certificate was in San Blas. Here was my last report card from the Escuela Municipal Numero 3 para Varones of Mazatlán, and so forth. Miss Hopley put things down in the book and my mother signed a card.

---

[8]**formidable** (fôr′mĭ də bəl): inspiring respectful fear.
[9]**obnoxious** (əb nŏk′shəs): extremely unpleasant or annoying.

As long as the questions continued, Doña Henriqueta could stay and I was secure. Now that they were over, Miss Hopley saw her to the door, dismissed our interpreter and without further ado took me by the hand and strode down the hall to Miss Ryan's first grade.

Miss Ryan took me to a seat at the front of the room, into which I shrank — the better to survey her. She was, to skinny, somewhat runty me, of a withering height when she patrolled the class. And when I least expected it, there she was, crouching by my desk, her blond radiant face level with mine, her voice patiently maneuvering me over the awful[10] idiocies of the English language.

During the next few weeks Miss Ryan overcame my fears of tall, energetic teachers as she bent over my desk to help me with a word in the pre-primer. Step by step, she loosened me and my classmates from the safe anchorage of the desks for recitations at the blackboard and consultations at her desk. Frequently she burst into happy announcements to the whole class. "Ito can read a sentence," and small Japanese Ito, squint-eyed and shy, slowly read aloud while the class listened in wonder: "Come, Skipper, come. Come and run." The Korean, Portuguese, Italian, and Polish first graders had similar moments of glory, no less shining than mine the day I conquered "butterfly," which I had been persistently pronouncing in standard Spanish as boo-ter-flee. "Children," Miss Ryan called for attention. "Ernesto has learned how to pronounce *butterfly*!" And I proved it with a perfect imitation of Miss Ryan. From that celebrated success, I was soon able to match Ito's progress as a sentence reader with "Come, butterfly, come fly with me."

Like Ito and several other first graders who did not know English, I received private lessons from Miss Ryan in the closet, a narrow hall off the classroom with a door at each end. Next to one

---

[10]**awful:** inspiring wonder, respect, or fear.

of these doors Miss Ryan placed a large chair for herself and a small one for me. Keeping an eye on the class through the open door she read with me about sheep in the meadow and a frightened chicken going to see the king, coaching me out of my phonetic ruts in words like *pasture, bow-wow-wow, hay,* and *pretty,* which to my Mexican ear and eye had so many unnecessary sounds and letters. She made me watch her lips and then close my eyes as she repeated words I found hard to read. When we came to know each other better, I tried interrupting to tell Miss Ryan how we said it in Spanish. It didn't work. She only said "oh" and went on with *pasture, bow-wow-wow,* and *pretty.* It was as if in that closet we were both discovering together the secrets of the English language and grieving together over the tragedies of Bo-Peep. The main reason I was graduated with honors from the first grade was that I had fallen in love with Miss Ryan. Her radiant no-nonsense character made us either afraid not to love her or love her so we would not be afraid, I am not sure which. It was not only that we sensed she was with it, but also that she was with us.

Like the first grade, the rest of the Lincoln School was a sampling of the lower part of town where many races made their home. My pals in the second grade were Kazushi, whose parents spoke only Japanese; Matti, a skinny Italian boy; and Manuel, a fat Portuguese who would never get into a fight but wrestled you to the ground and just sat on you. Our assortment of nationalities included Koreans, Yugoslavs, Poles, Irish, and home-grown Americans.

Miss Hopley and her teachers never let us forget why we were at Lincoln: for those who were alien, to become good Americans; for those who were so born, to accept the rest of us. Off the school grounds we traded the same insults we heard from our elders. On the playground we were sure to be marched up to the principal's office for calling someone a wop, a chink, a dago, or a greaser. The school was not so much a melting pot as a griddle where Miss

Hopley and her helpers warmed knowledge into us and roasted racial hatreds out of us.

At Lincoln, making us into Americans did not mean scrubbing away what made us originally foreign. The teachers called us as our parents did, or as close as they could pronounce our names in Spanish or Japanese. No one was ever scolded or punished for speaking in his native tongue on the playground. Matti told the class about his mother's down quilt, which she had made in Italy with the fine feathers of a thousand geese. Encarnación acted out how boys learned to fish in the Philippines. I astounded the third grade with the story of my travels on a stagecoach, which nobody else in the class had seen except in the museum at Sutter's Fort. After a visit to the Crocker Art Gallery and its collection of heroic paintings of the golden age of California, someone showed a silk scroll with a Chinese painting. Miss Hopley herself had a way of expressing wonder over these matters before a class, her eyes wide open until they popped slightly. It was easy for me to feel that

becoming a proud American, as she said we should, did not mean feeling ashamed of being a Mexican.

The Americanization of Mexican me was no smooth matter. I had to fight one lout who made fun of my travels on the *diligencia*, and my barbaric translation of the word into "diligence." He doubled up with laughter over the word until I straightened him out with a kick. In class I made points explaining that in Mexico roosters said "qui-qui-ri-qui" and not "cock-a-doodle-doo," but after school I had to put up with the taunts of a big Yugoslav who said Mexican roosters were crazy.

But it was Homer who gave me the most lasting lesson for a future American.

Homer was a chunky Irishman who dressed as if every day was Sunday. He slicked his hair between a crew cut and a pompadour. And Homer was smart, as he clearly showed when he and I ran for president of the third grade.

Everyone understood that this was to be a demonstration of how the American people vote for president. In an election, the teacher explained, the candidates could be generous and vote for each other. We cast our ballots in a shoe box and Homer won by two votes. I polled my supporters and came to the conclusion that I had voted for Homer and so had he. After class he didn't deny it, reminding me of what the teacher had said — we could vote for each other but didn't have to.

The lower part of town was a collage of nationalities in the middle of which Miss Nettie Hopley kept school with discipline and compassion. She called assemblies in the upper hall to introduce celebrities like the police sergeant or the fire chief, to lay down the law of the school, to present awards to our athletic champions, and to make important announcements. One of these was that I had been proposed by my school and accepted as a member of the newly formed Sacramento Boys Band. "Now, isn't that a wonderful

197

thing?" Miss Hopley asked the assembled school, all eyes on me. And everyone answered in a chorus, including myself, "Yes, Miss Hopley."

It was not only the parents who were summoned to her office and boys and girls who served sentences there who knew that Nettie Hopley meant business. The entire school witnessed her sizzling Americanism in its awful majesty one morning at flag salute.

All the grades, as usual, were lined up in the courtyard between the wings of the building, ready to march to classes after the opening bell. Miss Shand was on the balcony of the second floor off Miss Hopley's office, conducting us in our lusty singing of "My Country tiz-a-thee." Our principal, as always, stood there like us, at attention, her right hand over her heart, joining in the song.

Halfway through the second stanza she stepped forward, held up her arm in a sign of command, and called loud and clear: "Stop the singing." Miss Shand looked flabbergasted. We were frozen with shock.

Miss Hopley was now standing at the rail of the balcony, her eyes sparking, her voice low and resonant, the words coming down to us distinctly and loaded with indignation.

"There are two gentlemen walking on the school grounds with their hats on while we are singing," she said, sweeping our ranks with her eyes. "We will remain silent until the gentlemen come to attention and remove their hats." A minute of awful silence ended when Miss Hopley, her gaze fixed on something behind us, signaled Miss Shand and we began once more the familiar hymn. That afternoon, when school was out, the word spread. The two gentlemen were the Superintendent of Schools and an important guest on an inspection.

I came back to the Lincoln School after every summer, moving up through the grades with Miss Campbell, Miss Beakey, Mrs. Wood, Miss Applegate, and Miss Delahunty. I sat in the classroom

adjoining the principal's office and had my turn answering her telephone when she was about the building repeating the message to the teacher, who made a note of it. Miss Campbell read to us during the last period of the week about King Arthur, Columbus, Buffalo Bill, and Daniel Boone, who came to life in the reverie of the class through the magic of her voice. And it was Miss Campbell who introduced me to the public library on Eye Street, where I became a regular customer.

All of Lincoln School mourned together when Eddie, the blond boy everybody liked, was killed by a freight train as he crawled across the tracks going home one day. We assembled to say good-bye to Miss Applegate, who was off to Alaska to be married. Now it was my turn to be excused from class to interpret for a parent enrolling a new student fresh from Mexico. Graduates from Lincoln came back now and then to tell us about high school. A naturalist entertained us in assembly, imitating the calls of the meadow lark, the water ouzel, the oriole, and the killdeer. I decided to become a bird man after I left Lincoln.

In the years we lived in the lower part of town, La Leen-Con, as my family called it, became a benchmark in our lives, like the purple light of the Lyric Theater and the golden dome of the Palacio de Gobierno gleaming above Capitol Park.

Despite many obstacles, Ernesto finishes junior high and, with the help and advice of José and his friends, goes on to high school and college. Overcoming many misfortunes, and still proudly Mexican, he embraces America's possibilities.

Thinking and Discussing

What images and words does the author of *Barrio Boy* use to describe his first impressions of his new world? At what point in the story does he begin getting used to this world? How can you tell?

The author uses a number of Spanish words such as *mercado* or *barrio* in the beginning of the selection, but he uses fewer Spanish words as the selection continues. Why?

How does the author reveal Ernesto's strengths in the story?

Choosing a Creative Response

Making a Booklet Ernesto might have felt more comfortable if someone had given him tips on how to get along in his new world. Make a booklet of "Tips for New Kids" that would help new students adjust to your school and town.

Creating Your Own Activity Plan and complete your own activity in response to *Barrio Boy*.

Thinking and Writing

Imagine that you are Ernesto, and you are going to graduate from Lincoln School. In a farewell graduation speech, explain why you think that the teachers helped you.

Exploring Language

Look through the story to find Spanish words that have become familiar in English. List them with their meanings. Then add other Spanish words that you might use in your daily speech.

All of us have two

educations: one

which we receive

from others; another,

and the most valuable,

which we give

ourselves.

— *John Randolph*

Sister

BY
ELOISE
GREENFIELD

Doretha lives with her mother and older sister. Because her mother went to work when Doretha's father died, Doretha helps out by doing chores and most of the cooking. When Doretha was nine, she started a memory book — one page to remind her of each important memory. Now she is thirteen, and the book is filled with memories. One time when Aunt Mae came over . . .

"Sister! You deaf?" Aunt Mae called from the front room.

"I didn't hear you, Aunt Mae," Doretha called back. She folded the dishtowel and hung it over the rack.

"I guess not, the way you singing and carrying on. I said how long you going to take, washing those little bit of dishes?" She lowered her voice when she saw Doretha come into the room. "About time. The movie's coming on, and I hate to watch T.V. by myself." She turned several knobs on the television set. "How the devil you get this thing to stand still?"

Doretha made a fist and banged on the top of the set. The picture slid around once more and stopped. "I'm glad you came over," she said. "Mama's working late today."

"Thelma's going to let those folks at the laundry work her to death, you know that?" Aunt Mae sat down in the stuffed chair and crossed her legs. "Hey, why don't you run down to the corner and get us some potato chips? Keep me from biting my nails down to the quick[1] while I'm watching the movie. It's a murder mystery." She got her shoulder bag from the sofa and gave Doretha some change.

Doretha went to the closet for her coat. She put it on, tied a triangular scarf around her neck to hide the worn collar, opened the front door, and stopped suddenly.

---

[1]**quick** (kwĭk): the sensitive, tender flesh under the fingernails.

Illustrated by James Noel Smith.

"Why you just standing there?" Aunt Mae asked.

Doretha closed the door quietly. "They over there on Bernard's front," she said.

"Who?" Aunt Mae went to the window and lifted the yellow nylon curtain.

"The boys," Doretha said. "Aunt Mae! Don't let them see you looking!"

Aunt Mae dropped the curtain and stepped back. She put her hands on her hips. "Now, Sister," she said, "I know you not scared of boys."

"I'm not scared of them, I just don't like to walk by them. Coley's over there, and he acts so . . . so funny. Most of the time he doesn't even speak unless he's by himself."

"He knows you crazy about him, that's why," Aunt Mae said. She leaned her head to one side and widened her large eyes at Doretha. "And I guess when he feels like opening his mouth, you talk to him?"

Doretha didn't answer. She started taking her coat off.

"Put that coat right back on, Sister!"

"But, Aunt Mae . . ."

"I mean it. Put it on right now." She pulled the coat up on Doretha's shoulders. "I never heard anything so simple[2] in all my life. Can't go out your own house unless somebody goes out there first to see if the street's clear of boys. Now, all you got to do is like this. Watch me now." She walked across the room with a little bounce, making her accordion-pleated skirt swing. She was the size Doretha wanted to be, not really slim, but not fat either. "How you doing?" she said to the floor lamp standing beside the sofa. She waved her arm and kept walking. "Now you do it," she told Doretha.

---

[2]**simple**: having little common sense.

"I can't walk like you," Doretha said.

"Well, walk the way you walk, just don't draw all up like something's going to bite you."

Doretha felt silly, but she tried to imitate her aunt. She walked across the room and waved her arm. "How you doing?" she said.

"That's good, that's good," Aunt Mae said. "Now do it again and say it louder."

After the fourth time, Aunt Mae told her she was ready. "I'll be right here behind the curtain, watching," she said.

"They still there?" Doretha asked.

"Yeah, they still there, and if they weren't, I'd go find them. Thelma let you sit around here daydreaming all the time, you won't never learn how to deal."

Doretha put her hand on the doorknob, and a sudden thought made her panic. "What about when I'm coming back?" she asked.

"When you coming back, think about how good those potato chips going to be, and don't even look over there unless somebody says something to you."

When she got outside, Doretha didn't look across the street right away. She was concentrating on how she was walking. Not too fast, not too slow. She didn't hear a break in their laughing and talking, but when she turned her head to look at them, the boys were looking at her.

"How you doing?" she said with a quick wave.

"Hey Doretha, hey baby." Walter and Larry spoke, and Bernard gave her the black salute. But Coley stood still and cool with his hands in his pockets and his feet turned in just slightly. Doretha turned her head away.

At the store, she bought the potato chips from Mr. Carter and started back. She looked straight ahead and walked in rhythm with her thoughts. "Potato chips, potato chips." As soon as she passed the boys, she started to grin. Aunt Mae was laughing when she opened the door for her, and they leaned on it and closed it together. "I did it, I did it!" Doretha said, laughing and hugging her aunt.

Aunt Mae put her hands on her hips. "You bet your Aunt Mae's applecake you did it. And the next time that sometimey, jive joker tries to speak to you, you tell him where to go and what to do when he gets there. Now, come on watch the movie. You missed one murder already."

Thinking and Discussing

What dialogue and actions in *Sister* make the character of Doretha seem like a real person, someone you might know?

At the beginning of *Sister*, Doretha's answers to Aunt Mae's questions show how shy she is. How does the author use Doretha's dialogue with the boys and Aunt Mae to show Doretha's increased self-confidence?

Choosing a Creative Response

Giving Advice If Aunt Mae had a radio program called "Ask Aunt Mae," what kind of advice do you think she would give? With a partner, role-play one of Doretha's friends calling to "Ask Aunt Mae" about a problem, and Aunt Mae giving advice.

Creating Your Own Activity Plan and complete your own activity in response to *Sister*.

Thinking and Writing

Think of an incident that you would like to share with your classmates, and like Doretha, write your own memory page describing the incident. Say as much or as little as you wish, but try to make your writing clear and lively.

YEAR WALK

BY ANN NOLAN CLARK

In 1910 sixteen-year-old Kepa comes from the Basque provinces of Spain to herd his godfather Pedro's sheep in Idaho. Kepa is sent out for training with the most experienced herder, old Tío Marco. In Spain, Kepa looked after a flock of twenty sheep, but now he and Tío Marco are to take 2500 sheep on the 400-mile trip to the sheep buyers' camp. Kepa soon learns that Tío Marco speaks seldom, and only says what he has to. With no one to talk to or to care about him, Kepa is lonely and homesick.

Morning sun rose over the flattened land, tinting the earth and sky with the same bands of color. The sheep moved and began to graze. The lambs romped and played, flaunting their friskiness. Tío Marco and his dog, Kepa and the young dog following, climbed a small rise of desert sand to look down on the sheep. If they were quiet, calm and feeding, all was well.

The days moved along slowly; only the bad ones stood out to be counted. One afternoon wind brought a threat of rain. The sheep, sensitive to every weather change, scattered uphill. It was hours before the dogs and the herders had driven them down to the flat land near camp to bed down for the night. Another night Patto-Kak [Kepa's mule] broke his tether.[1] At dawn Kepa found him and led him back to camp to be loaded with the pack for the day's move to a new site.

The camp tender[2] came with his string of pack mules bringing camp supplies for the herders and salt for the sheep. He brought letters to Kepa from Paco and Manuel, from Mother and Father. They said everything was fine at home. They said they missed him.

---

[1]**tether**: a rope or chain for an animal.
[2]**tender**: a person who brings fresh supplies to the herders on the trail.

Illustrated by Mary Azarian

Somehow the letters made him lonelier than before. Tío Marco said, "Read your letters, boy, and be glad you get them. At first one writes a lot and the answers come pouring back. Then something happens. One stops writing and the folks stop answering. I guess it's difficult to answer letters that have not been written."

After the camp tender had gone, the days seemed more silent than ever. Kepa understood; it was not that Tío Marco did not want to talk but that he had lost the habit of talking. The old herder was a good teacher both for Kepa and the young dog. Kepa watched him give his signals by whistle, by hand, by shouted order. He watched the old dog respond to them and the young dog learn them. The boy learned them too. He also learned how to take care of his gun, how to keep it clean and dry, safe and always near at hand. He learned to shoot. The old herder's praise, "Good shot, boy," was a welcome one. He learned what plants are good for sheep at one season and poisonous at another. He learned to watch the sheep and know what caused them to act in certain ways at certain times.

The boy learned that sheep scatter uphill when they sense a coming storm, but move downhill when they sense danger from an enemy. When other dangers surround them, they make a circle with their bodies, putting the lambs in the center for safety. In trying to protect them, they smother them if the dogs and the herders do not keep the animals less tightly massed together. When a lamb strays and a ewe cannot find it, she will go back to the last place where it had been with her. When the lamb lags she will walk backward, coaxing it along the trails.

Kepa did not learn these things by being told about them. If the herder had told him, the boy would have listened, would have agreed, and probably would have forgotten them within a span of days. But now as he experienced them, they were explained to him. He lived them. They became part of him.

Again Alberto [the camp tender] came with his string of pack mules. Kepa was surprised to see him; he had not realized the visit was due. He thought, how slowly the days go by, and how fast the weeks. This time Godfather Pedro came with the camp tender. The boy was delighted to see him. He was someone from home. Best of all there was talk, good talk, around the evening cook fire and later by lantern light and starlight.

"Carlos is having trouble with the twin band," Pedro told them and then explained to Kepa, "We put the ewes with twin lambs in one band because it takes them twice as long to get half as far between now and autumn." At Kepa's look of surprise, he said, "A ewe won't feed one lamb alone. Both lambs must be fed at the same time. To get two lambs at the same place at the same time isn't even a miracle. It's an accident." He laughed, but then said seriously, "If I could get another herder I would put him with Carlos to help him, but all the good herders have been hired by this time of the year."

Godfather and Alberto stayed two nights. Before he left, Pedro said, "Chris wants to know how you like the dog." Kepa said, "I like him fine." There was more than liking in the boy's voice. There was longing and hurt. Pedro decided to talk of other things.

When Godfather and the camp tender left the next morning, Kepa missed them. Silence and monotony settled like dust around their campsite and the days followed each other in dreary succession.

Then everything went wrong. Patto-Kak broke tether again and this time went farther before Kepa found him, brought him back, and hobbled him. "You're staying here," Kepa told him, "Remember, I am more stubborn than you."

A ewe lost her lamb and Kepa and the young dog tracked her back to the last campsite, but a coyote had killed the lamb. It was

the first one they had lost. Coyote tracks, now that they were in the foothills, were numerous, and Kepa could hear their mocking, nighttime laughter in the surrounding hills.

There was not the rain there should have been for this time of year. Day after day hot winds blew across the land. The last water hole had been dry, and for days the sheep had not had water. If there had been dew on the shrubs and plants, the sheep could have gone waterless at least for a week, but there was no dew. The wind had dried everything in its sweep across the land.

Now that they had reached the hilly country of stunted juniper trees, the rock patches were more frequent, the shrubs farther apart, and each hour of travel became more difficult and slower. A half day's distance away, the old herder knew there was a large spring at the mouth of a stream. The dogs were urging the sheep band toward it. Twice the sheep had stampeded, trying to return to their last watering place. Tío Marco was impatient. "Stupid beasts," he grumbled, "If one sheep stampedes, every sheep in the band will stampede, and if one falls into a canyon, all of them will try to fall into the canyon."

Kepa agreed with him. He remembered the old shepherd at home telling him, "Sheep have a group mind. No matter how large the flock, they think as one sheep." Kepa grinned, thinking of his flock of twenty sheep in the valley of the Pyrenees.[3] Still, he thought, he had learned a lot from that small flock that was being put into use now.

Besides being impatient, Tío Marco was worried and uneasy. His unease communicated itself to the dogs and through them to the sheep. Kepa followed the herder's gaze. A thin line of dust curled against the distant horizon. "Sheep?" Kepa asked.

---

[3]**Pyrenees (pîr′ə nēz′):** a mountain range along the border between France and Spain.

"Cattle, I think. We must beat them to the spring. We can make it before sunset if these stupid sheep do not scatter again."

The noon sun burned the land and the dry wind stirred the hot air. The sheep rested fitfully.[4] Patto-Kak tried to rid himself of his hobbles.[5] The old dog lay near where the herder sat, but neither was napping. They were watching. The young dog lay by himself, but both he and Kepa, also, watched the sheep and the distant horizon.

A separate dust cloud had detached itself from the long, thin dust line. The man and the boy watched it moving in their direction. Tío Marco said, "We break camp now. By midafternoon when the sheep start to browse again, we will be ready to move them." They began loading the mules. An hour went by. The sheep moved, fanned out, began to graze. The pack mules were ready to go.

One of the last chores Kepa did for each camp move was to put dirt on the cooking-fire ashes to smother any tiny spark the wind might flame. As he was doing this, the expected horseman rode into camp. "He's one of a rustler band. I've had words with this man before," Tío Marco said to Kepa, going forward to meet the stranger. As usual, the old dog, when he was not with the sheep, was at his master's side. They went together — the old herder and the old dog — protecting the rights of the sheep under their care.

At first the rustler shouted in English, and the herder shouted as loudly in Basque. After a few minutes the horseman switched from English to Spanish. "I tell you, don't take your sheep to the spring up yonder, I need it for my cattle."

---

[4]**fitfully:** interrupted by brief bursts of activity.
[5]**hobbles:** ropes or straps placed around the legs of an animal to hamper but not completely prevent movement.

Tío Marco now also spoke in Spanish. "I need it for my sheep."

"Take your sheep some other place," the man said gruffly.

"That spring is never dry," Tío Marco answered reasonably. "There will be enough water for my sheep and the cattle you are driving." Kepa noticed that the old herder did not say, "your cattle."

Apparently the man had noticed it, too, which added to his rage. He said furiously, "My cattle won't drink after your sheep have muddied the water."

Now Tío Marco was angry. "My sheep muddy the water? Bah! It's the cattle that walk in the water and dirty it." The old herder turned his back on the horseman and gave the signal for the dogs to start moving the sheep.

Whirling his horse, the rustler rode back the way he had come, shouting, "I warned you!"

Tío Marco turned to look at him, also shouting, "My sheep need water. I take them to water!"

The dogs had trouble herding the sheep toward the spring. Time after time the band turned backward on the trail instead of forward as the dogs were urging. "I should think they would smell the water and travel toward it," Kepa said.

The herder answered impatiently, "They do smell water. That's why the stupid animals want to go back to where they remember they had it."

It was nearly sundown before they reached the spring, had driven the thirsty animals to the water's edge to drink, and later had seen them bedded down for the night. The old man said, "We won't put up the tents tonight. Tomorrow morning as soon as the sheep have been to water again, we will move on. It's only a two-day drive to the next water. They can make it." Then he added, looking back at the dust cloud on the distant skyline, "I want no trouble with that man. He's a bad one."

"Will he steal the sheep?"

"A lamb or two, maybe for their own meat supply, no more. Who could make a fast getaway with slow-moving sheep?"

At dusk the wind increased its flurry. "Blowing up a storm," the herder said. Rain clouds blotted out the moon and the stars. The dogs and the herders stood guard as they always did when the night was black. At dawn, the clouds hid the sunrise, but the sheep moved, went down to the edge of the spring and began to drink again. "The rustlers are on the move, too," Tío Marco said, looking at the nearing darker line against the banking rain clouds. "But we will be gone before they get here. They can have all the water they need."

Most of the band had finished drinking and were browsing on the grassy bank. Breakfast had been eaten; the cooking fire smothered; the cooking utensils cleaned and packed. Kepa took Patto-Kak's hobbles off and tethered the mule with a shortened rope. "When are you going to learn who is boss?" he asked, slapping the mule playfully as he prepared to put the pack saddle on. The mule flattened its ears and bared its teeth, but made no move to bite or kick. "I think we are beginning to understand each other," Kepa said, laughing.

The two herders packed steadily but unhurriedly. There would be plenty of time to get their band away from the spring before the rustlers and their stolen cattle would arrive. But the men came sooner than Tío Marco had thought. Less than three hours after sunrise, they rode into sheep camp, three men driving about fifty longhorn steers. Yesterday's visitor was in the lead. He had a gun in his hand. Tío Marco faced him, the old dog at his side. "Now that you are here, you can stay here," the rustler shouted. "A sheep band can't move without its dog." Raising his gun he took aim. There was a shot and a whimper of pain.

Kepa could not speak, could not move. He saw his own gun, where he had hung it on a branch of a juniper tree, but he could not reach out for it. The boy could only look in frozen horror at the old herder bending over his dog. Then, realizing the dog was dead, he shouted in anger, "Why didn't you get me instead of my dog? You cowards — to shoot a dog!"

The men and the steers thundered by. Instantly the sheep began to bunch, putting their lambs for protection into the center of their circling bodies. In a flash the young dog jumped among the flock, nipping the frightened sheep, driving them backward, giving the lambs room to breathe. Kepa went with the dog, pushing and shouting. The dog and the boy worked together, instinctively, neither one needing to give nor to have a signal.

It was long after midday before the sheep were calm and resting. Kepa went to find Tío Marco. The old man sat hunched by the fresh mound of earth where his dog lay buried. He needs hot food before we begin the new drive, the boy thought, unpacking the coffee pot, the frying pan, the tin of coffee, bacon and bread, and making a new campfire. When the food was ready he tried to lead the old herder to the campfire to eat, but the man refused to go. He kept saying, "Why did he do it? There was water for all of us." Tío has to eat, Kepa thought. Food will give him strength to walk away from what happened here. The boy brought the food to the old one, coaxing him, but again the herder refused it. Again he said, "Why did he do it? That dog was all I had."

The clouds, threatening since dawn, now opened and rain poured down. The sheep sought shelter in the sage. The boy was worried. He did not know which to do — give the signal, when the rain stopped, for the dog to start the sheep moving and perhaps from habit the old man would follow, or stay at this camp for another night. Alberto was due late today or sometime tomorrow, but he would think that the band would be a day or two farther along the trail. Since his schedule was to leave supplies first at Carlos' camp, then at Marco's, and at Juan's last, he would not come along this trail and would have no way of knowing that Marco's band was not where it was supposed to be. If they stayed here it would mean the camp tender and his string of mules would have to backtrack, which would cause delay. Kepa's grub supply was getting very low.

The rain stopped as abruptly as it had begun. The sheep moved out from the sheltering sage and began to browse. There was water and there were enough grass clumps and shrubs to feed on for awhile longer. The boy looked at Tío Marco. The old one was in no condition to travel. Kepa made his decision. They would stay where they were. Tío Marco might feel better after a night's sleep. Tomorrow's food would be tomorrow's problem.

The boy unpacked Tío Marco's mule and his own Patto-Kak and hobbled them. He put up Tío Marco's tent, but he left his own folded. Quicker packing for morning, he thought. He put the uneaten food on the ground for the young dog. "Eat it," he said gently. "As for me, I'm not hungry."

It was dusk now. He lighted the lantern and again went to where the old herder sat unmoving, uncaring. "Come to bed, Tío. Your bedroll is waiting beside the campfire."

The old man shook his head. "He slept beside me every night. Tonight it will be the same."

"That's fine, Tío. I'll bring your bedroll here." When Kepa brought the bedroll and stretched it out on the ground, Tío Marco said, "Good. Now I can sleep beside my dog."

Kepa made a last circle around the band. The young dog walked beside him. The sheep were sleeping. The boy went again to the new made mound. The old herder was asleep in his bedroll

beside it. Kepa raked the campfire so the coals would smolder and die, put out the lantern flame, and crawled into his own bedroll, exhausted, worried, and heavy-hearted.

The water in the spring lay clear and deep. The night wind whispered in the sagebrush[6] and the chaparral.[7] The young dog lay in the shadows. The young boy slept by the smoldering campfire. Moonlight bathed the rain-wet land, making it almost as light as day. The old man mumbled in his sleep. The night passed slowly, slowly giving way to the gray light of dawn.

Kepa wakened, startled, frightened, sitting upright, looking around him. His first thought was for the sheep, but they were quiet. Nothing disturbed them. He looked toward the place where the herder was sleeping. All was quiet there. The boy pushed himself back into his bedroll. Perhaps a dream had wakened him. Then he felt something against his body. He looked and at first could not believe what he saw. The young dog lay curled at his side. Kepa put his hand down gropingly, not daring to believe what he wanted to believe. His fingers, then his hand touched the young dog's head. The dog did not move but lay relaxed as if at last he had found where he belonged.

Kepa began to cry. As long as he could remember he had never really cried. He had not known what crying was, but now sobs choked him, caught in his throat, tore at his chest, making his body a holding place of his pain. At length his sobs quieted; his tears stopped. The boy crawled from his bedroll and stood in the moonlight looking down at his dog. "I'm a man now for sure," he told his new friend, "because I wasn't ashamed to cry." He felt

---

[6]**sagebrush** (sāj′brŭsh′): a shrub of dry regions of western North America, having strong-smelling silver-green leaves and clusters of small white flowers.

[7]**chaparral** (shăp′ə răl′): a dense growth of tangled, often thorny shrubs, especially in the southwestern United States and Mexico.

empty, but better, stronger, with certainty that he could face the new day that dawn would bring.

Sunrise in its bright-tinted garments lay upon the horizon, clothing the sky and the land alike in a blaze of color. Kepa and his dog walked to the top of a small sand hill, where they could look down on the band. The sheep were moving, wakened by the first hint of day.

The dog and the boy went back to the campsite. "Why did you suddenly decide to be my dog?" Kepa asked, then answered his own question. "I think I know. I think somehow you knew that now the responsibility for the sheep was yours," and he added proudly, "and mine."

Tío Marco had coffee and fried bread ready for the morning meal. Kepa quietly offered his first bit of bread to his dog. This was what all herders did, and it was what he had been longing to do. The dog took the bread from his master's hand, and now Kepa knew beyond all doubt that this was his dog for as long as they both would live.

Godfather Pedro gallops into camp the next day to find out if the rustlers have made trouble. He takes Tío Marco back to the home ranch, and Kepa continues to herd the band to the buyers' meeting place by himself. Before he sees the home ranch again, Kepa has many adventures and makes some important friends.

Responding to *Year Walk*

Thinking and Discussing

How does the author use the visits of the camp tender and Godfather Pedro to emphasize the herders' isolation and Kepa's loneliness?

Why, do you think, does the author describe Kepa's way of learning by observation and experience?

At the beginning of the selection, events happen slowly and calmly. How does the author use the appearance of the cattle rustlers to move the action along faster?

Choosing a Creative Response

Designing a Newspaper Ad Use the realistic details in *Year Walk* to write an ad for a newspaper in which you try to hire sheepherders for a ranch in the United States. Try to describe the personal qualities needed for the job in a few words that will appeal to the kind of person you want.

Planning a Documentary Imagine you are making a television documentary about sheepherders and their problems. Review the selection for ideas about the countryside, the sheep, and the advantages and disadvantages of the job. Work with a partner to plan an outline for the documentary.

Creating Your Own Activity Plan and complete your own activity in response to *Year Walk*.

Where the Red Fern Grows

By Wilson Rawls

Growing up in the Ozark Mountains, thirteen-year-old Billy Colman had always dreamed of having his own coonhounds. Then he saw an ad in a magazine for a pair of coonhound pups. Now, after two years of hard work, he has saved fifty dollars — the advertised price of the pups. Billy hurries to his grandfather's store to show him the pile of coins and to remind him of his promise to order the hound pups. His grandfather is delighted and amazed at his grandson's determination and says he'll write the dog kennel in the ad. He promises they'll find pups somewhere else if they have to. Billy thinks he has the finest grandpa in the world, but he can hardly stand the wait for the pups to arrive.

Day after day, I flew to the store. Grandpa would shake his head. Then on a Monday, as I entered the store, I sensed a change in him. He was in high spirits, talking and laughing with half a dozen farmers. Every time I caught his eye, he would smile and wink at me. I thought the farmers would never leave, but finally the store was empty.

Grandpa told me the letter had come. The kennels were still there, and they had dogs for sale. He said he had made the mail buggy wait while he made out the order. And, another thing, the dog market had gone downhill. The price of dogs had dropped five dollars. He handed me a ten-dollar bill.

"Now, there's still one stump in the way," he said. "The mail buggy can't carry things like dogs, so they'll come as far as the depot at Tahlequah, but you'll get the notice here because I ordered them in your name."

I thanked my grandfather with all my heart and asked him how long I'd have to wait for the notice.

He said, "I don't know, but it shouldn't take more than a couple of weeks."

I asked how I was going to get my dogs out from Tahlequah.

"Well, there's always someone going in," he said, "and you could ride in with them."

That evening the silence of our supper was interrupted when I asked my father this question: "Papa, how far is it to Kentucky?"

I may as well have exploded a bomb. For an instant there was complete silence, and then my oldest sister giggled. The two little ones stared at me.

With a half-hearted laugh, my father said, "Well, now, I don't know, but it's a pretty good ways. What do you want to know for? Thinking of taking a trip to Kentucky?"

"No," I said. "I just wondered."

My youngest sister giggled and asked, "Can I go with you?"

I glared at her.

Mama broke into the conversation, "I declare, what kind of a question is that? How far is it to Kentucky? I don't know what's gotten into that mind of yours lately. You go around like you were lost, and you're losing weight. You're as skinny as a rail, and look at that hair. Just last Sunday they had a haircutting over at Tom Rolland's place, but you couldn't go. You had to go prowling around the river and the woods."

I told Mama that I'd get a haircut next time they had a cutting. And I just heard some fellows talking about Kentucky up at the store, and wondered how far away it was. Much to my relief, the conversation was ended.

The days dragged by. A week passed and still no word about my dogs. Terrible thoughts ran through my mind. Maybe my dogs were lost; the train had a wreck; someone stole my money; or perhaps the mailman lost my order. Then, at the end of the second week, the notice came.

My grandfather told me that he had talked to Jim Hodges that day. He was going into town in about a week and I could ride in with him to pick up my dogs. Again I thanked my grandfather.

I started for home. Walking along in deep thought, I decided it was time to tell my father the whole story. I fully intended to tell him that evening. I tried several times, but somehow I couldn't. I wasn't scared of him, for he never whipped me. He was always kind and gentle, but for some reason, I don't know why, I just couldn't tell him.

That night, snuggled deep in the soft folds of a feather bed, I lay thinking. I had waited so long for my dogs, and I so desperately wanted to see them and hold them. I didn't want to wait a whole week.

In a flash I made up my mind. Very quietly I got up and put on my clothes. I sneaked into the kitchen and got one of Mama's precious flour sacks. In it I put six eggs, some leftover corn bread, a little salt, and a few matches. Next I went to the smokehouse and cut off a piece of salt pork. I stopped at the barn and picked up a gunny sack. I put the flour sack inside the gunny sack. This I rolled up and crammed lengthwise in the bib of my overalls.

I was on my way. I was going after my dogs.

Tahlequah was a small country town with a population of about eight hundred. By the road it was thirty-two miles away, but as the crow flies, it was only twenty miles. I went as the crow flies, straight through the hills.

Although I had never been to town in my life, I knew what direction to take. Tahlequah and the railroad lay on the other side of the river from our place. I had the Frisco Railroad on my right, and the Illinois River on my left. Not far from where the railroad crossed the river lay the town of Tahlequah. I knew if I bore to the right I would find the railroad, and if I bore to the left I had the river to guide me.

Some time that night, I crossed the river on a riffle[1] some-where in the Dripping Springs country. Coming out of the river bottoms, I scatted up a long hogback ridge, and broke out on top in the flats. In a mile-eating trot, I moved along. I had the wind of a deer, the muscles of a country boy, a heart full of dog love, and a strong determination. I wasn't scared of the darkness, or the mountains, for I was raised in those mountains.

On and on, mile after mile, I moved along. I saw faint gray streaks appear in the east. I knew daylight was close. My bare feet were getting sore from the flint rocks and saw briers. I stopped beside a mountain stream, soaked my feet in the cool water, rested for a spell, and then started on.

After leaving the mountain stream, my pace was much slower. The muscles of my legs were getting stiff. Feeling the pangs of hunger gnawing at my stomach, I decided I would stop and eat at the next stream I found. Then I remembered I had forgotten to include a can in which to boil my eggs.

I stopped and built a small fire. Cutting off a nice thick slab of salt pork, I roasted it, and with a piece of cold corn bread made a sandwich. Putting out my fire, I was on my way again. I ate as I trotted along. I felt much better.

I came into Tahlequah from the northeast. At the outskirts of town, I hid my flour sack and provisions, keeping the gunny sack. I walked into town.

I was scared of Tahlequah and the people. I had never seen such a big town and so many people. There was store after store, some of them two stories high. The wagon yard had wagons on top of wagons; teams, buggies, and horses.

Two young ladies about my age stopped, stared at me, and then giggled. My blood boiled, but I could understand. After all, I

---

[1]**riffle** (rĭf′əl): a rocky shoal or sandbar lying just below the surface of a waterway.

had three sisters. They couldn't help it because they were women-folks. I went on.

I saw a big man coming up the street. The bright shiny star on his vest looked as big as a bucket. I saw the long, black gun at his side and I froze in my tracks. I'd heard of sheriffs and marshals, but had never seen one. Stories repeated about them in the mountains told how fast they were with a gun, and how many men they had killed.

The closer he came, the more frightened I got. I knew it was the end for me. I could just see him aiming his big, black gun and shooting me between the eyes. It seemed like a miracle that he passed by, hardly glancing at me. Breathing a sigh, I walked on, seeing the wonders of the world.

Passing a large store window, I stopped and stared. There in the window was the most wonderful sight I had ever seen; everything under the sun; overalls, jackets, bolts of beautiful cloth, new harnesses, collars, bridles; and then my eyes did pop open. There were several guns and one of them had two barrels. I couldn't believe it — two barrels. I had seen several guns, but never one with two barrels.

Then I saw something else. The sun was just right, and the plate glass was a perfect mirror. I saw the full reflection of myself for the first time in my life.

I could see that I did look a little odd. My straw-colored hair was long and shaggy, and was bushed out like a corn tassel[2] that had been hit by a wind. I tried to smooth it down with my hands. This helped some but not much. What it needed was a good combing and I had no comb.

My overalls were patched and faded but they were clean. My shirt had pulled out. I tucked it back in.

---

[2]**corn tassel** (kôrn tăs'əl): the pollen-bearing flower cluster of a corn plant.

I took one look at my bare feet and winced. They were as brown as dead sycamore leaves. The spider-web pattern of raw, red scratches looked odd in the saddle-brown skin. I thought, "Well, I won't have to pick any more blackberries and the scratches will soon go away."

I pumped up one of my arms and thought surely the muscle was going to pop right through my thin blue shirt. I stuck out my tongue. It was as red as pokeberry juice and anything that color was supposed to be healthy.

After making a few faces at myself, I put my thumbs in my ears and was making mule ears when two old women came by. They stopped and stared at me. I stared back. As they turned to go on their way, I heard one of them say something to the other. The words were hard to catch, but I did hear one word: "Wild." As I said before, they couldn't help it, they were womenfolks.

As I turned to leave, my eyes again fell on the overalls and the bolts of cloth. I thought of my mother, father, and sisters. Here was an opportunity to make amends for leaving home without telling anyone.

I entered the store. I bought a pair of overalls for Papa. After telling the storekeeper how big my mother and sisters were, I bought several yards of cloth. I also bought a large sack of candy.

Glancing down at my bare feet, the storekeeper said, "I have some good shoes."

I told him I didn't need any shoes.

He asked if that would be all.

I nodded.

He added up the bill. I handed him my ten dollars. He gave me my change.

After wrapping up the bundles, he helped me put them in my sack. Lifting it to my shoulder, I turned and left the store.

Out on the street, I picked out a friendly-looking old man and asked him where the depot was. He told me to go down to the last street and turn right, go as far as I could, and I couldn't miss it. I thanked him and started on my way.

Leaving the main part of town, I started up a long street through the residential section. I had never seen so many beautiful houses, and they were all different colors. The lawns were neat and clean and looked like green carpets. I saw a man pushing some kind of a mowing machine. I stopped to watch the whirling blades. He gawked at me. I hurried on.

I heard a lot of shouting and laughing ahead of me. Not wanting to miss anything, I walked a little faster. I saw what was making the noise. More kids than I had ever seen were playing around a big red brick building. I thought some rich man lived there and was giving a party for his children. Walking up to the edge of the playground, I stopped to watch.

The boys and girls were about my age, and were as thick as flies around a sorghum[3] mill. They were milling, running, and jumping. Teeter-totters and swings were loaded down with them. Everyone was laughing and having a big time.

Over against the building, a large blue pipe ran up on an angle from the ground. A few feet from the top there was a bend in it. The pipe seemed to go into the building. Boys were crawling into its dark mouth. I counted nine of them. One boy stood about six feet from the opening with a stick in his hand.

Staring goggle-eyed, trying to figure out what they were doing, I got a surprise. Out of the hollow pipe spurted a boy. He sailed through the air and lit on his feet. The boy with the stick marked the ground where he landed. All nine of them came shooting out, one behind the other. As each boy landed, a new mark was scratched.

---

[3] **sorghum (sôr′gəm):** a grain-bearing grass grown as a source of syrup.

They ganged around looking at the lines. There was a lot of loud talking, pointing, and arguing. Then all lines were erased and a new scorekeeper was picked out. The others crawled back into the pipe.

I figured out how the game was played. After climbing to the top of the slide, the boys turned around and sat down. One at a time, they came flying down and out, feet first. The one that shot out the furthest was the winner. I thought how wonderful it would be if I could slide down just one time.

One boy, spying me standing on the corner, came over. Looking me up and down, he asked, "Do you go to school here?"

I said, "School?"

He said, "Sure. School. What did you think it was?"

"Oh. No, I don't go to school here."

"Do you go to Jefferson?"

"No. I don't go there either."

"Don't you go to school at all?"

"Sure I go to school."

"Where?"

"At home."

"You go to school at home?"

I nodded.

"What grade are you in?"

I said I wasn't in any grade.

Puzzled, he said, "You go to school at home, and don't know what grade you're in. Who teaches you?"

"My mother."

"What does she teach you?"

I said, "Reading, writing, and arithmetic, and I bet I'm just as good at it as you are."

He asked, "Don't you have any shoes?"

I said, "Sure, I have shoes."

"Why aren't you wearing them?"

"I don't wear shoes until it gets cold."

He laughed and asked where I lived.

I said, "Back in the hills."

He said, "Oh, you're a hillbilly."

He ran back to the mob. I saw him pointing at me and talking to several boys. They started my way, yelling, "Hillbilly, hillbilly."

Just before they reached me, a bell started ringing. Turning, they ran to the front of the building, lined up in two long lines, and marching like little tin soldiers disappeared inside the school.

The playground was silent. I was all alone, and felt lonely and sad.

I heard a noise on my right. I didn't have to turn around to recognize what it was. Someone was using a hoe. I'd know that sound if I heard it on a dark night. It was a little old white-headed woman working in a flower bed.

Looking again at the long, blue pipe, I thought, "There's no one around. Maybe I could have one slide anyway."

I eased over and looked up into the dark hollow. It looked scary, but I thought of all the other boys I had seen crawl into it. I could see the last mark on the ground, and thought, "I bet I can beat that."

Laying my sack down, I started climbing up. The farther I went, the darker and more scary it got. Just as I reached the top, my feet slipped. Down I sailed. All the way down I tried to grab on to something, but there was nothing to grab.

I'm sure some great champions had slid out of that pipe, and no doubt more than one world record had been broken, but if someone had been there when I came out, I know the record I set would stand today in all its glory.

I came out just like I went in, feet first and belly down. My legs were spread out like a bean-shooter stalk. Arms flailing the air,

232

I zoomed out and up. I seemed to hang suspended in air at the peak of my climb. I could see the hard-packed ground far below.

As I started down, I shut my eyes tight and gritted my teeth. This didn't seem to help. With a splattering sound, I landed. I felt the air whoosh out between my teeth. I tried to scream, but had no wind left to make a sound.

After bouncing a couple of times, I finally settled down to earth. I lay spread-eagled for a few seconds, and then slowly got to my knees.

Hearing loud laughter, I looked around. It was the little old lady with the hoe in her hand. She hollered and asked how I liked it. Without answering, I grabbed up my gunny sack and left. Far up the street, I looked back. The little old lady was sitting down, rocking with laughter.

I couldn't understand these town people. If they weren't staring at a fellow, they were laughing at him.

On arriving at the depot, my nerve failed me. I was afraid to go in. I didn't know what I was scared of, but I was scared.

Before going around to the front, I peeked in a window. The stationmaster was in his office looking at some papers. He was wearing a funny little cap that had no top in it. He looked friendly enough but I still couldn't muster up enough courage to go in.

I cocked my ear to see if I could hear puppies crying, but could hear nothing. A bird started chirping. It was a yellow canary in a cage. The stationmaster walked over and gave it some water. I thought, "Anyone that is kind to birds surely wouldn't be mean to a boy."

With my courage built up I walked around to the front and eased myself past the office. He glanced at me and turned back to the papers. I walked clear around the depot and again walked slowly past the office. Glancing from the corner of my eye, I saw the stationmaster looking at me and smiling. He opened the door and came out on the platform. I stopped and leaned against the building.

Yawning and stretching his arms, he said, "It sure is hot today. It doesn't look like it's ever going to rain."

I looked up at the sky and said, "Yes, sir. It is hot and we sure could do with a good rain. We need one bad up where I come from."

He asked me where I lived.

I told him, "Up the river a ways."

"You know," he said, "I have some puppies in there for a boy that lives up on the river. His name is Billy Colman. I know his dad, but never have seen the boy. I figured he would be in after them today."

On hearing this remark, my heart jumped clear up in my throat. I thought surely it was going to hop right out on the depot platform. I looked up and tried to tell him who I was, but something went wrong. When the words finally came out they sounded like the squeaky old pulley[4] on our well when Mama drew up a bucket of water.

I could see a twinkle in the stationmaster's eyes. He came over and laid his hand on my shoulder. In a friendly voice he said, "So you're Billy Colman. How is your dad?"

I told him Papa was fine and handed him the slip my grandpa had given me.

"They sure are fine-looking pups," he said. "You'll have to go around to the freight door."

I'm sure my feet never touched the ground as I flew around the building. He unlocked the door, and I stepped in, looking for my dogs. I couldn't see anything but boxes, barrels, old trunks, and some rolls of barbed wire.

---

[4]**pulley** (pool′ē): a freely turning grooved wheel through which a rope, chain, or cable runs.

The kindly stationmaster walked over to one of the boxes. "Do you want box and all?" he asked.

I told him I didn't want the box. All I wanted was the dogs.

"How are you going to carry them?" he asked. "I think they're a little too young to follow."

I held out my gunny sack.

He looked at me and looked at the sack. Chuckling, he said, "Well, I guess dogs can be carried that way same as anything else, but we'll have to cut a couple of holes to stick their heads through so that they won't smother."

Getting a claw hammer, he started tearing off the top of the box. As nails gave way and boards splintered, I heard several puppy whimpers. I didn't walk over. I just stood and waited.

After what seemed like hours, the box was open. He reached in, lifted the pups out, and set them down on the floor.

"Well, there they are," he said. "What do you think of them?"

I didn't answer. I couldn't. All I could do was stare at them.

They seemed to be blinded by the light and kept blinking their eyes. One sat down on his little rear and started crying. The other one was waddling around and whimpering.

I wanted so much to step over and pick them up. Several times I tried to move my feet, but they seemed to be nailed to the floor. I knew the pups were mine, all mine, yet I couldn't move. My heart started acting like a drunk grasshopper. I tried to swallow and couldn't. My Adam's apple wouldn't work.

One pup started my way. I held my breath. On he came until I felt a scratchy little foot on mine. The other pup followed. A warm puppy tongue caressed my sore foot.

I heard the stationmaster say, "They already know you."

I knelt down and gathered them in my arms. I buried my face between their wiggling bodies and cried. The stationmaster, sensing something more than just two dogs and a boy, waited in silence.

Rising with the two pups held close to my chest, I asked if I owed anything.

He said, "There is a small feed bill but I'll take care of it. It's not much anyway."

Taking his knife he cut two slits in the sack. He put the pups in it and worked their heads through the holes. As he handed the sack to me, he said, "Well, there you are. Good-bye and good hunting!"

Walking down the street toward town, I thought, "Now, maybe the people won't stare at me when they see what I've got. After all, not every boy owns two good hounds."

Turning the corner onto the main street, I threw out my chest.

I hadn't gone far before I realized that the reception I got wasn't what I thought it would be. People began to stop and stare, some even snickered. I couldn't understand why they were staring. Surely it couldn't be at the two beautiful hound pups sticking out of the gunny sack.

Thinking that maybe I had a hole in the seat of my britches, I looked over to my reflection in a plate-glass window. I craned my neck for a better view of my rear. I could see a patch there all right, and a few threadbare spots, but no whiteness was showing through. I figured that the people were just jealous because they didn't have two good hounds. . . .

I hurried on, wanting to get away from the stares and the snickers.

It wouldn't have happened again in a hundred years, but there they came. The same two old women I had met before. We stopped and had another glaring fight.

One said, "I declare."

The other one snorted, "Well, I never."

My face burned. I couldn't take any more. After all, a man can stand so much and no more. In a loud voice, I said, "You may have these people fooled with those expensive-looking feathers in your hats, but I know what they are. They're goose feathers painted with iodine."

One started to say something, but her words were drowned out by the roaring laughter from all around. Gathering up their long skirts, they swished on down the street.

All around me people began to shout questions and laugh. One wanted to know if I had the mother in the sack. Storekeepers stepped out and gawked. I could see the end of the street, but it looked as if it were a hundred miles away. My face was as red as a fox's tail. I ducked my head, tightened my grip on the sack, and walked on.

I don't know where they came from, but like chickens coming home to roost, they flocked around me. Most of them were about my age. Some were a little bigger, some smaller. They ganged around me, screaming and yelling. They started clapping their hands and chanting, "The dog boy has come to town. The dog boy has come to town."

My heart burst. Tears came rolling. The day I had waited for so long had turned black and ugly.

The leader of the gang was about my size. He had a dirty freckled face and his two front teeth were missing. I suppose he had lost them in a back alley fight. His shock of yellow sunburnt hair bobbed up and down as he skipped and jumped to the rhythm of the "dog boy" song. He wore a pair of cowboy boots. They were two sizes too big for him, no doubt handed down by an older brother.

He stomped on my right foot. I looked down and saw a drop of blood ooze out from under the broken nail. It hurt like the dickens but I gritted my teeth and walked on.

Freckle-face pulled the ear of my little girl pup. I heard her painful cry. That was too much. I hadn't worked two long years for my pups to have some freckle-face punk pull their ears.

Swinging the sack from my shoulder, I walked over and set it down in a doorway. As I turned around to face the mob, I doubled up my fist, and took a Jack Dempsey stance.[5]

Freckle-face said, "So you want to fight." He came in swinging.

I reached way back in Arkansas somewhere. By the time my fist had traveled all the way down to the Cherokee Strip, there was a lot of power behind it.

Smack on the end of Freck's nose it exploded. With a loud grunt he sat down in the dusty street. Grabbing his nose in both hands, he started rocking and moaning. I saw the blood squeeze out between his fingers.

Another one sailed in. He didn't want to fight. He wanted to wrestle. He stuck a finger in my mouth. I ground down. Shaking his hand and yelling like the hoot owls were after him, he ran across the street.

Another one bored in. I aimed for his eye, but my aim was a little low. It caught him in the Adam's apple. A sick look came over his face. Bending over, croaking like a bullfrog that had been caught by a water moccasin, he started going around in a circle.

But there were too many of them. By sheer weight and numbers, they pulled me down. I managed to twist over on my stomach and buried my face in my arms. I could feel them beating and kicking my body.

All at once the beating stopped. I heard loud cries from the gang. Turning over on my back, I was just in time to see the big marshal plant a number-twelve boot in the seat of the last kid. I just knew I was next. I wondered if he'd kick me while I was down.

---

[5]**Jack Dempsey stance:** the boxing position of Jack Dempsey (1895–1983), famous American heavyweight boxer.

239

I lay where I was. He started toward me. I closed my eyes. I felt a hand as big as an anvil[6] clamp on my shoulder. I thought, "He's going to stand me up, and then knock me down."

He raised me to a sitting position. His deep friendly voice said, "Are you all right, son?"

I opened my eyes. There was a smile on his wide rugged face. In a choking voice, I said, "Yes, sir. I'm all right."

He helped me to my feet. His big hands started brushing the dust from my clothes.

"Those kids are pretty tough, son," he said, "but they're really not bad. They'll grow up some day."

"Marshal," I said, "I wouldn't have fought them, but they pulled my pup's ears."

He looked over to my sack. One pup had worked its way almost out through the hole. The other one's head and two little paws were sticking out. Both of them were whimpering.

A smile spread all over the big marshal's face. "So that's what started the fight," he said.

Walking over, he knelt down and started petting the pups. "They're fine-looking dogs," he said. "Where did you get them?"

I told him I had ordered them from Kentucky.

"What did they cost you?" he asked.

"Forty dollars," I said.

He asked if my father had bought them for me.

"No," I said. "I bought them myself."

He asked me where I got the money.

"I worked and saved it," I said.

"It takes a long time to save forty dollars," he said.

"Yes," I said. "It took me two years."

"Two years!" he exclaimed.

---

[6]**anvil (ăn′vĭl):** a heavy block of iron or steel, on which metals are shaped by hammering.

240

I saw an outraged look come over the marshal's face. Reaching up, he pushed his hat back. He glanced up and down the street. I heard him mutter, "There's not a one in that bunch with that kind of grit."[7]

Picking up my sack, I said, "Thanks for helping me out. I guess I'd better be heading for home."

He asked where I lived.

I said, "Up the river a way."

"Well, you've got time for a bottle of pop before you go, haven't you?"

I started to say "No," but looking at his big friendly smile, I smiled back and said, "I guess I have."

Walking into a general store, the marshal went over to a large red box and pulled back the lid. He asked what kind I wanted. I'd never had a bottle of pop in my life, and didn't know what to say.

Seeing my hesitation, he said, "This strawberry looks pretty good."

I said that would be fine.

The cool pop felt wonderful to my hot dry throat. My dark little world had brightened up again. I had my pups, and had found a wonderful friend. I knew that the stories I had heard about marshals weren't true. Never again would I be scared when I saw one.

Back out on the street, I shook hands with the marshal, saying as I did, "If you're ever up in my part of the country come over and see me. You can find our place by asking at my grandfather's store."

"Store?" he asked. "Why, the only store upriver is about thirty miles from here."

"Yes," I said, "that's my grandpa's place."

He asked if I was afoot.

---

[7]**grit:** courage.

"Yes," I said.

"You won't make it tonight," he said. "Will you?"

"No," I said. "I intend to camp out somewhere."

I saw he was bothered.

"I'll be all right," I said. "I'm not scared of the mountains."

He looked at me and at my pups. Taking off his hat, he scratched his head. Chuckling deep down in his barrel-like chest, he said, "Yes, I guess you will be all right. Well, good-bye and good luck! If you're ever in town again look me up."

From far down the street, I looked back. The marshal was still standing where I had left him. He waved his hand. I waved back.

On the outskirts of town, I stopped and picked up a can and my provisions.

I hadn't gone far before I realized that I had undertaken a tough job. The sack became heavier and heavier.

For a while my pups cried and whimpered. They had long since pulled their heads back in the sack. I would peek in at them every once in a while. They were doing all right. Curled up into two little round balls on my bundles, they were fast asleep.

Deep in the heart of the Sparrow Hawk Mountains, night overtook me. There, in a cave with a stream close by, I put up for the night.

Taking my pups and bundles from the gunny sack, I used it to gather leaves to make us a bed. My pups followed me on every trip, whimpering and crying, tumbling and falling over sticks and rocks.

After the bed was made I built a fire. In a can of water from the mountain stream, I boiled three eggs. Next, I boiled half of the remaining salt pork. Cutting the meat up in small pieces, I fed it to my pups. Each of us had a piece of candy for dessert. My pups enjoyed the candy. With their needle-sharp teeth, they gnawed and worried with it until it was melted away.

While they were busy playing, I dragged up several large timbers and built a fire which would last for hours. In a short time the cave grew warm and comfortable from the heat. The leaves were soft, and felt good to my tired body and sore feet. As I lay stretched out, my pups crawled all over me. I played with them. They would waddle up to the front of the cave, look at the fire, and come scampering back to roll and play in the soft leaves.

I noticed the boy dog was much larger than the girl dog. He was a deeper red in color. His chest was broad and solid. His puppy muscles knotted and rippled under the velvety skin. He was different in every way. He would go closer to the fire. I saw right away he was bold and aggressive.

Once he went around the fire and ventured out into the darkness. I waited to see if he would come back. He came wobbling to the mouth of the cave, but hesitated there. He made several attempts to come back, but the flames were leaping higher by the minute. The space between the fire and the wall of the cave was much hotter than when he had ventured out. Whimpering and crying, he kept trying to get around the fire. I said not a word; just watched.

Puppy though he was, he did something which brought a smile to my face. Getting as close as he could to the side of the cave, he turned his rear to the fire. Hopping sideways, yipping at every jump, he made it through the heat and sailed into the pile of leaves. He had had enough. Curling up in a ball close to me, he went to sleep.

The girl pup was small and timid. Her legs and body were short. Her head was small and delicate. She must have been a runt in the litter. I didn't have to look twice to see that what she lacked in power, she made up in brains. She was a much smarter dog than the boy dog, more sure of herself, more cautious. I knew when the trail became tough, she would be the one to unravel it.

I knew I had a wonderful combination. In my dogs, I had not only the power, but the brains along with it.

I was a tired boy. My legs were stiff, and my feet sore and throbbing. My shoulders were red and raw from the weight of the sack. I covered my pups up in the leaves and moved my body as close to them as I could. I knew as night wore on, and the fire died down, the chill would come. Tired but happy, I fell asleep.

Along in the silent hours of night, I was awakened. I opened my eyes, but didn't move. I lay and listened, trying to figure out what it was that had aroused me. At first I thought one of my pups had awakened me by moving and whimpering. I discarded this thought for I could see that they were both fast asleep. I decided it was my imagination working.

My fire had burned down, leaving only a glowing red body of coals. The cave was dark and silent. Chill from the night had crept in. I was on the point of getting up to rebuild my fire, when I heard what had awakened me. At first I thought it was a woman screaming. I listened. My heart began to pound. I could feel the strain all over my body as nerves grew tighter and tighter.

It came again, closer this time. The high pitch of the scream shattered the silence of the quiet night. The sound seemed to be all around us. It screamed its way into the cave and rang like a blacksmith's anvil against the rock walls. The blood froze in my veins. I was terrified. Although I had never heard one, I knew what it was. It was the scream of a mountain lion.

The big cat screamed again. Leaves boiled and stirred where my pups were. In the reflection of the glowing coals, I could see that one was sitting up. It was the boy dog. A leaf had become entangled in the fuzzy hair of a floppy ear. The ear flicked. The leaf dropped.

Again the hellish scream rang out over the mountains. Leaves flew as my pup left the bed. I jumped up and tried to call him back.

Reaching the mouth of the cave, he stopped. Raising his small red head high in the air, he bawled his challenge to the devil cat.

The bawl must have scared him as much as it had startled me. He came tearing back. The tiny hairs on his back were standing on end.

My father had told me lions were scared of fire. I started throwing on more wood. I was glad I'd dragged up a good supply while making camp.

Hearing a noise from the bed, I looked back. The girl pup, hearing the commotion, had gotten up and joined the boy dog. They were sitting side by side with their bodies stiff and rigid. Their beady little eyes bored into the darkness beyond the cave. The moist tips of their little black noses wiggled and twisted as if trying to catch a scent.

What I saw in my pups gave me courage. My knees quit shaking and my heart stopped pounding.

I figured the lion had scented my pups. The more I thought about anything harming them, the madder I got. I was ready to die for my dogs.

Every time the big cat screamed, the boy dog would run to the mouth of the cave and bawl back at him. I started whooping and throwing rocks down the mountainside, hoping to scare the lion away. Through the long hours of the night, I kept this up.

The lion prowled around us, screaming and growling; first on the right, and then on the left, and above and below. In the wee hours of morning, he gave up and left to stalk other parts of the mountains. I'm sure he thought he didn't stand a chance against two vicious hounds and a big hunter.

Responding to *Where the Red Fern Grows*

Thinking and Discussing

How does Billy react to his new experiences in the town? What are some of the details that make Billy's reactions realistic?

A boy starts to talk with Billy in the schoolyard. How does the author use their dialogue to show some differences between the boys?

Choosing a Creative Response

Describing an Unfamiliar Object Billy is puzzled by an unfamiliar piece of playground equipment. Think of a piece of equipment that might also puzzle someone seeing it for the first time. Describe it and ask your classmates to figure out what it is.

Drawing a Map Draw a map of Tahlequah as you imagine it from the author's description. Mark the places Billy visits.

Creating Your Own Activity Plan and complete your own activity in response to *Where the Red Fern Grows*.

Thinking and Writing

Imagine that Billy has arrived home and is describing to a friend what he saw and did in the schoolyard in Tahlequah. Write this conversation as a dialogue between the two friends.

LIFE
IN THE
OZARKS

The Ozark Mountains, where Billy Colman grew up, cover 200 square miles in Missouri, Arkansas, Kansas, and Oklahoma.

In the 1920's, when Billy Colman walked thirty miles to fetch his coonhound pups, life in the Ozarks hadn't changed much since settlers first arrived more than a hundred years before. Farm families like Billy's had to produce everything they needed. Men raised corn, wheat, and hogs. They hunted and fished to add to the family food supply. Women raised chickens and vegetables. They spun thread and wove cloth for their families' clothes. Doctors were few so the farmers treated illnesses with herbs. They made baskets, rag rugs, feather beds, and patchwork quilts.

People worked hard, but they had fun, too, especially when they square-danced to bluegrass music.

Because the Ozark Mountains are hard to get to, pioneer ways survived there long after they disappeared in other parts of the country. But by the 1940's, the old ways of life began to disappear.

Because many people in the Ozarks are descended from English and Scottish immigrants, some of them still use very old words and expressions from the England and Scotland of several hundred years ago. They also have developed many colorful expressions of their own.

Some Old English Expressions

To get your ears lowered (to get a haircut): "I see you've got your ears lowered."

To jump the broomstick (to get married): "I hear you two jumped the broomstick."

To have swamp measles (to be dirty): "Seems like every time the kids play outside, they come down with swamp measles."

Some Comparisons

Jumpier than a truckload of starving kangaroos

Nervous as a porcupine in a balloon factory

Slick as a wax snake on a marble floor

Papa's Parrot

by Cynthia Rylant

Though his father was fat and merely owned a candy and nut shop, Harry Tillian liked his papa. Harry stopped liking candy and nuts when he was around seven, but, in spite of this, he and Mr. Tillian had remained friends and were still friends the year Harry turned twelve.

For years, after school, Harry had always stopped in to see his father at work. Many of Harry's friends stopped there, too, to spend a few cents choosing penny candy from the giant bins or to sample Mr. Tillian's latest batch of roasted peanuts. Mr. Tillian looked forward to seeing his son and his son's friends every day. He liked the company.

When Harry entered junior high school, though, he didn't come by the candy and nut shop as often. Nor did his friends. They were older and they had more spending money. They went to a burger place. They played video games. They shopped for records. None of them were much interested in candy and nuts anymore.

A new group of children came to Mr. Tillian's shop now. But not Harry Tillian and his friends.

The year Harry turned twelve was also the year Mr. Tillian got a parrot. He went to a pet store one day and bought one for more money than he could really afford. He brought the parrot to his shop, set its cage near the sign for maple clusters and named it Rocky.

Harry thought this was the strangest thing his father had ever done, and he told him so, but Mr. Tillian just ignored him.

Rocky was good company for Mr. Tillian. When business was slow, Mr. Tillian would turn on a small color television he had sitting in a corner, and he and Rocky would watch the soap operas. Rocky liked to scream when the romantic music came on, and Mr. Tillian would yell at him to shut up, but they seemed to enjoy themselves.

The more Mr. Tillian grew to like his parrot, and the more he talked to it instead of to people, the more embarrassed Harry became. Harry would stroll past the shop, on his way somewhere else, and he'd take a quick look inside to see what his dad was doing. Mr. Tillian was always talking to the bird. So Harry kept walking.

At home things were different. Harry and his father joked with each other at the dinner table as they always had — Mr. Tillian teasing Harry about his smelly socks; Harry teasing Mr. Tillian about his blubbery stomach. At home things seemed all right.

But one day, Mr. Tillian became ill. He had been at work, unpacking boxes of caramels, when he had grabbed his chest and fallen over on top of the candy. A customer had found him, and he was taken to the hospital in an ambulance.

Mr. Tillian couldn't leave the hospital. He lay in bed, tubes in his arms, and he worried about his shop. New shipments of candy and nuts would be arriving. Rocky would be hungry. Who would take care of things?

Harry said he would. Harry told his father that he would go to the store every day after school and unpack boxes. He would sort out all the candy and nuts. He would even feed Rocky.

So, the next morning, while Mr. Tillian lay in his hospital bed, Harry took the shop key to school with him. After school he left his friends and walked to the empty shop alone. In all the days of his life, Harry had never seen the shop closed after school. Harry didn't even remember what the CLOSED sign looked like. The key stuck in the lock three times, and inside he had to search all the walls for the light switch.

The shop was as his father had left it. Even the caramels were still spilled on the floor. Harry bent down and picked them up one by one, dropping them back in the boxes. The bird in its cage watched him silently.

Harry opened the new boxes his father hadn't gotten to. Peppermints. Jawbreakers. Toffee creams. Strawberry kisses. Harry traveled from bin to bin, putting the candies where they belonged.

"Hello!"

Harry jumped, spilling a box of jawbreakers.

"Hello, Rocky!"

Harry stared at the parrot. He had forgotten it was there. The bird had been so quiet, and Harry had been thinking only of the candy.

"Hello," Harry said.

"Hello, Rocky!" answered the parrot.

Harry walked slowly over to the cage. The parrot's food cup was empty. Its water was dirty. The bottom of the cage was a mess. Harry carried the cage into the back room.

"Hello, Rocky!"

"Is that all you can say, you dumb bird?" Harry mumbled. The bird said nothing else.

Harry cleaned the bottom of the cage, refilled the food and water cups, then put the cage back in its place and resumed sorting the candy.

"Where's Harry?"

Harry looked up.

"Where's Harry?"

Harry stared at the parrot.

"Where's Harry?"

Chills ran down Harry's back. What could the bird mean? It was like something from "The Twilight Zone."

"Where's Harry?"

Harry swallowed and said, "I'm here. I'm here, you stupid bird."

"You stupid bird!" said the parrot.

Well, at least he's got one thing straight, thought Harry.

"Miss him! Miss him! Where's Harry? You stupid bird!"

Harry stood with a handful of peppermints.

"*What?*" he asked.

"Where's Harry?" said the parrot.

"I'm *here*, you stupid bird! I'm here!" Harry yelled. He threw the peppermints at the cage, and the bird screamed and clung to its perch.

Harry sobbed, "I'm here." The tears were coming.

Harry leaned over the glass counter.

"Papa." Harry buried his face in his arms.

"Where's Harry?" repeated the bird.

Harry sighed and wiped his face on his sleeve. He watched the parrot. He understood now: someone had been saying, for a long time, "Where's Harry? Miss him."

Harry finished his unpacking, then swept the floor of the shop. He checked the furnace so the bird wouldn't get cold. Then he left to go visit his papa.

Thinking and Discussing

Why is it more effective for the boy to learn how his father feels through the parrot than directly from the father?

How does Harry's changing attitude toward candy reflect his changing feelings as he begins growing up?

Choosing a Creative Response

Performing a Puppet Play With a partner, create a puppet show that features Harry and the parrot. Write a dialogue in which the puppets act out their feelings about the situation with the father. Perform the skit in front of the class.

Creating Your Own Activity Plan and complete your own activity in response to "Papa's Parrot."

Thinking and Writing

Imagine that you are Harry, and you must create a sign explaining your father's absence from the store. How might you let people know about your father's situation? Write a large sign explaining why the store is closed.

Thinking About Realism

Creating a Diorama In your opinion, which selection setting in "Becoming" is the most vivid and believable? You might like to make a shoebox diorama of this setting. Scan the selection and note any details you find about where and when the story takes place. Add details about the characters' food, clothing, and shelter. Look around for things to use in your diorama, such as twigs for trees, or a bottlecap for a picture frame.

Giving a Special Gift Think about the six main characters in the selections in "Becoming." With a partner, choose one who seems like a real person, someone you both would enjoy having as a friend. Decide on a special gift you might give this friend. You may want to illustrate or describe your gift and ask your classmates to guess which character you intend the gift for. Explain why your gift is especially appropriate.

Having a Panel Discussion Imagine that you are the moderator of a teen-age panel discussion on growing up. You have invited Hideyo, Kepa, Billy, Doretha, Harry, and Ernesto to be panel members. The panel will discuss the ways older friends or relatives can help the growing-up process. With your group, role-play the panel discussion.

Dramatizing a Scene With a group, choose your favorite scene from one of the stories in "Becoming" that you would like to dramatize. Create a script, construct sets and costumes, and perform your scene for your classmates. Be sure to capture in your performances the changes the characters go through in the scene. You may wish to videotape your dramatization if a camera is available.

257

About the Authors

Ann Nolan Clark was born in the late 1800's in Las Vegas, New Mexico. She started her career teaching in a university but soon changed to work with Native American children. During this time, she wrote books such as *In My Mother's House*, which won the New York Herald Spring Festival award, *Little Navajo Herder, Buffalo Caller*, and *Bringer of the Mystery Dog*. Later Clark began writing books for and about Latin Americans. One of these, *Secret of the Andes*, won the Newbery Medal in 1952.

Dan D'Amelio was born in Italy in 1927. He received a bachelor's degree from New York University and went on to work on the editorial staff of CBS. In addition to *Taller Than Bandai Mountain*, D'Amelio's writing includes books about his experiences in journalism and about the education of children with severe mental disabilities.

Ernesto Galarza was born in 1905 in Jalcocotán, Mexico. To escape the violence of the Mexican Revolution, Galarza's family moved frequently, settling down in Sacramento, California. Galarza wrote several books on the history of farm workers in America, a volume of poetry, and *Barrio Boy*, his autobiography. Galarza died in San Jose, California, in 1984.

Eloise Greenfield was born in Parmele, North Carolina, in 1929. She has written biographies of Rosa Parks, Paul Robeson, and Mary McLeod Bethune. Other books by Greenfield include *Honey, I Love, and Other Love Poems*, which was named an ALA Notable Book; *Africa Dream*, which won the Coretta Scott King Award in 1978; and *Childtimes: A Three-Generation Memoir*, a book of memories recalled by Eloise Greenfield, her mother, and her grandmother.

Wilson Rawls was born in Oklahoma in 1913. He was taught to read and write by his mother. Throughout his years as a laborer, he never lost his secret ambition to be a writer. In 1961, his award-winning book *Where the Red Fern Grows*, based on Rawls's boyhood, was published. Rawls's second book for young people, *Summer of the Monkeys*, was published in 1976, and received numerous awards from libraries and universities all over the country.

Cynthia Rylant's first book, *When I Was Young in the Mountains*, won four awards. Other books of hers include *Waiting to Waltz: A Childhood*, *Every Living Thing*, *A Blue-Eyed Daisy*, *The Relatives Came*, and *A Fine White Dust*, which was a Newbery Honor Book in 1987.

Staying on Track

. . . and now Miguel
by Joseph Krumgold
(Houghton, 1991;
Crowell, 1953)

Miguel lives on a
sheep farm in New
Mexico. He longs to
join the men when
they take the sheep to
the Sangre de Cristo
Mountains. The trip
promises to be excit-
ing — and dangerous.

**Homesick: My
Own Story**
by Jean Fritz
(Putnam, 1982)

Born and raised
in China, young Jean
Fritz felt fiercely
American and longed
for a land she hadn't
seen. She developed
an enthusiasm for
American history that
has never left her.

Queen of Hearts
by Vera and
Bill Cleaver
(Lippincott, 1978)

Wilma spends the
summer living with her
strong-minded grand-
mother. As the two
come to understand
each other, they share
good times and make
some difficult adjust-
ments.

On My Honor by Marion Dane Bauer (Clarion, 1986)

Tony dares Joel to swim in the dangerous river. They both go in, but Tony disappears. Joel's best friend has drowned. How will he overcome his guilt? How will he tell his father the terrible truth?

Whose Side Are You On? by Emily Moore (Farrar, 1988)

Barbara becomes interested in her math tutor T.J. in spite of herself. Together Barbara and T.J. solve all kinds of family and school problems — more complicated than any in her math book.

Moving In by Alfred Slote (Lippincott, 1988)

Robby is tired of moving after his mother's death. Now he and his sister have to deal with a bigger problem when their father's new business partner wants to marry Dad. Robby and his sister cook up a plan to stop the marriage.

POETRY

images

SOUNDS

SONGS

images

sounds

songs

The Blue Window by Henri Matisse, summer 1913, oil on canvas

GRAVEL PATHS

I feel crinkled when I walk on gravel paths.
The gravel crinkles me
And I become gravel,
Crunched under five thousand footsteps.
I know what it is to be gravel,
Pecked at by pigeons,
Searching for crumbs of park picnics.
Gravel gets tired,
Being poked at by sparrows and pigeons,
Being squashed under grown-up feet,
Being combed by park men's tickling rakes.
Gravel would rather play,
Explode in skittery sprays under running sneakers.
At least, I think it would,
And I should know,
Having run crinkled
And sneaker-shod
Up many gravel paths.

Patricia Hubbell

Boots with Laces
by Vincent van Gogh,
1886,
oil on canvas

Cardinal

Red as a shout
he stamps himself
like a Chinese signature
on the clean snow
under the dark juniper tree
in the park.

He is a scarlet stroke
of ink
brushed in —
a feathered ending
to a poem about
snow.

In the whole city
pale and dusted with
snow
only his wings are ablaze
with poppies!

Barbara Esbensen

From some tall grass
a meadow mouse
leaps up
to feel the morning
empty
all around her.

Joanne Ryder

Northern Cardinal
by John James Audubon, 1822,
watercolor on paper

Sudden Shower at Ohashi by Utagawa Hiroshige, 1857, color woodcut

Nag's Head, Cape Hatteras

Etched against a leaden sky,
Birds delicately fly
Frozen in the motion of their flight.
The clouds, motionless,
Are permanently fixed, without relief,
Varying shades of gray.

At a distance
The restless dunes,
Lonely, desolate, beckon
With their straggly reeds
Given motion
By the endless winds.
The roaring waves
Crash blindly
On the jetty
"Closed until the summer."
There is no other sign of life.

The night is velvet ebony.
There is only dark.
There is no beginning: there is no end:
Only the waves in their incessant crashing.
All is suspended in timelessness.

The wind rises
Then subsides, then rises again.

Javier Honda

The Sea B by Emil Nolde, 1930, oil on canvas

Rags

The night wind
rips a cloud sheet
into rags,

then rubs, rubs
the October moon
until it shines
like a brass doorknob.

Judith Thurman

In the Morning

In the morning
a little bird
that has no name
flies westward
pulling away
the dark blanket of the night.

Siv Cedering Fox

The wild geese returning
Through the misty sky —
Behold they look like
A letter written
In faded ink!

Tsumori Kunimoto

Check

The night was creeping on the ground;
She crept and did not make a sound
Until she reached the tree, and then
She covered it, and stole again
Along the grass beside the wall.

I heard the rustle of her shawl
As she threw blackness everywhere
Upon the sky and ground and air,
And in the room where I was hid:
But no matter what she did
To everything that was without
She could not put my candle out.

So I stared at the night, and she
Stared back solemnly at me.

James Stephens

Steam Shovel

The dinosaurs are not all dead.
I saw one raise its iron head
To watch me walking down the road
Beyond our house today.
Its jaws were dripping with a load
Of earth and grass that it had cropped.
It must have heard me where I stopped,
Snorted white steam my way,
And stretched its long neck out to see,
And chewed, and grinned quite amiably.

Charles Malam

Lectern Sentinel by David Smith, 1961,
stainless steel

271

WHAT IS BLACK?

Black is the night
When there isn't a star
And you can't tell by looking
Where you are.
Black is a pail of paving tar.
Black is jet
And things you'd like to forget.
Black is a smokestack
Black is a cat,
A leopard, a raven,
A high silk hat.
The sound of black is
"Boom! Boom! Boom!"
Echoing in
An empty room.
Black is kind —
It covers up
The run-down street,
The broken cup.
Black is charcoal

And patio grill,
The soot spots on
The window sill.
Black is a feeling
Hard to explain
Like suffering but
Without the pain.
Black is licorice
And patent leather shoes
Black is the print
In the news.
Black is beauty
In its deepest form,
The darkest cloud
In a thunderstorm.
Think of what starlight
And lamplight would lack
Diamonds and fireflies
If they couldn't lean against
Black. . . .

Mary O'Neill

Responding to

Thinking and Discussing

Poets paint with words. If you were to paint one of the poems in this section, which one would you choose? Why? What specific words and phrases does the poet use to "paint" the image clearly?

Poetry helps you see things in a new and different way. Look through these poems to find comparisons that you might not normally make. Choose one poem, and think about the two things it compares. Then explain how the poem helps you see something in an unusual way.

Choosing a Creative Response

Making Images Think of a scene such as a city street, the woods after a snowfall, or your own personal make-believe world. Imagine that you are there, and describe the scene with images that appeal to your senses. Jot down the words that describe these images. Then either draw a picture of this scene or write your own poem with the words that you have chosen.

Creating Your Own Activity Plan and complete your own activity in response to the poems in "Images."

authors

Barbara Esbensen worked as an art teacher; her poems often capture the visual arts in poetic form.

Siv Cedering Fox has won awards for both poetry and photography.

Javier Honda is a Texan whose poetry has appeared in numerous publications.

Patricia Hubbell says that writing poetry is "arranging and rearranging. . . . Somehow a pattern emerges, and reflects your delight in some aspect of the world."

Tsumori Kunimoto was a Japanese Shinto priest who lived during the eleventh century. He wrote poetry as a hobby.

Charles Malam wrote poetry and drama. He won many literary awards for his promising work as a writer.

Mary O'Neill has published over a dozen books. One of these, *Hailstones and Halibut Bones,* was selected in 1961 as one of the hundred best books for children

Joanne Ryder's books introduce young people to nature, often through fantasy.

James Stephens grew up in Dublin, Ireland; he remained passionately devoted to Ireland and loved to tell Irish stories and sing Irish songs.

Judith Thurman not only writes poetry for young people, but she also writes about women writers.

The Starry Night by Vincent van Gogh, 1889, oil on canvas

SOUNDS

night
and a
distant
church

Forward abrupt
                         up
then mmm
                    mmm
wind mmm   m
      mmm
             m

upon
the mm
          mm
wind mmm   m
      mmm
into the mm wind
rain now and again
the mm
            wind
     ells
b
       ells
    b

Russell Atkins

snowspell

Look, it is falling a little
faster than falling, hurrying
straight down on urgent business
for snowbirds, snowballs, glaciers.

It is covering up the afternoon.
It is bringing the evening down
on top of us and soon the night.
It is falling fast as rain.

It is bringing shadows wide
as eagles' wings and dark
as crows over our heads.
It is falling, falling fast.

Robert Francis

Icicle in sun
flashing blue fire, melts. Dripping,
dripping, crystal bells.

Doris Johnson

Plunging Gull by Milton Avery, 1960, oil on canvas

snow toward evening

Suddenly the sky turned gray,
The day,
Which had been bitter and chill,
Grew intensely soft and still.
Quietly
From some invisible blossoming tree
Millions of petals cool and white
Drifted and blew,
Lifted and flew,
Fell with the falling night.

Melville Cane

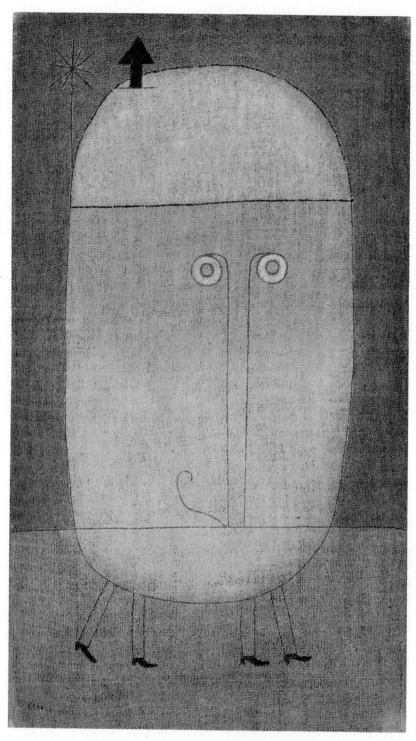

Mask of Fear by Paul Klee, 1932, oil on burlap

WINDY NIGHTS

Whenever the moon and stars are set,
    Whenever the wind is high,
All night long in the dark and wet,
    A man goes riding by.
Late in the night when the fires are out,
Why does he gallop and gallop about?

Whenever the trees are crying aloud,
    And ships are tossed at sea,
By, on the highway, low and loud,
    By at the gallop goes he.
By at the gallop he goes, and then
By he comes back at the gallop again.

Robert Louis Stevenson

HOUSE FEAR

Always — I tell you this they learned —
Always at night when they returned
To the lonely house from far away
To lamps unlighted and fire gone gray,
They learned to rattle the lock and key
To give whatever might chance to be
Warning and time to be off in flight:
And preferring the out- to the in-door night,
They learned to leave the house-door wide
Until they had lit the lamp inside.

Robert Frost

WHERE HAVE YOU BEEN DEAR?

Where
Have you been dear?
What
Have you seen dear?
What
Did you do there?
Who
Went with you there?
Tell me
What's new dear?
What's
New with you dear?
Where
Will you go next?
What
Will you do?

"I do this and I do that.
I go here and I go there.
At times I like to be alone.
There are some thoughts that are my own
I do not wish to share."

Karla Kuskin

Angry General with Decorations by Enrico Baj, 1961, oil and collage on canvas

Responding to

SOUNDS ‖‖‖

Thinking and Discussing

Poets use rhyme, rhythm, and repetition of sounds to convey meaning. Compare the poems in this section. How do their sounds represent different meanings? Do they enrich the poems? Why or why not?

Compare the way the sounds in these poems create mood. Then choose the poem you liked most. What sound effects are used to create a special mood? How does this mood make the poem come alive?

Choosing a Creative Response

Identifying the Galloping Man Make up a story that will tell your listeners what "Windy Nights" leaves out — who the man is and why he gallops about. You may wish to tape your story, creating the special sound effects of the galloping horse.

Writing a Poem of Sounds "Night and a Distant Church" is based on the sounds of the wind and the bells. Create a poem of sounds that you like to hear.

Creating Your Own Activity Plan and complete your own activity in response to the poems in "Sounds."

AUTHORS

Russell Atkins, an Afro-American poet and composer, has often set his work to music.

Melville Cane's long life of 101 years was devoted to law and poetry. His last book, published in 1974, was named after the poem "Snow Toward Evening."

Robert Francis chose to live a simple, solitary life so that he could devote himself to writing poetry.

Robert Frost, one of the most popular American poets of the twentieth century, spent most of his life in rural New England, farming, teaching, and writing poetry.

Doris Johnson is an author and musician who is very interested in the Orient and its literature.

Karla Kuskin's more than forty books illustrate her philosophy that "poetry can be as natural and effective a form of self-expression as singing or shouting."

Robert Louis Stevenson wrote many books and stories that are now classics, including *Treasure Island* and *The Strange Case of Dr. Jekyll and Mr. Hyde*.

Carnival of Harlequin by Joan Miró, 1924-1925, oil on canvas

This old hammer
Shine like silver,
Shine like gold, boys,
Shine like gold.

Well don't you hear that
Hammer ringing?
Drivin' in steel, boys,
Drivin' in steel.

Can't find a hammer
On this old mountain
Rings like mine, boys,
Rings like mine.

I've been working
On this old mountain
Seven long years, boys,
Seven long years.

I'm going back to
Swannanoa Town-o,
That's my home, boys,
That's my home.

Take this hammer,
Give it to the captain,
Tell him I'm gone, boys,
Tell him I'm gone.

(*Traditional Ballad*)

The Hero by David Smith, 1952,
painted steel

JOHNNY APPLESEED

Of Jonathan Chapman
Two things are known
That he loved apples,
That he walked alone.

At seventy-odd
He was gnarled as could be,
But ruddy and sound
As a good apple tree.

For fifty years over
Of harvest and dew,
He planted his apples
Where no apples grew.

The winds of the prairie
Might blow through his rags,
But he carried his seeds
In the best deerskin bags.

From old Ashtabula
To frontier Fort Wayne,
He planted and pruned
And he planted again.

He had not a hat
To encumber his head.
He wore a tin pan
On his white hair instead.

He nested with owl,
And with bear cub and 'possum,
And knew all his orchards
Root, tendril, and blossom.

A fine old man,
As ripe as a pippin,
His heart still light,
And his step still skipping.

The stalking Indian,
The beast in its lair
Did no hurt
While he was there.

For they could tell,
As wild things can,
That Jonathan Chapman
Was God's own man.

Why did he do it?
We do not know.
He wishes that apples
Might root and grow.

He has no statue.
He has no tomb.
He has his apple trees
Still in bloom.

Consider, consider,
Think well upon
The marvelous story
Of Appleseed John.

Rosemary Carr Benét

FROG WENT A-COURTIN'

Frog went a-courtin' and he did ride, unh-hunh,
Frog went a-courtin' and he did ride, unh-hunh,
Sword and pistol by his side, unh-hunh, unh-hunh,

Rode till he came to Miss Mousie's door, unh-hunh,
Rode till he came to Miss Mousie's door,
He gave three raps and a very loud roar, unh-hunh, unh-hunh.

He said, 'Miss Mouse, are you within?' etc.
'Yes, I just sat down to spin.'

He went right in and took her on his knee,
And he said, 'Miss Mouse, will you marry me?'

Miss Mouse, she said, 'I can't answer that
Until I see my Uncle Rat,

'Uncle Rat's in London Town,
And I don't know when he'll be down.

'Without my Uncle Rat's consent,
I wouldn't marry the President.'

Uncle Rat came riding home;
'Who's been here since I've been gone?'

'A very worthy gentleman,
He said he'd marry me if he can.'

When Uncle Rat gave his consent,
The weasel wrote the publishment.

'Where shall the wedding supper be?'
'Out in the woods in an old hollow tree.'

'Who shall the wedding guests be?'
'A little lady bug and a bumblebee.'

Mister Frog was dressed in a pea green,
Mistress Mouse she looked like a queen.

First that came was a little lady bug,
And she had cider in her jug.

Next that came was a bumblebee
Dancing a jig with a two-legged flea.

'What shall the wedding supper be?'
'Two blue beans and a black-eyed pea.'

First came in a little moth
For to lay the tablecloth.

The owl did hoot, the birds, they sang,
And through the woods the music rang.

Next came in was a little red ant,
She always says, 'I can't, I can't.'

The next came in was an old gray mare,
Hip stuck out and shoulder bare.

The next came in was a little black dog,
Chased Miss Mousie in a hollow log.

The next came in was an old tomcat,
Swallowed Miss Mousie as slick as a rat.

Mr. Frog he went down to the lake,
And there he was swallowed by a big black snake.

Big black snake he swam to land,
And was killed by a bad old man.

Bad old man he went to France,
And that's the end of my romance.

So here's the end of one, two, three,
The snake, the frog, and Miss Mousie.

There's bread and cheese upon the shelf,
If you want any, just help yourself.

(Traditional Ballad)

Conversation Piece by J. N. Eaton, circa 1830-1845, oil on wood panel

Scarborough Fair

Are you going to Scarborough Fair?
Sing parsley, sage, rosemary, and thyme,
Remember me to one who lives there,
For once she was a true love of mine.

Tell her to buy me an acre of land,
Sing parsley, sage, rosemary, and thyme,
Beneath the wild ocean and yonder sea strand,
And she shall be a true love of mine.

Tell her to make me a cambric shirt,
Sing parsley, sage, rosemary, and thyme,
Without any stitching or needlework,
And she shall be a true love of mine.

Tell her to wash it in yonder dry well,
Sing parsley, sage, rosemary, and thyme,
Where water ne'er sprung nor a drop of rain fell,
And she shall be a true love of mine.

Tell her to dry it on yonder sharp thorn,
Sing parsley, sage, rosemary, and thyme,
Which never bore blossom since Adam was born,
And she shall be a true love of mine.

(Traditional Ballad)

Louise by Modigliani, oil on canvas

HOPE

Sometimes when I'm lonely,
Don't know why,
Keep thinkin' I won't be lonely
By and by.

Langston Hughes

Responding to

SONGS

Thinking and Discussing

Many poems were originally sung. What musical qualities do the poems in "Songs" display? Why do you think these songs might have such lasting appeal?

You might know the music that accompanies some of the poems in "Songs." If you were to set one of these poems to your own music, which one would you choose? What type of music might you use for it? Do you think the poem would be better as a song? Explain why or why not.

Choosing a Creative Response

Forming a Chorus of Song Choose one "song" from this section, and with a group, practice reading or singing it chorally. You might want to tape-record it, adding background music to complement the poem's tone or mood.

Adapting a Ballad Look back at the incidents in the ballad you liked best. Have you read about someone whose life story might make a similar ballad? Retell this story, trying to imitate the style of the ballad you liked.

Creating Your Own Activity Plan and complete your own activity in response to the poems in "Songs."

Horse's Head Covering by a Cheyenne Indian, circa 1825-1875, vegetable-dyed porcupine quills on buckskin

Authors

In 1933 **Rosemary Carr Benét** and her Pulitzer Prize– winning husband, Stephen Vincent Benét, wrote *A Book of Americans*, verse biographies of historical characters.

Langston Hughes was the best-known writer of the Harlem Renaissance, a period during the 1920's when many black writers produced innovative work. Hughes experimented with using blues and jazz rhythms in his poetry.

Violet-Orange by Wassily Kandinsky, October 1935, oil on canvas

Thinking About Poetry

Coloring a Poem The color black in Mary O'Neill's poem "What Is Black?" recalls animals, objects, sounds, and feelings. Work with a group to write a collective poem about another color. Create as many images as you can, appealing to all the senses. Then read the poem to your class. You might want to add visual and sound effects to your color poem.

Creating a Poets' Hall of Fame Create an exhibit on poets whose verse you particularly liked. Write biographical sketches, and include pictures of the poets; exhibit several other poems by these writers; and reproduce fitting quotations or anecdotes to introduce them. Display your presentations in a "Poets' Hall of Fame."

Displaying Poetry Cover your bulletin board with blank construction paper. Then use this as a display on which to write your own poetry. You might also want to include poems that have impressed you that you have read in other books, magazines, or newspapers. Add to your wall anytime you find or create a new masterpiece.

Play with Poetry

The Dream Keeper and Other Poems by Langston Hughes (Knopf, 1932, 1986) uses songs, blues, and lyrical poems to show the hopes and concerns of black Americans.

I Like You, If You Like Me: Poems of Friendship selected by Myra Cohn Livingston (McElderry, 1987) includes poems from many cultures on all aspects of friendship.

Sports Pages by Arnold Adoff (Lippincott, 1986) covers all types of players and sports, using blank verse that moves with the power and grace of a fine athlete.

This Delicious Day: 65 Poems selected by Paul B. Janeczko (Orchard, 1987) presents short poems for your funny bone, your sweet tooth, and your mind's eye.

You Come Too: Favorite Poems for Young People by Robert Frost (Holt, 1959, 1967) brings together this popular poet's better-known verses about nature and people.

*Rhythm, Joy of Lif*e by Robert Delaunay, 1930, oil on canvas

SOCIAL STUDIES

BOOK 5

DISCOVERING

ANCIENT EGYPT

The pyramids at Giza

HELP WANTED
Archaeological Dig in Egypt

Discover tombs of the Pharaohs. Break open massive doors of stone. Enter burial chambers and catalogue treasures. Bring the history of ancient Egypt to life.

Discoveries

From *A Message of Ancient Days,* a social studies textbook

The Gift of the Nile

Key Terms

- cataract
- delta
- papyrus
- dynasty
- pharaoh

➤ *In this scene at
Aswan in south Egypt,
the fertile riverbank
contrasts sharply with
the barren desert.*

Grain was scarce, and fruit was dried up. People robbed their neighbors. Babies were crying, and old men were sad as they sat on the ground with their legs bent and their arms folded.

So begins an ancient legend about the Nile River. The Egyptians depended on the flooding of the Nile to water their fields. During years of "high Niles," crops grew well and people had plenty to eat. Years of "low Niles" provided barren fields.

The legend tells of a time of low Niles, when Egypt had seven years of famine. This time fell during the reign of King Zoser, who ruled in the 2600's B.C. The king watched the crops withering, and he saw his people starving. He turned to his chief advisor, Imhotep, for help. The answer, said Imhotep, was to learn the name of the god of the Nile so they could pray to him. Later, he told the king that the Nile slept in two caverns below a temple near Egypt's southern border. When it was time, the ram-god Khnum (kə nōōm´) opened the floodgates, and the Nile rushed toward Egypt. That night Zoser dreamed that Khnum spoke to him: "I am Khnum. I know the Nile. When it covers the fields, it gives them life. Now the Nile will pour over the land without stopping. Plants will grow, bowing down with fruit. The years

of starvation will be over."

When the king awoke, he told the people that they must honor Khnum by giving a portion of each year's harvest to his temple. The high Niles returned, and the seven years of hunger ended.

The Geography of the Nile

Egypt is on the northeastern coast of Africa. Look at the map and locate Egypt on the globe in the inset. Now find the Nile River on the large map.

As the ancient legend shows, the Nile is Egypt's lifeline. Without it, most of the land would be desert. It is the longest river in the world, traveling over 4,000 miles from its source in the lakes and marshes of central Africa to its outlet in the Mediterranean Sea.

At six places along the Nile's winding course, stone cliffs and boulders force its waters through narrow channels. The water rushes through, forming waterfalls and rapids called **cataracts**. The first cataract marked the southern boundary of ancient Egypt. Find it on the map.

From the first cataract, the Nile flows north for about 600 miles. For most of this journey, it flows as a single

▼ *Some have compared the shape of Egypt with that of a lotus flower. Can you see the flower's blossom and stem?*

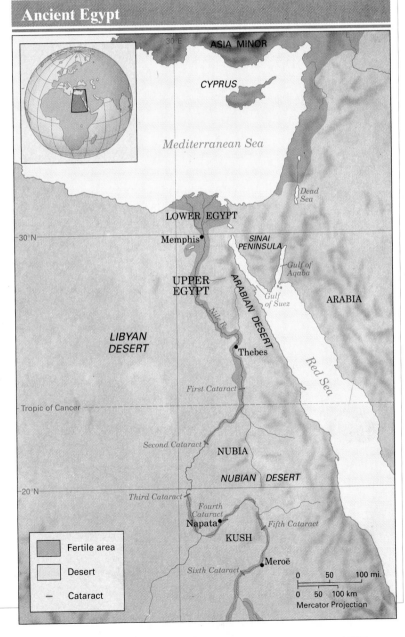

Ancient Egypt

30°E
ASIA MINOR
CYPRUS
Mediterranean Sea
Dead Sea
LOWER EGYPT
30°N
Memphis
SINAI PENINSULA
Gulf of Aqaba
UPPER EGYPT
ARABIAN DESERT
Gulf of Suez
ARABIA
Nile R.
LIBYAN DESERT
Thebes
Red Sea
First Cataract
Tropic of Cancer
Second Cataract
NUBIA
NUBIAN DESERT
20°N
Third Cataract
Fourth Cataract
Napata
Fifth Cataract
KUSH
Meroë
Sixth Cataract

Fertile area

Desert

— Cataract

0   50   100 mi.

0   50 100 km
Mercator Projection

301

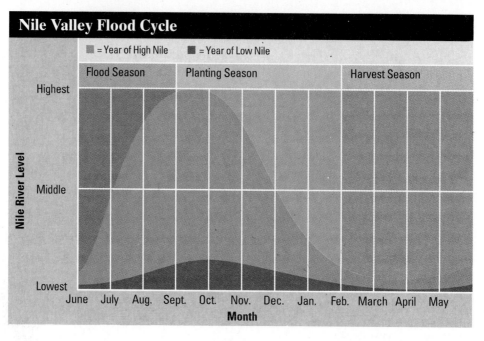

Nile Valley Flood Cycle

■ = Year of High Nile   ■ = Year of Low Nile

| Flood Season | Planting Season | Harvest Season |

Nile River Level

Highest

Middle

Lowest

June July Aug. Sept. Oct. Nov. Dec. Jan. Feb. March April May

Month

▲ *Which months made up each of Egypt's three seasons? How did the years of high Niles differ from the years of low Niles? What might you be doing now if you were a farmer in ancient Egypt?*

➤ *The Egyptians used stone nilometers like this one to measure the yearly flood level of the Nile.*

river. But just south of what is today Cairo (**kī´rō**) it divides into many smaller channels and streams. This triangle of marshy wetlands is called the **delta**.

A Dry Climate

From the air much of the Nile looks like a brown snake wriggling north across a vast desert. Its narrow banks are green with crops and palms. Abruptly they turn into desert — red stone and hot sands. The people who lived there 4,000 years ago called their fertile, dark-soiled valley the Black Land. The desert was the Red Land.

Egypt gets almost no rain. The deserts on the east and the west are parts of the Sahara, the great desert that covers much of North Africa. Desert on two sides, mountains on the south, and the Mediterranean on the north — these natural barriers isolated ancient Egypt and protected it from invaders.

A Seasonal Cycle

In this desert land, the Egyptians depended on the Nile for water and for life. The amount of water the Nile carried on its journey to the Mediterranean varied from season to season. When heavy rains fell in central Africa and snows began to melt high in the mountains of east Africa, the water level of the river rose. By the time the river

the river, dividing the year into three seasons. During the season of flooding, from June through September, the Nile overflowed its banks and covered the fields. When the Nile returned to its normal level, from October to February, the farmers planted their crops. From March until June, with the river at its lowest level, the farmers harvested their crops. This cycle of flooding, planting, and harvesting gave a pattern to Egyptian life.

The River's Gifts

About 2,500 years ago Herodotus (hĭ **rŏd´**ə təs), a Greek visitor to ancient Egypt, called this land the "gift of the Nile." The Egyptians sang special hymns of praise to the river. The example below was written down in the New Kingdom.

*H*ail to thee O Nile that issues from the earth and comes to keep Egypt alive! . . . He that waters the meadows which Ra created.
Hymn to the Nile, from papyrus documents, 1350–1100 B.C.

◄ *Notice the fine carving and bright coloring in this small wooden statue of a woman carrying an offering.*

reached Egypt, it overflowed its banks. Egypt's farmers depended on the annual flooding to water their crops.

The floods of Egypt were predictable. They came at about the same time each year. Farmers knew when the Nile would rise, and they planned ahead for that time. In fact, the Egyptians measured time by

To take advantage of the annual flooding of the Nile, the people built irrigation channels to carry water into the fields. They also built dams to hold back the water for use during dry seasons. In some

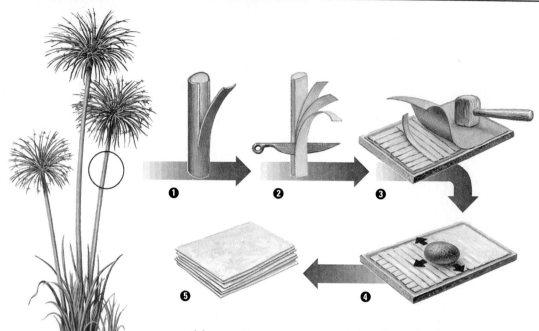

▲ *Paper-makers cut the stem of the papyrus and removed the inner pith. This clockwise series of images shows how they cut the pith into strips, put one layer across another, beat the layers into a single sheet, and polished each sheet with a stone and trimmed the edges.*

■ *Explain how water, mud, plants, and animals were all "gifts of the Nile" to the Egyptians.*

ways this was the same thing done by the ancient Sumerians, the people of an older civilization. But the floods were predictable in Egypt, and farming was easier. The Egyptians needed less cooperation than the Sumerians to get the work done. As a result, they did not develop cities until much later.

Besides water, another gift of the Nile was the thick, black mud left behind in the annual flooding. This mud enriched the soil and made the farmland extremely productive.

The Nile gave other gifts as well. Ducks, geese, and other edible water birds made their homes in the marshes of the delta. **Papyrus** (pə pī′rəs), a long, thin reed, grew wild along the riverbanks. The Egyptians harvested the papyrus and made it into baskets, boats, sandals, and a lightweight writing material. Our word *paper* comes from the word *papyrus*.

The Nile also served as a highway. Boats going north traveled swiftly downstream with the current. Boats going south used sails to travel upstream.

The Egyptians used the gifts of the Nile wisely. Here in this land of contrasts — fertile riverbanks and barren deserts, Black Land and Red Land — they built a remarkable civilization. ■

The Union of Two Lands

Ancient Egypt had two parts, Upper Egypt and Lower Egypt. Upper Egypt, the south part, stretched for over 500 miles from Aswan north to the beginning of the Nile Delta.

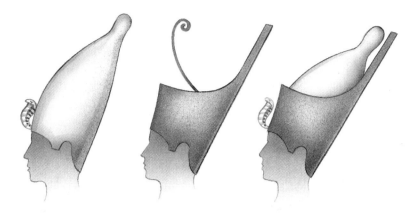

Lower Egypt, the north part, was the area of the Nile Delta. Lower Egypt was only 100 miles long but many times wider than Upper Egypt.

Red and White Crowns

By about 3300 B.C., both Upper Egypt and Lower Egypt had kings. The king of Upper Egypt wore a tall, white pear-shaped crown. The king of Lower Egypt wore a short, boxy red crown with a tall spike at the back and a curlicue at the front.

Much of our knowledge of Egypt in this prehistoric time is mixed with legend. One famous legend tells about Menes (mē′nēz), a king of Upper Egypt. Around 3100 B.C., Menes defeated the king of Lower Egypt, united the two lands, and named himself King of Upper and Lower Egypt.

The legend goes on to tell how Menes designed a new crown to celebrate his victory. This double crown, which combined those of Upper and Lower Egypt, stood for the union of the two lands. Menes and his family went on to form the first Egyptian dynasty. A **dynasty** is a series of rulers from the same family. After Menes died, his son became king, and later his grandson.

During its almost 4,000-year history, 30 different dynasties ruled Egypt.

Menes chose the city of Memphis as his capital. Find Memphis on the map on page 301. How do you think the location of Memphis helped Menes keep firm control of both parts of his newly united kingdom?

Over 2,000 Years of History

History for ancient Egypt began around 3000 B.C., with the invention of hieroglyphic writing. Within the history of ancient Egypt, historians have

The slate palette of Narmer is from around 2950 B.C. King Narmer, who is wearing the white crown, is striking a kneeling prisoner.

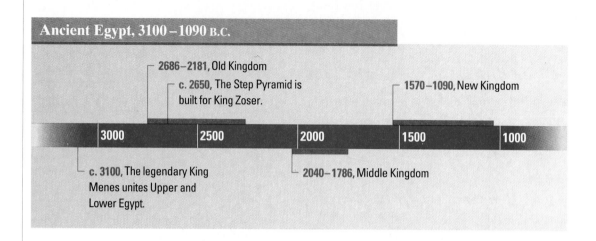

Ancient Egypt, 3100 – 1090 B.C.

2686–2181, Old Kingdom

c. 2650, The Step Pyramid is built for King Zoser.

1570–1090, New Kingdom

3000   2500   2000   1500   1000

c. 3100, The legendary King Menes unites Upper and Lower Egypt.

2040–1786, Middle Kingdom

identified three periods when many important events took place.

In the Old Kingdom, from 2686 to 2181 B.C., the Egyptians built the great pyramids. In the Middle Kingdom, from 2040 to 1786 B.C., Egypt became stronger, and the Egyptians achieved a great deal in literature, art, and architecture. In the New Kingdom, from 1570 to 1090 B.C., Egypt became a world power by conquering other nations and building a great empire. Sometime in the New Kingdom period, the Egyptian people began to call their kings **pharaoh**. In the two earlier periods the word pharaoh, meaning "great house," had been the name for the king's palace. In the New Kingdom,

■ *What were some important early accomplishments of the Egyptians?*

pharaoh came to mean the king who lived in the palace.

In the years between these periods, weak kings ruled, or foreigners gained control of Egypt. These in-between periods were times of great confusion.

In the 1,000 years before the Old Kingdom began, the Egyptian people accomplished many things. They learned to irrigate their fields, and they raised both grain and livestock. They formed governments, with kings as rulers. They invented hieroglyphic writing. Finally, they created the belief systems and customs that made Egyptian life unique. These early achievements formed the basis of ancient Egyptian society. ■

R E V I E W

1. What did the ancient Egyptians accomplish because of the "gifts of the Nile"?
2. Explain how the geography of Egypt affected its early development as a civilization.
3. The ancient Egyptians valued a quiet, orderly life. They did not want things to change. How might these preferences help to explain why the story of Menes was important to them?

Life in Ancient Egypt

The photo below may surprise you if you have seen pictures of pyramids in Egypt. This pyramid is different. It is called the Step Pyramid, and the name fits. To find out more about this unusual structure, we will revisit King Zoser.

Sometime in the middle of the 2600's B.C., King Zoser began to plan for his burial. He called on Imhotep, his chief advisor and also a fine architect, to design his tomb. Until then, a royal tomb was a flat-topped, mud-brick structure built over a burial chamber that lay deep under the ground. Imhotep designed a grander, more permanent tomb for the king, and he did not build it of mud brick, but of stone.

No one knows whether Imhotep planned the design in advance or thought of it as the work went along. At any rate, his builders put one flat-topped structure on top of another. They made each level a few feet smaller than the one below it.

When Imhotep's pyramid was finished, a chamber for the king's body lay about 80 feet under the ground. A mile-long, 133-foot-high stone wall surrounded the tomb. The wall had 14 doors, only one of which actually opened.

Later architects and engineers built on Imhotep's ideas to design and construct

THINKING FOCUS

Describe the religious ideas and the social structure of the ancient Egyptians.

Key Terms

- afterlife
- embalm
- mummy
- hieroglyphics

◄ *Zoser's Step Pyramid, the first large-scale stone structure in the world, was built in the mid -2600's B.C. on a plateau overlooking the ancient city of Memphis.*

pyramids even grander than the Step Pyramid. King Zoser had launched an age of pyramid building that would last for more than 1,000 years.

Pyramid building reached its peak during the Old Kingdom. More than 80 pyramids survive as reminders of that distant age.

The Egyptian Religion

King Zoser's pyramid was more than just a new idea in architecture. It reflected the religious beliefs of the Egyptian people. Early Egyptian literature pictured the king climbing to heaven on a stairway formed by the rays of the sun. People may have thought of that stairway when they looked at the Step Pyramid. The shape of the later pyramids might also have seemed like the slope of the sun's rays. In that way, the later pyramids, too, might have pictured a king's passage to heaven.

Preparing for the Afterlife
The Egyptians believed in an **afterlife,** a life that would

continue after death. This belief was so strong and important to the people that great preparation was made for death and burial. Pyramid building was just one part of it.

Another was the preparation of the body itself. Before an Egyptian's body was placed in a pyramid or other tomb, it had to be prepared for the afterlife.

The Egyptians believed that without a body, a person's spirit couldn't eat, drink, dance, or enjoy the other pleasures that the afterlife would offer. If the body decayed, the spirit would die too. So the Egyptians developed a process called **embalming**, treating the

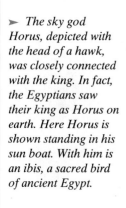

➤ *The sky god Horus, depicted with the head of a hawk, was closely connected with the king. In fact, the Egyptians saw their king as Horus on earth. Here Horus is shown standing in his sun boat. With him is an ibis, a sacred bird of ancient Egypt.*

body to protect it from decay. This process preserved the body as a **mummy.**

Once the mummy had been prepared, it was placed into a coffin made of wood or stone. The coffin was left in the tomb along with items for use in the afterlife. These items ranged from food and drink to gold and jewelry. They included many objects that were useful in daily life, such as clothes, games, and hand mirrors. Some tombs even held mummies of cats, dogs, horses, and apes. Some contained small carved statues of servants. Some tomb walls were painted with scenes from the everyday life of the dead person.

Most of these objects and paintings were found in the tombs of royal or wealthy families. But even many of the less privileged were buried with some favorite possessions.

According to Egyptian belief, the objects and paintings in the tomb would help ensure that the person would continue to enjoy the good things of this life. The Egyptians loved life in this world. Because they believed the afterlife would be much like this life, they wanted to be buried with the things they would need.

After a mummy was placed in its tomb, priests recited prayers or chanted magic spells. They called on the gods to help the person make the trip from this world to the next. These words appear on the tomb of an Old Kingdom ruler named Pepi: "Gates of sky, open for Pepi, Gates of heaven, open for Pepi, Pepi comes to you, make him live!"

The Book of the Dead

Hymns, prayers, and magic spells from the tombs are found in the Egyptian *Book of the Dead*. One part describes a trial in which the soul of a dead person argues its case before a jury of the gods. "In life, I fed the hungry," says the soul. "I respected my parents."

The soul also tells what it did not do. "I never stole." The gods then weigh the heart of the dead person against the feather of truth. The Egyptians believed the heart was the center of intelligence and memory. If the soul was too heavy with sin, they believed, it died a second death from which there was no returning. But the soul that passed the test would go on to a happy afterlife. Such a judgment scene is shown in the picture on page 311.

The Gods of the Egyptians

The religion of ancient Egypt was a form of polytheism, belief in a number of gods. Not surprisingly, many of the Egyptians' gods were connected with death and the afterlife. Osiris (ō sī′ rĭs) was the chief god of the underworld, or home of the dead. One of Osiris's helpers was

▲ *The Egyptians' love for animals can be seen in their portrayal of gods with animal heads, their animal sculptures, and animal mummies like this one of a cat.*

Anubis (ə nōō´bĭs), who had the body of a human and the head of a jackal. His job was to prepare the bodies of the dead for the afterlife.

The Egyptians had great gods that they believed created and ruled the world. One of these was Ra (rä) the sun god, who was later joined by another great god, Amon (ä´mən), to become Amon-Ra (ä´mən rä).

Some Egyptian gods, like Anubis, had a human body and the head of an animal.

Hathor (hă´thôr´), the goddess of love, had the head of a cow. Horus, the sky god, had the head of a hawk.

Each Egyptian village and city had its own local god. There were also gods of music and dancing, of love and beauty, and of healing and learning. Commoners in Egyptian society built small shrines at home and dedicated them to their favorite gods. Especially popular in households was a dwarflike god named Bes, the god of the family. ■

■ *What religious beliefs account for the pyramids and mummies of ancient Egypt?*

UNDERSTANDING THE IDEA OF AN AFTERLIFE

To us, the ancient Egyptians sometimes seem more interested in death than life. We marvel at the time, energy, and other resources they put into making pyramids and mummies. Yet we know that their love of life caused them to do these things. They thought an afterlife would be like this one, only better.

In every time and place, people have asked, "Is there life beyond this life?" and if so, "What kind of life is it?" These questions ask about the afterlife — life that continues after death.

A Place of Darkness

The Mesopotamians, the people of another ancient culture, painted a gloomy picture of the afterlife. For them, the world of the dead was under the earth. One of their stories called it a place "where they see no light and live in darkness." Their hero-king Gilgamesh tried but failed to gain a happy afterlife.

A Happy Afterlife

People's ideas about an afterlife are tied to their ideas about God or the gods. In our own twentieth-century Western society, many people are believers in Judaism, Christianity, or Islam. Followers of these faiths believe in one God. Most of them also believe in a human soul that will never die. They look forward to an afterlife in which they will live with God and with other human souls. Like the Egyptians, many believe in an afterlife that will be happier and better than this life. However, few cultures have placed more importance on the idea of an afterlife than the ancient Egyptians.

A Writing System

The earliest Egyptian writing, called **hieroglyphics** (hī´ər ə glĭf´ĭks), used pictures to stand for objects, ideas, and sounds. The system was not easy to decipher. In fact, linguists and archaeologists studied the symbols for years without success.

Then, in 1799, French soldiers near Rosetta, a village in the Nile Delta, unearthed a black stone slab. On it the same passage was written in three ways: in Greek, in hieroglyphs, and in a cursive form of Egyptian.

For 20 years, scholars tried in vain to decode the hieroglyphic writing on the Rosetta Stone. Then a brilliant Frenchman named Jean Champollion found the key.

Champollion could read Greek. He knew that all three parts said the same thing, praising Ptolemy V for gifts he had given the temples in

195 B.C. One summer day in 1822, Champollion was comparing the hieroglyphs with the Greek words. He identified

and compared proper names like *Ptolemy* and *Cleopatra*. He matched sounds from the names with the hieroglyphs that spelled them, as follows:

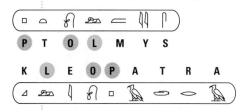

Now at last Champollion had the key he needed. He decoded the Rosetta stone and went on to publish a dictionary of ancient Egyptian.

Fortunately, the Egyptians left us many written texts. Once scholars could decode hieroglyphic writing, they could read laws, songs, tales, spells, jokes, and business contracts. From these texts and others, scholars have learned about Egypt's past.

The hieroglyphic system was complex. It had over 700 signs that a person must memorize to master it. Young peo-ple who wanted to be scribes spent years attending special schools. The school day was long, sometimes lasting from just after sunrise to sunset. Teachers expected their students to pay attention, and punishments could be harsh. One father sent these words of advice to his son, who was learning to be a scribe: "Learn to write, for this will be of greater advantage to you than all the trades. One day at school is useful to you and the work done there will last forever, like mountains."

Few Egyptian students, studying hard and copying the same lines over and over, would have found these words encouraging. However, those who completed the training would be well rewarded. Only a small number of dedicated ancient Egyptians learned to read and write. As experts with special skills, they would have good jobs and respected places in society. ■

■ *In what ways did the decoding of the Rosetta Stone expand our knowledge of ancient Egypt?*

A Social Pyramid

Scribes and farmers, potters and brickmakers — all Egyptians had a place in the social class system of ancient Egypt. A diagram of Egyptian society would look something like a pyramid.

Pharaoh and Priests

At the top of the social pyramid was the pharaoh. The Egyptians believed their pharaohs were gods.

The Egyptian pharaoh was all powerful. He owned all the land and had complete control of the people. All workers, from farmers to artists, served the pharaoh, directly or through royal officials. The members of the royal family were just below the pharaoh on the social pyramid.

The priests served the gods to which the temples were dedicated. Some people who worked at other occupations, such as law or medicine, also served in the temple.

Officials and Scribes

The pharaoh relied on government officials, who were also in the upper level of society. He counted on them to assist him in governing the country. Many were tax collectors. Some were responsible for the royal storehouses.

The scribes, another group of officials, held a privileged position. They were Egypt's writers and record keepers. Scribes might work at the pharaoh's palace, travel with high officials, or serve as public letter writers.

Skilled Workers and Farmers

Below scribes on the social pyramid were the artisans and other skilled workers. These included carpenters, painters, jewelers, brickmakers, and stonemasons. Many of these skilled workers provided goods for the pharaoh and his family.

For example, they might create furniture, make jewelry, weave fine cloth, and paint pictures inside the royal tombs.

Farmers formed the large base of the Egyptian social pyramid. Most people were farmers, and they spent their lives growing and marketing farm products. In this way, they supported all the other levels of Egyptian society.

But the farmers did not provide food only. During the flood season, they could not work in the fields. They were required to work on royal building projects. These included the irrigation works, the pyramids, and later the temples. The great stone monuments they helped to build have outlasted both pharaohs and commoners. ■

▲ *This fine painted woodcarving of a plowing scene was found in a Middle Kingdom tomb of around 2000 B.C. Why do you think it was put in the tomb? Where would these farmers have been on the social pyramid?*

■ *What were the occupations of people at the top, middle, and bottom of the Egyptian social pyramid?*

REVIEW

1. Describe the religious ideas and the social structure of the ancient Egyptians.
2. How did the annual flooding help the Egyptian pharaohs to complete their building projects?
3. What was the importance of farming to the economy of ancient Egypt?
4. Why do you think scribes held privileged positions in ancient Egyptian society? What can be learned today from ancient texts?

Responding to *A Message of Ancient Days*

Thinking and Discussing

What are the many "gifts of the Nile" discussed in the text? Why is the Nile important to the people of Egypt?

How did the Nile's cycle of flooding give a pattern to life in ancient Egypt? What effect did the flooding cycle have on the building of pyramids and temples?

How did ancient Egyptian religious beliefs lead to the practices of mummification, tomb painting, and the stocking of tombs with the dead person's possessions?

Applying Historical Concepts

Drawing a Social Pyramid With a group of classmates, make a pyramid diagram that illustrates the social structure of ancient Egypt. Draw the pyramid and divide it into the various levels from top to bottom. For each level, draw pictures of what those people did as they went about their lives.

Being a Historian Historians often ask questions that begin with "What if . . ." in order to help themselves better understand historical events. Be a historian, and answer any of the following questions in a presentation to your classmates: What if the ancient Egyptians did not develop a writing system? What if Imhotep did not serve as Zoser's architect? What if ancient Egypt did not have a system of government?

Advice to Schoolboys

In ancient Egypt, students learned to read and write by copying texts with messages like this one:

I place you at school along with the children of notables, to educate you and to have you trained for this enhancing calling.

Behold, I relate to you how it fares with the scribe when he is told: "Wake up and at your place! The books lie already before your comrades! Place your hand on your clothes and look to your sandals!"

When you get your daily task, be not idle and read diligently from the book. When you reckon in silence, let no word be heard.

Write with your hand and read with your mouth. Ask counsel of them who are clever. Be not slack, and spend not a day in idleness, or woe betide your limbs! Enter into the methods of your teacher and hear his instructions. Behold, I am with you every day!

Writing a Problem Solution

The chapter you have just read describes the Nile as Egypt's lifeline. Since Egypt has almost no rainfall, its farmers were dependent on the annual flooding of the Nile to irrigate their crops. Periods of little or no flooding meant famine and starvation.

Like the people of ancient Egypt, modern societies face the threat of water shortages and other environmental problems. Write a proposal in which you suggest solutions to one of these problems. Or, if the selections give you another idea, write about that one instead.

1. Prewriting

With a partner, discuss the problems facing the environment, and think of possible solutions to those that concern you most. It might help you to go to the library to research the topics. Decide to write about one environmental problem and the solutions that you think will work best. Remember that you have to be convincing.

2. Write a First Draft

As you write, think about your purpose and audience. What are you trying to achieve? How can you convince your audience that your solutions to the problem are worth considering? Write your ideas down on paper as quickly as you can. You may correct any errors in spelling, punctuation, or grammar at a later step. Try to write persuasively.

3. Revise
Review your first draft with a partner. Are your opinions stated clearly? Have you checked your facts for accuracy? Are your arguments logical and convincing?

Make any changes that will improve your proposal.

4. Proofread
Check your proposal carefully for correct grammar, spelling, capitalization, and punctuation. Your proposal will be more effective if your readers are not distracted by mistakes.

5. Publish
Decide on a way to share your proposal. You might want to publish it in the form of an editorial in your school newspaper or a letter to the mayor of your city or town.

Akhenaten pictured as a sphinx beneath the rays of the sun

WORSHIP OF THE SUN

from *Signs and Symbols of the Sun* by Elizabeth Helfman

The sun-god Ra was at the very center of the religion of the ancient Egyptians. It was Ra who ruled the earth. He was so powerful and so complicated a god that he was given many names and many shapes. Countless legends were told about Ra, and he appeared in symbolic form over and over again in paintings and writing and sculpture. Sometimes he was represented by a simple disk, sometimes by a hawk or by a disk with a hawk's wings or by other creatures — a beetle, a phoenix,[1] a lion, or a cat. The stories and the beliefs varied from place to place, and they changed with the passing of time. But though the Egyptians believed in many gods, the god of the sun remained supreme.

---

[1] **phoenix:** fē′nĭks.

Ra, the sun-god, pictured in his boat

The Egyptians believed that the sun-god made his great journey across the sky in a boat with gracefully curved posts at bow and stern. He was called Ra in the heat of midday. At sunset he merged with Osiris, god of all growing plants. Osiris as sun-god spent each night fighting huge evil serpents in the mist and darkness. In the morning the sun-god would appear as Horus, the ancient god of the sky. Horus took the form of a sacred hawk as he lit the sky at dawn.

To the Egyptians this daily journey of the sun symbolized the struggle between the powers of Light and Life and the power of Darkness. This was a struggle that the people felt going on within themselves. When the sun reappeared each morning as the glorious young Horus, people rejoiced. Evil had been conquered during the long night. Good had triumphed, and by midday the great god Ra would shine down again on the broad fields of Egypt beside the River Nile. The grain would ripen and life would go on.

Sometimes, it was said, Horus assumed the form of a great disk, ancient symbol of the sun. One morning, with his hawk's wings flapping out on each side of the disk, Horus flew up to the sun to wage war against the enemies of the god Ra. Wildly he descended upon these enemies and destroyed them all.

This story is the source of one of the most famous Egyptian symbols of the sun, a disk with outstretched wings. Carved in stone, it was often placed over the doors of temples and other buildings, where it was supposed to banish evil. On the entrances of tombs it

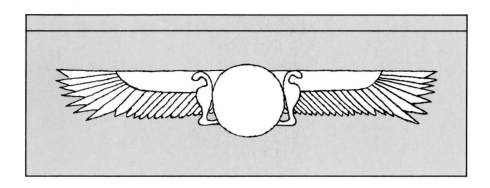

was meant to protect the dead from harm. Because it was first of all a sun symbol, it may also have signified life after death when it was used on tombs. The Egyptians believed that the human soul was born again after death, just as the sun appeared each day at dawn, though it had seemed to die the night before.

The disk, or circle, was of course a very early symbol of the sun, known in many parts of the world. In Egyptian writing the hieroglyph, or written sign, for sun was a circle with a dot in its center. This may have represented an egg, with the dot signifying the new life within it. The Egyptians sometimes represented the sun as an egg that was laid every morning by a Great Sky Goose.

The dot within a circle is still used by astronomers and astrologers as a sign meaning the sun. It is also the Chinese sign for the sun.

The disk of the sun appears often in Egyptian painting and sculpture. Sometimes the sun-god was portrayed as a bright disk with rays ending in small hands, as if to show that the sun gave life to the world.

There were still other Egyptian symbols for the sun. Ra was sometimes a beetle rolling before him a flaming ball that was the sun. This idea came from the Egyptians' observation of the scarab[2] beetle which rolled its egg about in a ball of earth. They believed the beetle created itself in this ball. So, too, the sun re-created itself each day.

---

[2]scarab: skăr′əb.

Bast, the cat-goddess

An Egyptian sphinx

In some parts of Egypt a cat-goddess named Bast was worshiped as daughter and wife of the sun-god. Egyptian paintings often showed a cat biting off the head of the serpent of darkness, while Ra himself, or another form of the sun-god, looked on with approval. Any Egyptian who killed a cat, whether intentionally or not, was sentenced to die.

Other creatures were associated with the sun by the ancient Egyptians. One was the fabulous phoenix. From very early times this mythological bird had symbolized life on earth and life after death. When the phoenix had lived five hundred years or more, people said, it would make for itself a secret nest of rare spices. In the heat of the sun, fanned by the wings of the bird, the nest would burst into flames. The phoenix would be reduced to ashes, but from these ashes it would arise, young again, ready to begin the same pattern of life, death, and rebirth. In Egypt the phoenix was still another form of the sun-god Ra.

The famous sphinx of Egypt is yet another form of Horus. A number of statues of the sphinx still exist, but the most famous is at Gizeh. It is a huge stone lion with a human head, facing the rising sun, which it symbolizes. The sphinx was meant as a colossal home for the spirit of the sun-god, where the god could dwell while he watched over the souls of the dead.

It was believed that the Egyptian king, the Pharaoh, was himself a sun-god, directly descended from Ra. The Pharaohs built their own tombs. These were pyramids, enormous stone structures pointing upward toward the sun. The Pharaohs built obelisks,[3] too, four-sided tapering shafts of stone that reached for the sky and were symbols of the rays of the sun. One obelisk, called Cleopatra's Needle, was presented by Egypt to the United States in the nineteenth century. It stands in Central Park in New York City,

---

[3] obelisk: ŏb'ə lĭsk'

sixty-nine feet high and weighing two hundred tons. Two other Cleopatra's Needles had been cut from the same piece of stone. One was presented to England and one to France.

One Egyptian Pharaoh, Akhenaten,[4] is remembered above all because he proclaimed that there were not many gods, but only one, Ra the sun-god. Akhenaten built a city for Ra, a glorious city of the sun. There each morning Akhenaten the Pharaoh celebrated the rising of the sun. At night his wife Nefertiti[5] celebrated its setting. Akhenaten did not doubt that he himself was divine, a son of Ra. But he believed that all people were brothers, whether Egyptians or foreigners, whether men or women.

Akhenaten composed a great hymn to the sun. Here is part of it (Aten was Akhenaten's name for the sun-god):

> *You rise glorious at the heavens' edge, O living*
> *Aten!*
> *You in whom all life began.*
> *When you shone from the eastern horizon*
> *You filled every land with your beauty. . . .*
> *You have made far skies so that you may shine*
> *in them,*
> *Your disk in its solitude looks on all that you have*
> *made,*
> *Appearing in its glory and gleaming both near*
> *and far.*
> *Out of your singleness you shape a million forms —*
> *Towns and villages, fields, roads and the river.*
> *All eyes behold you, bright Disk of the Day.*

---

[4]**Akhenaten:** ä′kə nä′tn.
[5]**Nefertiti:** nĕf′ər tē′tē.

Cleopatra's Needle in New York City's Central Park, originally from the Temple of Heliopolis

Akhenaten's bright city, his single god, and his ideas of brotherhood were the greatest tribute to the great Ra that had ever been made. But Akhenaten failed. The Egyptians were not ready to believe in one god or in peace and brotherhood. No other Pharaohs followed Akhenaten's way. Ra remained a symbol of light and life, but in Egypt after Akhenaten's time the sun was never again worshiped as a single god of the universe.

Responding to "Worship of the Sun"

Thinking and Discussing

In what ways was the sun connected to the ideas of birth and rebirth in the lives of the ancient Egyptians?

How did Akhenaten's belief in only one sun-god make him different from the other Pharaohs? What did other ancient Egyptians think of Akhenaten's ideas?

Applying Historical Concepts

Identifying the Forms of Ra The text discusses many forms of the ancient Egyptian sun-god, as well as the creatures that represent them. Make a list of all the forms and creatures, listing them in the order in which they appear in the text. How, according to Egyptian religious belief, are the different forms and creatures related to the sun?

Drawing the Sun's Journeys Draw a picture of Ra's journey across the sky, Horus's war against the enemies of Ra, or any other story that tells about one of the sun-god's many forms. You may wish to imitate the style of the art of ancient Egypt or use your own artistic technique.

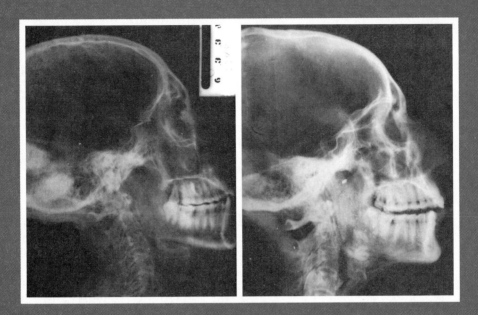

X-rays such as these, which show similarities in the skulls of Amenhotep II and his son Thutmosis IV, are one of the few means of identifying ancient Egyptian family relationships.

Seeing the Unseen

from *Tales Mummies Tell* by Patricia Lauber

A single mummy can tell a lot about the life, health, and death of one person. The many, many mummies of ancient Egypt can tell about whole classes of people. What diseases did the Egyptians suffer from? How did diet affect their health? How long did they live? The answers to those and many other questions are in the mummies.

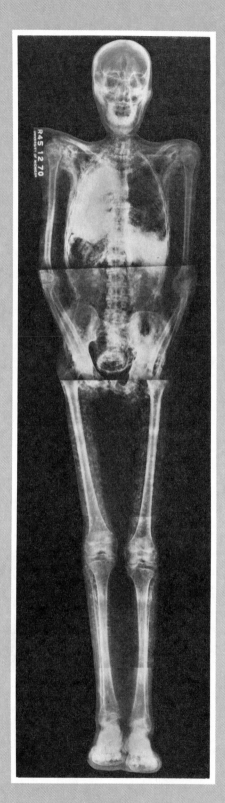

This mummy was once believed to be that of Thutmosis I, who died at the age of fifty after a very successful reign; however, x-rays of the mummy revealed a teen-ager's long leg bones. Was Thutmosis I a child-king? Did Thutmosis have a disease that affected his legs? Is this really the mummy of Thutmosis? Scientists have yet to solve this mystery.

Getting at the answers was a problem for many years. One way to study mummies is to unwrap them and do an autopsy,[1] but this destroys the mummies. Many mummies are too precious to destroy. Another way is to x-ray them. In the past this meant moving the mummies to hospitals or other places where the x-ray machines were. Many mummies were so fragile that moving them might have damaged them. Finally the development of a portable x-ray machine solved the problem. Now the machine can be taken to the mummies.

The x-ray pictures provide views of mummies never unwrapped — of pharaohs, queens, nobles, priests. The shape of the face appears, as do magic charms of gold and semiprecious stones within the wrappings. The pictures show that some mummies have been wrongly identified, that they cannot be the person they were thought to be. They have helped to clarify family relationships. They have produced some surprises and puzzles. Most of all, they have yielded important information about health in ancient Egypt. In the bones medical scientists can read age at death, signs of disease, fractures that healed.

X-rays show that the Egyptians suffered from many diseases known in the modern world — tuberculosis, polio, arthritis, gall-stones, hardening of the arteries. They also show that the most serious health problems arose from the environment, from the Nile and the desert.

The Nile was the lifeblood of Egypt. Its yearly floods dropped soil that enriched the river valley. Its waters, drawn off in canals, irrigated fields and pastures. From the fields came barley and wheat, fruits, vegetables, herbs. The cattle grazing the pastures supplied milk and eventually became meat on the tables of the rich.

---

[1] **autopsy** (ô′tŏp′sē): a medical examination of a dead human body, especially to determine the cause of death.

By studying x-rays and hair samples, scientists have concluded that the mummy above, known as the Elder Lady, is probably the mummy of Queen Tiye, Tut-ankh-Amen's grandmother. Small marks on the face of the mummy of Rameses V, pictured below, led scientists to believe that he may have contracted and died of smallpox.

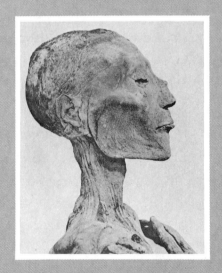

There were wild fowl to trap in the marshes of the Nile and fish from the river itself. The many tomb paintings of banquets and lists of grave foods make clear that the Egyptians enjoyed food and drink and that they ate well.

But the life-giving river was also a source of disease. It was a source of waterborne parasites — small animals that invade another creature, using its body as a place to live and feed but doing nothing that benefits the host. Most of the parasites that infected the ancient Egyptians were worms with complicated life cycles. But in general they spent part of their lives in human hosts and part in fresh water — canals, wet fields, marshes. Some kinds invaded their hosts through the skin, some were swallowed in drinking water. All caused misery, such as sores, rashes, and a growing weakness over a number of years. The remains of parasites and their eggs appear in x-rays of many mummies. They were a major reason why the life span of the average Egyptian was 35 to 40 years.

At the edge of the Nile Valley was the desert. Its dust storms filled the air with tiny particles of sand. The sand scarred the lungs of the Egyptians, and its effect on their teeth was equally serious.

The chief dental problem among the ancient Egyptians was extreme wear. It showed in the teeth of skeletons and mummies that medical scientists had examined earlier. Now the x-rays of pharaohs, priests, and nobles showed that their teeth too had rapidly worn down. The only possible explanation was sand. Somehow sand from the desert must have got into the food. As the Egyptians chewed, particles of sand ground down their teeth.

How that much sand got into their food was something of a puzzle until 1971. In that year the Manchester Museum in England was having an Egyptian exhibition. Among the displays were a large number of pieces of ancient Egyptian bread. X-rays showed that each piece contained vast quantities of mineral fragments. Some of the minerals were kinds that came from the soil in which the grain

A wooden model of a granary found in a tomb

had grown. Some came from the kind of stones used to grind the grain. But most of the fragments were the pure quartz of desert sand. Dust storms must have added sand to grain when it was being harvested, winnowed, and stored. The sand went into bread along with the flour. Because the Egyptians ate large amounts of bread, they also chewed large amounts of sand.

Sometimes sand may have been added on purpose. A scientist at the Manchester Museum tried making flour with ancient Egyptian grinding stones. After 15 minutes of work, the grain was still whole. But when he did what other ancient peoples are reported to have done and added sand to the grain, he was quickly able to make fine flour.

Sand in their daily bread caused serious tooth problems for peasants and pharaohs alike. It wore down the hard parts of their teeth, the outside enamel and the underlying dentine. In some people new dentine formed. In most, teeth wore down faster than new dentine could form. Then the inside of the tooth was exposed. This is the pulp chamber, which houses the nerves and blood supply for the tooth. Without dentine as a barrier, disease-causing bacteria could invade the tooth's root canals. Painful infections followed and sometimes led to death.

Responding to "Seeing the Unseen"

Thinking and Discussing

What were the main health problems suffered by the ancient Egyptians? Which were caused strictly by their environment?

Applying Historical Concepts

Charting the Help of X-rays Based on the selection, make a chart showing how effective x-rays have been in helping scientists who study ancient Egyptian mummies. Arrange your chart in two columns. In the left column, list the questions that scientists have been able to answer through the use of x-rays. In the right column, list the answers they found and the evidence that x-rays provided.

Giving Modern Medical Advice Imagine you could have given the ancient Egyptians some advice based on what you know about modern medicine and health concerns. What would you tell them? Write your recommendations in the form of a health newsletter.

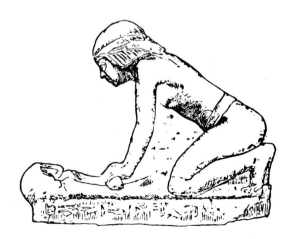

An Egyptian grinding grain

Grave robbers stripped most of the tombs of ancient Egypt, but one royal burial place lay untouched for centuries. Its amazing treasure was unearthed in 1922 by English archaeologist Howard Carter and his partner Lord Carnarvon.

From *Lost Worlds: The Romance of Archaeology* by Anne Terry White

THE TOMB OF TUT-ANKH-AMEN

Now Carnarvon and Carter were not planning to dig at random in the Valley of the Tombs of the Kings. They were on the lookout for a particular tomb, the tomb of the Pharaoh Tut-ankh-Amen, and they believed they had worked out the very location where it lay.

To the eyes of most people their undertaking seemed absurd.

The solid gold death mask placed on Tut-ankh-Amen's mummy is perhaps the most famous treasure from the ancient Pharaoh's tomb. The mask is believed to be a good likeness of Tut-ankh-Amen.

Nearly everybody was convinced that Tut-ankh-Amen's tomb had already been found. But Lord Carnarvon and Mr. Carter were not to be dissuaded, for they believed that the pit-tomb containing the fragments bearing the figures and names of Tut-ankh-Amen and his queen was far too small and insignificant for a king's burial. In their opinion the things had been placed there at some later time and did not indicate that the Pharaoh himself had been buried on the spot. They were convinced that the tomb

of Tut-ankh-Amen was still to be found, and that the place they had chosen — the center of the Valley — was the best place to look for it. In that vicinity had been unearthed something which they considered very good evidence — two jars containing broken bits of things that had been used at the funeral ceremonies of King Tut-ankh-Amen.

Nevertheless, when in the autumn of 1917 the excavators came out to look over the spot they had chosen and to begin their Valley campaign in earnest, even they thought it was a desperate undertaking. The site was piled high with refuse thrown out by former excavators. They would have to remove all that before they could begin excavating in virgin soil. But they had made up their minds and meant to go through with it; even though it took many seasons, they would go systematically over every inch of the ground.

In the years that followed, they did. They went over every inch, with the exception of a small area covered with the ruins of stone huts that had once sheltered workmen probably employed in building the tomb of Rameses VI. These huts lay very near the tomb of the Pharaoh on a spot which Carter and Carnarvon had not

In this photograph taken in the Valley of the Kings, the entrance to the tomb of Rameses VI is shown at the center. Buried beneath the huts of the workmen who built Rameses' tomb was the entrance to the tomb of Tut-ankh-Amen, discovered fifteen years after this picture was taken.

touched for reasons of courtesy. The tomb of Rameses VI was a popular show-place in the Valley, and digging in the area of the huts would have cut off visitors to the tomb. They let it be, and turned instead to another site which they felt had possibilities.

The new ground proved, however, no better than the old, and now Lord Carnarvon began to wonder whether with so little to show for six seasons' work they were justified in going on. But Carter was firm. So long as a single area of unturned ground remained, he said, they ought to risk it. There was still the area of the huts. He insisted on going back to it. On November first, 1922 he had his diggers back in the old spot.

And now things happened with such suddenness that Carter afterward declared they left him in a dazed condition. Coming to work on the fourth day after the digging on the little area had started, he saw at once that something extraordinary had happened. Things were too quiet; nobody was digging and hardly anybody was talking. He hurried forward, and there before him was a shallow step cut in the rock beneath the very first hut attacked! He could hardly believe his eyes. After all the disappointments of the past six seasons, was it possible that he was actually on the threshold of a great discovery? He gave the command to dig, and the diggers fell to work with a will. By the next afternoon Carter was able to see the upper edges of a stairway on all its four

sides, and before very long there stood revealed twelve steps, and at the level of the twelfth the upper part of a sealed and plastered doorway.

Carter's excitement was fast reaching fever pitch. Anything, literally anything, might lie beyond. It needed all his self-control to keep from breaking the doorway down and satisfying his curiosity then and there. But was it fair to see what lay beyond that door alone? Although Lord Carnarvon was in England, was it not his discovery as much as Carter's? To the astonishment of the workmen, the excavator gave orders to fill the stairway in again, and then he sent the following cable off to Carnarvon: "At last have made wonderful discovery in Valley. A magnificent tomb with seals intact. Recovered same for your arrival. Congratulations."

In two weeks' time Lord Carnarvon and his daughter were on the spot. Carter now ordered his men to clear the stairway once more, and there on the lower part of the sealed doorway the explorers beheld what almost took their breath away — the seal of the Pharaoh Tut-ankh-Amen. Now they knew. Beyond this doorway lay either the Pharaoh's secret treasure store or else the very tomb for which they were searching. Yet one thing made them uneasy. They noticed that part of the door was patched up and that in the patched-up part there stood out clearly the seal of the cemetery. It was evident that the door had been partly broken down — by robbers, of course — and then patched up again by cemetery officials. Had the robbers been caught in time? Did at least some of Tut-ankh-Amen's glory yet remain behind that twice-sealed doorway? Or would perhaps only barren walls reward their years of tedious toil?

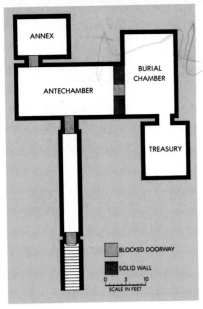

ANNEX

BURIAL CHAMBER

ANTECHAMBER

TREASURY

BLOCKED DOORWAY
SOLID WALL

0   5   10
SCALE IN FEET

With pounding hearts they broke down the door. Beyond lay only another obstacle to their progress — a passage filled with stone. Had the robbers got beyond that? They began slowly to clear away the stone, and on the following day — "the day of days," Carter called it, "and one whose like I can never hope to see again" — they came upon a second sealed doorway, almost exactly like the first and also bearing distinct signs of opening and reclosing.

His hands trembling so that he could scarcely hold a tool, Carter managed to make a tiny hole in the door and to pass a candle through it. At first he could see nothing, but as his eyes grew accustomed to the light, "details of the room slowly emerged from the mist, strange animals, statues, and gold — everywhere the glint of gold."

"Can you see anything?" Carnarvon asked anxiously as Carter stood there dumb with amazement.

"Yes, wonderful things!" was all the explorer could get out.

And no wonder. What he saw was one of the most amazing sights anybody has ever been privileged to see. It seemed as if a whole museumful of objects was in that room. Three gilt couches, their sides carved in the form of monstrous animals, and two statues of a king, facing each other like two sentinels,[1] were the most prominent things in the room, but all around and between were hosts of other things — inlaid caskets, alabaster vases, shrines, beds, chairs, a golden inlaid throne, a heap of white boxes (which they later found were filled with trussed ducks and other food offerings), and a glistening pile of overturned chariots. When Carter and Carnarvon

---

[1] **sentinel** (sĕn′tə nəl): something that serves to guard or give warning of approaching danger.

got their senses together again, they realized all at once that there was no coffin in the room. Was this then merely a hiding place for treasure? They examined the room very intently once again, and now they saw that the two statues stood one on either side of a sealed doorway. Gradually the truth dawned on them. They were but on the threshold of their discovery. What they saw was just an antechamber.[2] Behind the guarded door there would be other rooms, perhaps a whole series of them, and in one of them, beyond any shadow of doubt, they would find the Pharaoh lying.

But as they thought the thing over, the explorers were by no means certain that their first wild expectations would actually come to pass. Perhaps that sealed doorway, like the two before it, had also been re-opened. In that case there was no telling what lay behind it.

---

[2]**antechamber** (ăn′tē chām′bər): a waiting room at the entrance to a larger and more important room.

On the following day they took down the door through which they had been peeping, and just as soon as the electric connections had been made and they could see things clearly, they rushed over to the doubtful door between the royal sentinels. From a distance it had looked untouched, but when they examined it more closely, they saw that here again the robbers had been before them; near the bottom was distinct evidence that a small hole had been made and filled up and re-sealed. The robbers had indeed been stopped, but not before they had got into the inner chamber.

It took almost as much self-command not to break down that door and see how much damage the robbers had done as to have filled in the staircase after it had once been cleared. But Carter and Carnarvon were not treasure-seekers; they were archaeologists, and they would not take the chance of injuring the objects within the antechamber just to satisfy their curiosity. For the moment they let that go and turned their attention to the things already before them.

There was enough there to leave them altogether bewildered. But while they were yet going crazily from one object to another and calling excitedly to each other, they stumbled upon yet another discovery. In the wall, hidden behind one of the monstrous couches, was a small, irregular hole, unquestionably made by the plunderers and never re-sealed. They dragged their powerful electric light to the hole and looked in. Another chamber, smaller than

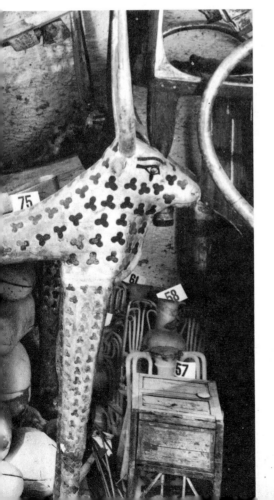

The treasures in the antechamber of Tut-ankh-Amen's tomb

343

Above, a child's gilt chair inlaid with ivory, perhaps used by the young Tut-ankh-Amen

At left, a carved relief of Tut-ankh-Amen making an offering to the god Osiris

the one they were in, but even more crowded with objects! And everything was in the most amazing mess they had ever seen. The cemetery officials had made some attempt to clean up the antechamber after the robbers and to pile up the funeral furniture in some sort of order, but in the annex they had left things just as they were, and the robbers had done their work "about as thoroughly as an earthquake." Not a single inch of floor space remained unlittered.

Carter and Carnarvon drew a long breath and sobered down. They realized now that the job before them was going to take months and months. It would be a monumental task to photograph, label, mend, pack and ship all this furniture, clothing, food, these chariots, weapons, walking sticks, jewels — this museumful of treasures.

All the time they were working, Carter and Carnarvon were, of course, feverishly anxious to know what lay beyond the guarded door. Many a time they glanced at it, but never once did they weaken. Not until every article was safely stowed away and the last bit of dust sifted for a possible bead or bit of inlay did they permit themselves to think of exploring farther.

But at length the day came, and in a hushed stillness — they had invited about twenty people to witness the opening of the door — Carter mounted a platform and with trembling hands very carefully chipped away the plaster and picked out the stones that made up the upper part. Then, when the hole was large enough to look through, he put his electric light on the other side and saw at a distance of a yard from him, and stretching as far as he could see, what appeared to be a wall of solid gold. He removed a few more stones, and then he understood. This was indeed the burial chamber, and the golden wall was an immense gilt shrine built to cover and protect the sarcophagus.[3]

---

[3]**sarcophagus** (sär **kŏf'ə** gəs): a stone coffin.

It took two hours to remove the doorway. Carter then let himself down into the burial chamber, which was some four feet below the level of the antechamber, and Lord Carnarvon came on behind through the narrow passage between the shrine and the wall. It was immense, that shrine. It practically filled the room, rising to nine feet and measuring seventeen on the long side and eleven on the short. And from top to bottom it was overlaid with gold.

Carter and Carnarvon did not stop to examine the decorations. At one end of the shrine were great folding doors, and to these they hurried, disregarding everything else. The all-absorbing question was: had the thieves got inside? They drew the bolts, swung back the doors. Inside was a second shrine with bolted doors just as before, and upon the bolts a seal — unbroken. The king was safe. In time they would remove one by one the encasing shrines and before them in full regalia[4] would lie a king of Egypt, unseen by human eyes, untouched by human hands, for three thousand and three hundred years.

With hearts at ease the explorers now moved to examine everything there was to see. They unrolled the wire of their electric light and passed on to the farthest end of the chamber.

To their astonishment, instead of coming to a dead wall, they saw a low door. It stood open as if inviting them into the room beyond, and passing through, they saw at the first glance that, though smaller than the outer ones, this room contained the greatest treasures of the tomb. Facing the doorway stood a monument so lovely that they gasped with wonder. It was a chest, shaped like a shrine, and overlaid with gold. On the top were sculptured cobras, and about them statues of the four goddesses of the dead, standing with outstretched arms, protecting and guarding the shrine. Directly in front of the entrance stood the emblems of the underworld — the jackal-god Anubis, lying on a shrine resting on

---

[4]**regalia** (rĭ gāl′yə): the emblems and symbols of royalty.

a sled, and behind him the head of a bull on a stand. A great number of black shrines and chests stood on one side of the chamber, all closed save one through the open doors of which the explorers could see statues of Tut-ankh-Amen standing on black leopards. Miniature coffins, model boats and yet another chariot stood in various places about the room, while in the center were a number of caskets of ivory and wood. The thieves had certainly been there, but they could not have taken much because the seals on most of the caskets were still intact.

Carter and Carnarvon felt now as Prince Yuaa's excavators had felt. These were not the relics of a life of three thousand years ago. These were the things of yesterday, of a year or two ago. Tut-ankh-Amen had not reigned in 1400 B.C. He had but just died and they — two Englishmen strangely suspended in time and space — were taking part in the ceremonies of his burial. Not the unbelievable tomb, but the actual world of the twentieth century seemed unreal to these enchanted explorers.

It was their plan to go on immediately with the work of dismantling the shrines. But for some unfortunate reason the Government now started an argument with the excavators. The work had to be postponed. And while they waited, Lord Carnarvon died.

It was thus with a heavy sense of loss that Carter returned to the tomb to dismantle the shrines — a hard task even for a light heart. The sarcophagus practically filled the chamber, leaving scarcely any room to work in. The sections of the outer shrine, moreover, weighed from a quarter to three-quarters of a ton each. They were almost impossible to handle without injury. And to prove his patience further, Carter found not two but four shrines about the sarcophagus. Eighty days passed before he could get them safely removed.

But at last the sarcophagus stood free, a magnificent chest carved from a single block of yellow quartzite, and sculptured in high relief[5] with goddesses so placed that their outstretched arms and wings encircled the sarcophagus. Strangely enough, the lid of the chest was made not of quartzite but of granite, cracked and patched, though stained to match the quartzite. The workmen, Carter decided, must have dropped the original lid, and there being no time to make another to match, granite had been used instead. That, too, had been cracked in the narrow quarters, and Carter, who had the task of removing the ton and a quarter of stone, understood why the Egyptians had decided to let well enough alone.

In all these many weeks the excavator's emotions had been steadily mounting, for with every day that passed the final mystery drew closer. Even the moment when he had first looked into the antechamber seemed to Carter less dramatic than the one he was looking forward to now as the workmen hauled up the lid of the sarcophagus. In an intense silence it was raised from its bed.

At first sight the contents were disappointing. Linen shrouds swathed whatever lay within and prevented his seeing anything. But when Carter had feverishly pushed back the folds on folds of linen, he saw a coffin of such unsurpassed beauty that he was speechless. It was in the form of the king himself and was decorated for the most part in low relief, but the head and hands were fully sculptured in the round, in massive gold. The hands, crossed over the breast, held the Crook and Flail, the face was wrought in sheet gold, the eyes were of aragonite and obsidian, the eyebrows and eyelids of lapis lazuli glass. Upon the forehead of the boy king in brilliant inlay were worked the Cobra and the Vulture, the symbols of Upper and Lower Egypt, and about these was twined a tiny wreath of flowers, which Carter guessed must have been the farewell offering of the widowed girl queen. "Among all that regal splendor," Carter afterwards said, "there was nothing so beautiful as those few withered flowers, still retaining their tinge of color.

---

[5]**relief:** the projection of a sculptured figure from a flat background.

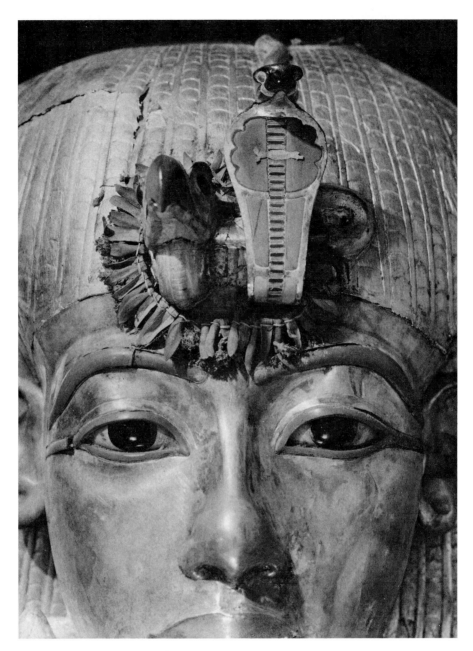

The small wreath of flowers found on the forehead of Tut-ankh-Amen's likeness on the outermost coffin

The process of opening Tut-ankh-Amen's coffins in the burial chamber of his tomb was complicated. In the stage pictured, ropes lowered the bottom half of the outer coffin, while wires suspended the second coffin. Howard Carter wondered about the great weight of the coffins until he discovered that the third coffin was made of solid gold.

They told us what a short period three thousand three hundred years really was — but Yesterday and the Morrow."

To raise the lid of the coffin was the next task. Carter already guessed there would probably be another coffin nested inside. That is what he found. The inner coffin was also in human form, presenting another portrait of the king, and was sumptuously inlaid with colored glass on gold foil. But when the lid of this coffin was raised, there lay within it a third coffin, strangely heavy, and proving to be of solid gold.

The onlookers could not believe their eyes. They had been led to suppose that the funeral glory of the Pharaohs was very great, but so much they had not even dreamed. No wonder the robbers had always managed to find the royal tombs! The value of the gold in the coffin alone was $2,500,000. And Tut-ankh-Amen was but the least of Egypt's kings, a mere boy who ruled in the least glamorous period of Egypt's history. What must have been the funeral trappings of the great Pharaohs in the prime of Egypt's glory!

These were the thoughts that passed through the dazed spectators' minds while they stood awestruck about the innermost coffin of Tut-ankh-Amen. Then the final lid was raised by its golden handles. The mummy of the king lay disclosed. Over the face was a mask of beaten gold — another portrait of the ruler — while about the body was disposed layer after layer of beautiful objects. Beneath the mask was a lovely diadem, about the neck a heap of amulets[6] and necklaces, on the chest breastplates of gold, along the right thigh the Vulture of Upper Egypt, along the left thigh the Uraeus of Lower Egypt, emblems detached from the crown. Over the legs were four collarettes, over the feet were gold sandals, over the toes and fingers gold stalls,[7] about the arms bracelets of gold

---

[6]**amulet** (ăm′yə lĭt): a charm worn to ward off evil or injury, especially one worn around the neck.
[7]**stall:** a protective covering for a finger or thumb.

and silver inlaid with precious stones. Altogether one-hundred-and-forty-three objects were disposed about the body in one-hundred-and-one separate groups!

With trembling fingers Carter examined the treasures. How privileged above all men he had been to do that which others had dreamed of all their lives! Never before had such a find been made. Never had fancy even conjured up such magnificence. What was it worth? Fifteen million? Twenty? What did the money value matter! Carter knew that as an emblem of a lost civilization, the tomb of Tut-ankh-Amen was priceless. Of all those royal tombs it alone — and only in part — had baffled the greed of man, but it alone would suffice to bring to life the buried world of the Pharaohs, that never-equaled world of glamor and glitter and slavery and toil, of terror and magic and beauty and skill.

A painted frieze in the Pharaoh Tut-ankh-Amen's burial chamber pictures the following scenes, from right to left: Tut-ankh-Amen's successor Ay; the Pharaoh's mummy dressed as Osiris, the god of the dead; the Pharaoh standing before the goddess Nut; Tut-ankh-Amen, followed by his spirit double, being welcomed to the underworld by Osiris.

Thinking and Discussing

What was the reasoning that led Carter and Carnarvon to dig where they did, or even to dig for the tomb of Tut-ankh-Amen at all?

Why did Carter and Carnarvon not go on immediately from the antechamber to the inner chamber? Do you think they did the right thing in waiting? Why? Do you think you could have waited? Why or why not?

What did the vastness of Tut-ankh-Amen's treasures indicate about the wealth and burial customs of ancient Egyptian kings?

Applying Historical Concepts

Writing a News Story Carter and Carnarvon invited about twenty people to watch the opening of the burial chamber. Imagine that you, a newspaper reporter, are one of those people. Write a news story describing the two men as Carter pokes the hole in the door and peers into the chamber. Describe their actions and what they say to each other. Tell how the assembled people react. Give your story a headline.

Howard Carter and Lord Carnarvon at Tut-ankh-Amen's burial chamber entrance

TREASURES OF TUT-ANKH-AMEN'S TOMB

A gold collar in the shape of the vulture-goddess Nekhbet, inlaid with colored glass, was placed on Tut-ankh-Amen's mummy for magical protection.

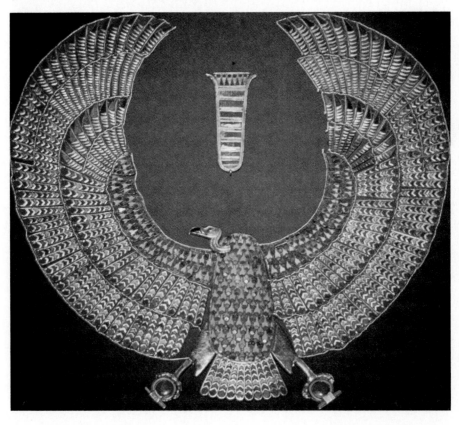

Above, royal emblems written in hieroglyphics stand for "Tut-ankh-Amen, ruler of On of Upper Egypt [Thebes]" and the Pharaoh's throne name, "Nebkheperura." At left, a sculpture of Tut-ankh-Amen depicts the Pharaoh moments before he throws a harpoon at a hippopotamus belonging to Seth, the god of evil.

At right, a gold buckle pictures Tut-ankh-Amen as a triumphant warrior. Below, a necklace represents the moon's journey across the night sky. Below right, a detail of the necklace shows the moon floating above lotus blossoms and poppies.

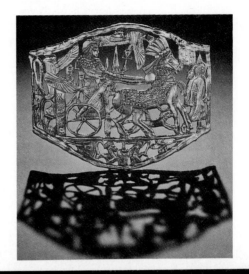

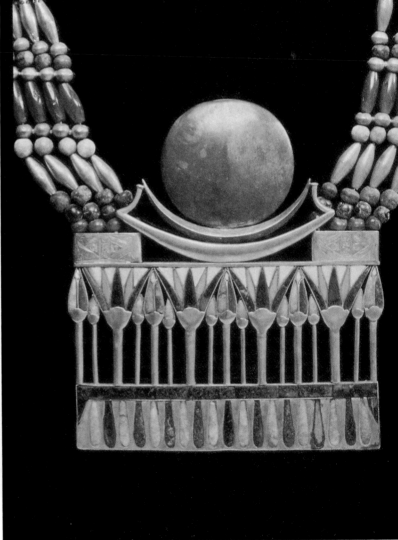

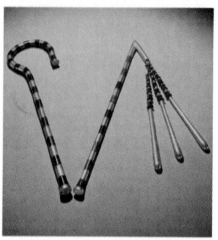

At left from top to bottom, a hand mirror is made in the shape of *ankh*, the hieroglyph meaning "life"; a crook is pictured with a flail that has the inscription "Tut-ankh-Aten," the original form of Tut-ankh-Amen's name; and an alabaster vase glows with light. Above, gold rings represent important ancient Egyptian gods.

357

Thinking About History

Planning a Tomb Painting Imagine that you are an ancient Egyptian artist who has been asked to create paintings for a tomb. You are to depict the colorful, pleasant scenes of daily life that will come alive in the afterworld. Jot down notes for the paintings you would make. Then write detailed descriptions of the paintings. If you wish, create the paintings using colored markers or watercolors.

Investigating the Ancient Past Explore other great civilizations that existed in ancient times. Research the ancient culture of Greece, Central America, or another land that interests you.   Present your findings in writing or in an oral report. You may wish to include photographs or drawings.

Describing School Days Imagine you are away at school learning to become a scribe. One of your assignments is to write a letter home, telling how you like — or dislike — school. Give an account of your days, your teachers, what type of schoolwork you do, even your writing materials: reed pens and papyrus. You might wish to include a description of the type of job you hope to get when you graduate.

Creating a Poster The ruins and remains of ancient Egypt offer many striking visual images to today's visitor. Create a travel poster that uses several of these images to attract tourists. Make people want to visit Egypt to explore its ancient past. You may use markers, paints, or crayons. Include a short, catchy slogan or message that fits in with your artwork.

About the Authors

Elizabeth S. Helfman was born in Massachusetts in 1911. She taught elementary school for many years before she became a full-time writer. Two of her books, *Signs and Symbols Around the World* and *Signs and Symbols of the Sun*, deal with the history of written communication. Her other books include *Celebrating Nature*, *This Hungry World*, and *The Bushmen and Their Stories*.

Patricia Lauber was born in New York City in 1924. Before she began to write books, Lauber was the chief editor of the science and mathematics division of *The New Book of Knowledge*. Her *Tales Mummies Tell* was named a New York Academy of Sciences Honor book in 1986, and *Volcano: The Eruption and Healing of Mt. St. Helens* was named a Newbery Honor Book in 1987.

Anne Terry White was born in 1896 in the Ukraine in Russia and raised in the United States. Most of her books grew out of her fascination with the geological history of the earth and the cultural history of its people. She has written a series of science books called *All About* that discusses stars, rocks, rivers, and mountains. Her other books include *Prehistoric America*, *North to Liberty: The Story of the Underground Railroad*, and *Lost Worlds: The Romance of Archaeology*.

Future
Expeditions

PYRAMID

DAVID MACAULAY

HIS MAJESTY,
QUEEN HATSHEPSUT
Dorothy Sharp Carter

362

Mummies, Tombs, and Treasure: Secrets of Ancient Egypt by Lila Perl (Clarion, 1987)

This is a fascinating, thorough description of Egyptian mummies. It includes discussions of how the process of mummifying was discovered, how mummies are prepared, and how efforts are made to prevent theft of valuable items from burial places.

Pyramid by David Macaulay (Houghton, 1975)

Finely detailed drawings show the step-by-step process of pyramid building in ancient Egypt.

Hieroglyphs, the Writing of Ancient Egypt by Norma Jean Katan (Atheneum, 1981)

This book offers a good, clear introduction to hieroglyphs, with interesting examples found on tombs, statues, and other objects of the dead. It also gives instructions for drawing and deciphering hieroglyphs.

His Majesty, Queen Hatshepsut by Dorothy Sharp Carter (Lippincott, 1987)

This fictionalized account of a queen in ancient Egypt who declared herself Pharaoh includes fascinating characters and offers excellent historical background.

Cat in the Mirror by Mary Stolz (Dell, 1978)

A time-travel fantasy follows two girls — one in New York City and the other in ancient Egypt. Erin and Irun are both loners, and each longs for a pet cat against her parents' wishes.

TRADITIONAL TALES

BOOK 6

TIMELESS TALES

TIMELESS TALES

Stories are handed on from the older generation to the younger. It is all done by word of mouth — the art is in the telling, the pleasure in listening. Each speaker is an individualist telling the story in his own way. Some legends are sacred, and whoever relates them will make an effort to tell the story just as he heard it from his grandfather, in the same words if possible. Others are fun stories which can be improved upon with each telling. One family tells a legend one way, another family knows it differently. Some stories die because there is nobody left to tell them and nobody to remember. Luckily that does not happen very often. . . .

RICHARD ERDOES
The Sound of Flutes and Other Indian Legends

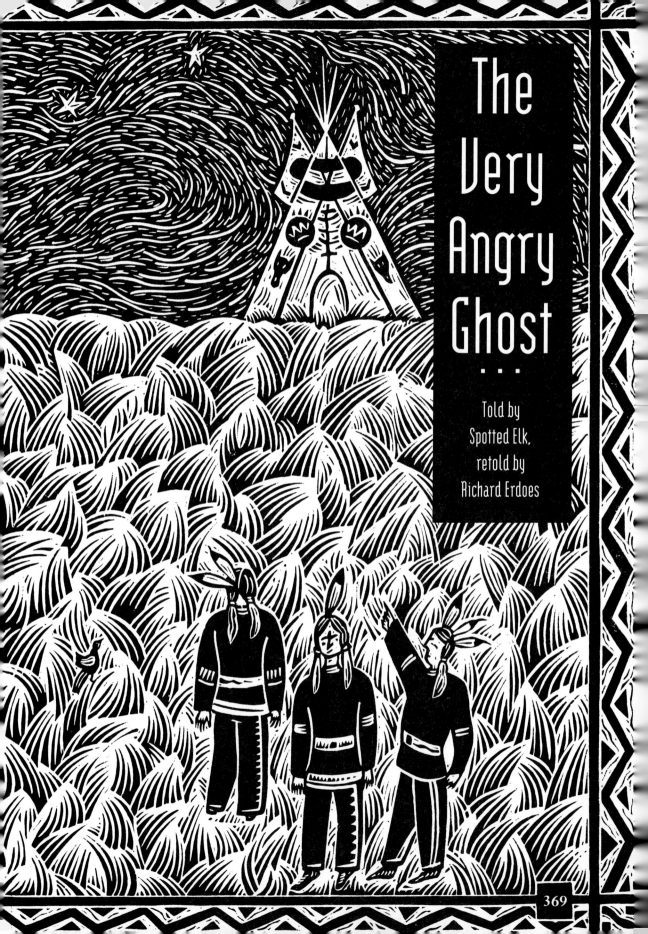

The Very Angry Ghost

Told by
Spotted Elk,
retold by
Richard Erdoes

Y • • • oung men never know how to behave themselves. They should learn good manners from
their elders, but they seldom do.

One day, long ago, an old warrior who
had counted many coups[1] in his days took
three young braves with him on a raid to steal
• • • horses from the Pawnees, ancient enemies
of the Sioux.

"Stealing horses" — this is what the white men call
it. But it was really a sport practiced by all the Plains
tribes. To creep into an enemy village noiselessly,
unseen, and to make off with their herd right under the
noses of the horse guards — to outwit, outthink, and
outride them — took great skill and brought fame and
honor to a warrior.

On this raid, though, the four Sioux had no luck.
They were discovered by the enemy before they could
even get near the horse herd. They had to be happy to
get out of this scrape alive by running away and hiding
themselves in a ravine. They had left on foot, and on
foot they went home. Their moccasins had holes in
them from their many days of hard walking. They were
hungry, tired, and empty-handed.

---

[1]**counted coups (koun′tĭd ko͞oz):** In battle, the Plains Indians "counted coup"
on an enemy by touching him with a "coup stick." This was considered to
require more bravery than killing an enemy.

Halfway home, they passed a hill on top of which they spied a lonely tipi,[2] all by itself, and without any signs of life. They wondered what it was doing there on the wild prairie, and went up to investigate. They found that it was a burial tipi — a splendid one made of sixteen large buffalo hides and painted all over with pictures of war and hunting.

Inside they found the body of a man, his face painted in the sacred scarlet color, lying in state in a resplendent war shirt and beautifully beaded leggings. His fine weapons, his quilled moccasins, and all his other possessions were spread about him to take along to the spirit world.

The young men looked admiringly at all these fine things. "What a stroke of luck," they said. "We will take all this to bring home, turning failure into success."

"A fine success," chided the old warrior. "To steal horses from an enemy brings honor, but to rob the dead is shameful. How wrong I was to pick youths of low mind like you to accompany me. Don't you know that only great chiefs and famous warriors are buried thus?"

They left and went down the hill again, making their camp near a stream. But the young men were still thinking of all the splendid things left in the lone tipi.

---

[2]**tipi** (tē′pē): a form of the word teepee; a tent.

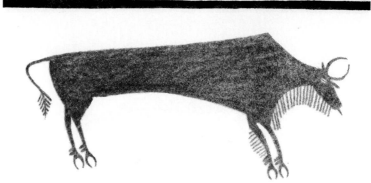

"I think it was stupid to leave it all there," said one of them. "We should have taken everything," said the second. "Let us go right now and do it," said the third.

"I really showed bad judgment in picking you to go with me on a raid," the old man told them. "I will never be able to make good warriors out of you!"

But the young men would not listen. "Old one, show some sense," they answered him. "Those fine things are of no use to one who is dead, but they are of much use to us who are alive."

"Well, I guess you better go without me then," said the old warrior. So they left him to go up that hill again. Quickly the old man ran to the stream and smeared himself all over with cold mud. He took a fur pouch he wore, made two holes in it, and put it over his head as a mask. He looked like a ghost from another world. He ran fast, circling the hill, coming up on the far side, and sat down in the entrance of the lone tipi before the three young braves arrived.

When they got there, they heard an eerie hollow voice, resounding from the tipi. "Who has come here to rob a great chief? I will take them to the spirit world with me." Out from under the entrance flap rose the specter of a frightful ghost, the pale moonlight making it look still more terrible to the young men, who were so petrified with fright that their hair stood on end.

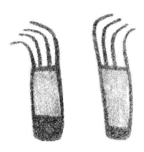

They stood stock-still and open-mouthed for a few seconds. Then, all together, they dropped their bows, turned around, and took to their heels, running down the hill as fast as their feet would carry them.

It was not very fast. They were so scared, they didn't know where to put their feet. They stumbled, they stepped on cactus and prickly pear, they got stuck in the underbrush. The ghost got nearer and nearer, gaining on them fast. At last the hindmost felt a cold, clammy hand touching his bare shoulder and a hollow voice whispering in his ear, "Friend, I have come for you!" The young man was so frightened he fell down in a dead faint.

Then it was the next young man's turn to feel the icy hand, and to hear the ghostlike voice. He, too, fainted. And so did the third and last one.

The old man got back to the campsite well ahead of them. He took off his mask and washed the mud from his body in the cold stream. He was warming himself by the fire as the bedraggled young men came in one by one.

"Where are all those fine things you wanted to take from that dead chief?" asked the old warrior.

"We did not find the tipi," said the young men. "And we did not feel like taking those things after all."

The old warrior said nothing.

Back home in their village, the three young men were sitting in the camp circle telling the people about their raid. Suddenly the old warrior came and sat down among the others. He put on his fur mask and laid a muddy hand on a pretty girl's shoulder. "Does that frighten you, *wincincala*?"[3] he asked the girl.

"You are a funny old man," said the girl, giggling.

"There are some here who were very frightened," said the old warrior, "so frightened that they fainted." And he told the story of how he had fooled them.

Everybody had a good laugh at the young men's expense. They were shamed, but this was good for them. It taught them a lesson, how to act and how to behave, so that they turned out to be good men and brave warriors.

Opening illustration by Patti Green
In-text illustrations by Paul Goble

---

[3]**wincincala:** a young girl.

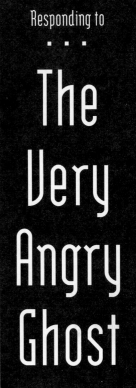

Responding to . . .

The Very Angry Ghost

Thinking and Discussing

Why did the old warrior trick the young men?
Did he achieve his purpose? Why or why not?

Choosing a Creative Response

Holding a Trial Plan and hold a mock trial to judge
the three young warriors. Members of your group
can take the parts of the jury, judge, lawyers, and witnesses.
At the end of the trial, the jury can decide whether or not the
young men are guilty of a crime. The judge can come up with
a just punishment if they are found guilty.

Creating Your Own Activity Plan and complete your own activity in response to "The Very Angry Ghost."

Thinking and Writing

Suppose the three young braves were humble men of honor.
How would they respond to their unsuccessful raid? How
would the story's outcome be affected? Write a summary of
the plot as it would take place this way.

Writing A Story

Traditional tales have entertained people for centuries. They often feature animal characters or beings with magical powers. The characters are often engaged in struggles or contests. They sometimes embark on journeys or quests for special objects, places, or persons.

As you read the stories here, think about writing a folktale of your own. You may want to use your folktale to teach a lesson or simply to entertain readers. Start writing whenever you are ready. If these tales give you a different idea that you would like to explore, write about that.

1. *Prewriting* Before you begin, choose a story idea and think about the setting, characters, and plot. Answer the following questions to help you organize your ideas.

- Where does my story take place? In my own neighborhood, a foreign country, or an enchanted land? In a mysterious forest or a vast desert?

- When does my story happen? In the past or present? During the summer or the winter?

- What do my characters look like? Are they animals, people, or both? How do they behave?

- Does my story teach a lesson or offer advice?

2. *Write a First Draft* Use descriptive language, dialogue, and a clear plot line to bring your story to life. Remember not to worry too much about making mistakes at this stage. Answer these questions as you write your first draft.

- Who will hear or read my folktale? My classmates? My family? Adults? Children?
- Do I wish to use a storyteller's tone? How will I accomplish this?

3. *Revise* Read your first draft to a partner and answer the following questions together.

- Does the plot make sense?
- Is the setting clear?
- Where can I add dialogue, details, or actions to add life to my characters?
- Is the lesson of the folktale clear to the reader?
Make any necessary changes.

4. *Proofread* Check your folktale for errors in spelling, punctuation, and capitalization. If you created unusual names for characters, places, or objects, be sure that you spell them the same way throughout the story.

5. *Publish* Decide on a way to share your tale. You may wish to illustrate exciting, important, or scary parts of your story. You might also do a dramatic reading of your tale, either on tape or to a live audience.

URBAN LEGENDS

People today continue to participate in the oral tradition. Our modern folklore includes the kind of story that tells about something that happened to a friend of a friend of your uncle's dentist's sister-in-law. Such stories may be based on real events, but in the retelling, they have become so distorted and exaggerated that they are no longer believable. Such stories are called **urban legends.**

Famous people, animals, and consumer products are popular subjects for urban legends. These tales spread rapidly from one part of the country to another. Some have spread around the world. If an urban legend is heard often enough, and if it is exciting enough, people may believe it to be true.

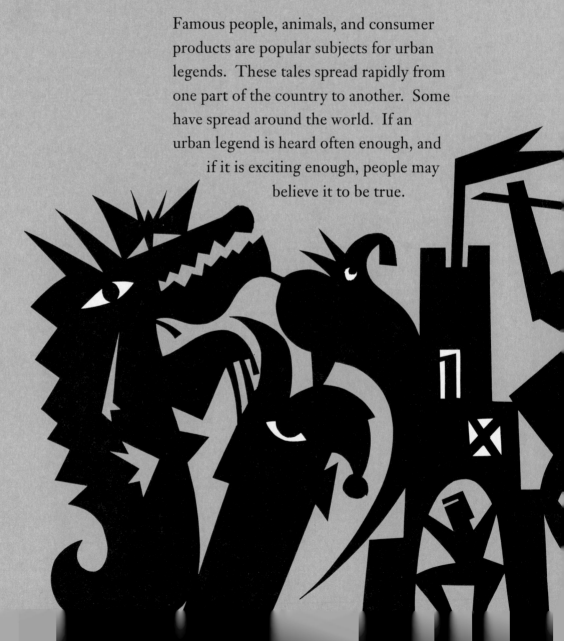

There are often several versions of an urban legend that differ only in details. One such tale involves a driver's picking up a hitchhiker who suddenly disappears into thin air. Later, the driver learns that the hitchhiker was a ghost. Another urban legend concerns the alligators that supposedly inhabit the sewer systems of large cities.

The Lazy Fox

Retold by Genevieve Barlow

T here was once a fox who was known throughout the land for being a lazy scamp as well as a scheming rascal. He was too lazy to work on his own little farm, and he was so scheming nobody would work for him. The fox was as full of tricks as a fig is of seeds.

One morning he looked at his barren fields and sighed, "Unless my fields are planted, I shall go hungry. But what can I do?"

He sat on his haunches and thought and thought. Finally, an idea popped into his head.

"I'll get that slow, stupid armadillo to plant my fields for me and I'll promise him a share of the crops. Of course," the fox added slyly, "it will be a very *small* share."

So the fox hurried down the path to the home of his neighbor. He found him sitting under a *quebracho* tree, telling stories to his children.

"Good day, friend armadillo," the fox called. "I have been thinking about you this morning, and I want to help you."

"Help me?" asked the armadillo, not able to believe his ears.

"Yes, indeed. Your ground is rocky and poor. Why don't you plant on my good land? I will ask only a small share of the crop as payment."

"That is very generous of you," the armadillo replied.

Now the armadillo knew he was no match for the cunning fox, and suspected a trick, but he did want to grow food on that rich soil.

"You may choose whatever you want to plant," urged the fox, "and I will take only half of it."

"That is fair enough," said the armadillo slowly.

"Better yet," suggested the fox, swishing his bushy tail, "I'll take only the part of the crop that grows beneath the soil. You may have all that grows above the ground."

"That is more than fair," the armadillo agreed.

Early the next morning, the armadillo and his family got busy in the fields. By the time the fox sauntered past, they were well along with their work. The fox was pleased to see how well his scheme was working, but he never bothered to ask what crop was being planted.

Raindrops fell on the dark, thirsty earth. Warm fingers of the sun reached down to the fields, caressing the new plants. How they grew! At last it was time to harvest the crop.

The armadillo brought his entire family to help him. And what a fine field of wheat they harvested! By the time the lazy fox went out to get his share, all that remained were the tasteless roots.

He was not only very angry, but he was very hungry, too. Hurrying over to the farm of the armadillo, he found him resting under his favorite tree, looking sleek and contented.

"You made a terrible blunder," the fox shouted at his neighbor. "I cannot eat roots! Surely you know that the good part of the wheat grows above the ground. But I forgive you. Next season we will work together again. Then what is below the soil will be yours, and I shall take what grows above."

"It seems a fair bargain," the armadillo said. "Do you want to choose the crop?"

"No, but you must choose it wisely. Just let me know when the food is ready to eat."

The next season the armadillo planted potatoes. Again the crop was large, but the fox could not eat the tops, which were above ground and lay withering in the sun.

He went to the farm of his neighbor. "Last season I thought you made a stupid mistake. But now I believe you are tricking me.

I cannot eat the vines of the potato plants."

The armadillo squirmed in his suit of armor, and remained silent.

"I have made a great sacrifice to help you," the fox continued, "but you never think of me when you plant your crop. See how thin and weak I am."

"It is true that you are thin, but your coat fits you much better that way."

The fox glared at him. "We are going to try another plan. Next season, I shall take the tops of the plants as well as what grows beneath the soil. You may take what grows in the middle of the plants."

The armadillo remained silent.

"It is only right," added the fox, "that I have a larger share next year, because I have had nothing of the first two crops."

At last the armadillo replied, "Well, it seems a fair enough bargain." And he agreed.

The fox went happily up the path, sure that he could not be tricked again.

When planting time came again, the armadillo planted corn. The crop was large, with ears full and tender, but they grew in the middle of the stalk. There was nothing left for the fox but roots and husks.

The armadillo and his family were munching on the tempting ears of corn when they saw the fox running down the path toward them. His bushy tail trailed straight out behind him.

"You are just in time for a feast," greeted the armadillo. "Sit down and have a roasted ear and we shall talk of next season's crop."

"We shall not! For three seasons, you have tricked me."

The armadillo blinked his heavy eyelids. "I am sorry, but I gave you the part of the crop you asked for."

The fox looked hungrily at the corn, but he didn't sit down with his neighbors. Instead, he stared at the armadillo, wondering why he had ever been stupid enough to call *him* stupid!

"Next year I shall plant my crop, and keep all of it." With that the fox went back up the path, his tail dragging in the dust.

The armadillo reached for another ear of corn, and seated himself under the *quebracho* tree. He was laughing so merrily that he had to hang on to his bony armor to keep it from cracking.

Responding to
The Lazy Fox

Thinking and Discussing

What does the armadillo know about the fox's personality that helps him outwit the fox?

What lesson do you think this story teaches?

Choosing a Creative Response

Drawing a Comic Strip Think about the lesson this story teaches. Try portraying this lesson in a comic strip. You may want to see if you can create a new story with your own characters that teaches the same lesson. Share your comic strip with your classmates.

Constructing a Display Make a display showing what the armadillo plants, what parts of the crops he gives to the fox, and what parts he keeps for himself. With your partner or group, think of other plants the armadillo could use to outwit the fox, and add them to the display.

Creating Your Own Activity Plan and complete your own activity in response to "The Lazy Fox."

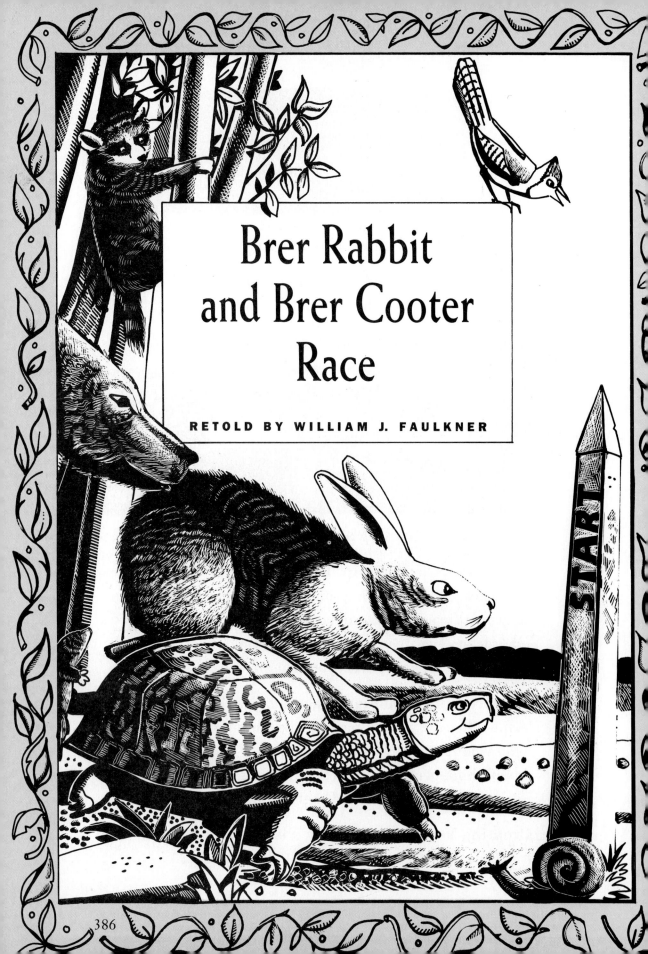

Brer Rabbit
and Brer Cooter
Race

RETOLD BY WILLIAM J. FAULKNER

Along time ago, when the creatures lived together in villages the way people do today, Brer[1] Rabbit and Brer Box Cooter were neighbors. But Brer Rabbit used to poke fun at Brer Cooter because, like all turtles, he had to carry his house on his back wherever he went and he always moved about so slowly.

"Brer Cooter, I feel sorry for you sometimes," said Brer Rabbit one day. "You travel around so slowly on those short legs of yours that it's a wonder you can get out of a shower of rain. And you look so funny carrying your house on your back. I declare there isn't but one other creature in the whole world that's slower than you — and he carries his house on his back, too. It's Brer Snail. Ho! Ho! Ho! That is funny! You and Brer Snail are the slowest creatures in the world." And Brer Rabbit doubled up with laughter as he looked down at Brer Cooter. This hurt Brer Cooter's feelings and made him angry.

"Hold on there, Mister Smart-Aleck," said Brer Box Cooter. "Don't talk too fast. The old folks say, 'An empty wagging makes a heap of fuss.' And that's what I think about you. Just because your legs are long and you can pick them up quick, it doesn't mean you can outrun me in a footrace. In a fair race, man to man, I'll run your long ears off you," challenged Brer Cooter.

This was more than Brer Rabbit could stand. His ears were big and long, but for once he was too amazed to believe them. The idea of Brer Cooter, the slowest creature in town, outrunning Brer Rabbit, the fastest runner in town except possibly for Brer Deer,

---

[1]**Brer** (brûr): a southern expression meaning "brother." Also used to refer to a friend or comrade.

was just too much for Brer Rabbit. He rolled over and over on the ground and laughed and laughed until he looked silly.

Finally he caught his breath and managed to say, "Brer Cooter, that's too funny to be sensible. Fact is, it's impossible. Cooter outrun rabbit in a footrace? No living creature's ever heard tell of such a thing. Why, Brer Cooter, it's so impossible that I'll bet you a whole bushel of pinders[2] that you can't outrun me. And I'll even let you lay out the racetrack and set up the mile posts yourself."

Brer Box Cooter appeared to be well pleased to run a race with Brer Rabbit. Especially since Brer Fox and Brer Wolf and other creatures of the village had come up and overheard much of the big talk, and Brer Rabbit was strutting all around the street, boasting of his speed before the crowd. Brer Cooter's pride would not let him back out of the race now.

"All right, Brer Rabbit," he said, "we'll run the race this coming Saturday afternoon, straight across the field for two miles. And I'll set up the mileposts myself."

Now, it did not take long for such exciting news to spread all over the countryside, and by Saturday morning the creatures from miles around began gathering for the footrace. Brer Cooter had laid out the racecourse very carefully, taking special care to run it across a few gullies[3] and high places.

Brer Rabbit paid no attention to all of this, but spent his time boasting of how he would beat Brer Cooter. He went so far as to tell his wife to be on the front piazza[4] to watch him raise dust when he

---

[2]**pinder** (pĭn′dər): peanut.
[3]**gully** (gŭl′ē): a ditch or channel cut in the earth by running water, especially after a rain.
[4]**piazza** (pē ăz′ə): a porch.

passed Brer Cooter on the way to the last milepost. For, you see, Brer Cooter had placed three posts in the ground a mile apart: the first one at the start, the second one in the middle, and the last one at the end.

Everybody from the Deep Woods and the villages nearby was on hand to see the race and to root for his or her favorite. At the signal to go, Brer Rabbit and Brer Cooter dashed away from the first post at top speed. In an instant, Brer Rabbit had passed Brer Cooter and kicked up dust in his face. Brer Cooter went steadily on.

Brer Rabbit soon was so far ahead that he said to himself, "Aw shucks, I've left Brer Box Cooter so far behind, I'm going to lie down and take a nap."

And he did. And while he was asleep, Brer Cooter disappeared in a gully.

After a while, Brer Rabbit awoke and dashed off across the field toward the second post. Brer Cooter was nowhere in sight. So, as Brer Rabbit neared the post, he called out, "Hello there, Brer Cooter! Where are you?"

Instantly Brer Cooter struck his shell against the post and said, "Here I am, Brer Rabbit! I've been here so long my head is in my house." And his head actually was in his shell.

Brer Rabbit was so surprised he couldn't believe what he saw. Nevertheless, he said to Brer Cooter, "Come on, slowpoke. I slept too long back there. But you won't beat me to the last post. Good-bye, I'm gone."

With that, Brer Rabbit left the turtle far behind again as he galloped across the field. But Brer Rabbit had not gone very far before he came to his house, and then he stopped.

"Hello, honey!" he said to his wife. "I just thought I'd stop by and

talk with you a bit. You see, I left that old slowpoke of a cooter so far behind, he couldn't see me for my dust."

"Come on in, dear, and sit down on the piazza for a spell," encouraged his wife. "You must be hot and tired from running on a day like this. I'll bring you some lemonade." So Brer Rabbit took a seat on the piazza and soon lost track of time as he talked and drank lemonade.

Finally he remembered the race, ran down the steps, jumped over the fence, and was off again at top speed. He looked like a whirlwind coming across the field, he was raising so much dust. Not seeing Brer Box Cooter again, he yelled out as he neared the milepost, "Where are you, Brer Cooter?"

Instantly came back the answer, "Here I am, Brer Rabbit. I've been here so long my head is in my house." And Brer Cooter rapped the milepost with his shell as Brer Rabbit dashed up just a moment too late to win the race.

So Brer Cooter won the footrace and the bushel of pinders, while Brer Rabbit became the laughingstock of all the creatures for miles around. And, strange to say, Brer Rabbit never found out that Brer Box Cooter had planted one of his cousins in the ground with only his head showing at the last two posts.

When the cousins had seen Brer Rabbit coming, they'd jumped out of the ground and said, "Here I am, Brer Rabbit. I've been here so long my head is in my house."

And from this race with Brer Cooter, Brer Rabbit learned a good lesson — that it never pays to brag or to poke fun at another creature.

THINKING AND DISCUSSING

How is the behavior of the animals in this tale similar to human behavior? What conclusions can you then draw about human nature from this story?

CHOOSING A CREATIVE RESPONSE

Drawing a Map Create a map showing all the events of the race between Brer Rabbit and Brer Cooter.

Holding a Debate Divide your group into two teams and debate the following question: "Who really wins the race?" Have one team defend Brer Cooter and the other team defend Brer Rabbit.

Creating Your Own Activity Plan and complete your own activity in response to "Brer Rabbit and Brer Cooter Race."

THINKING AND WRITING

Write a sports article about the race between Brer Rabbit and Brer Cooter. Include an interview with one of the two competitors telling why he won or lost.

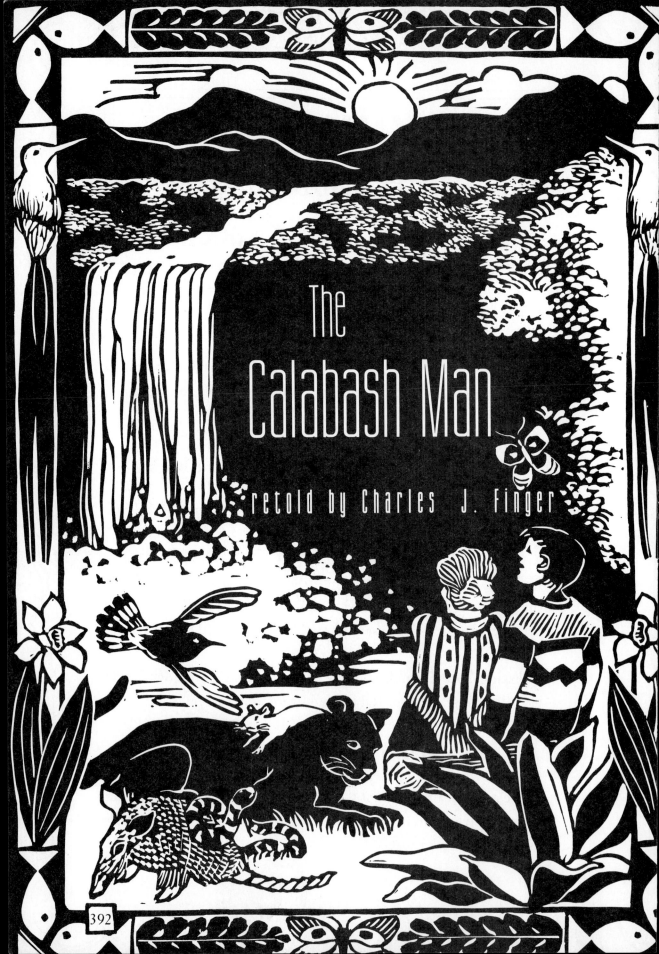

The Calabash Man

retold by Charles J. Finger

 here was once a woman who had an only son, and they lived in great contentment in a little house by the side of the lake and at the foot of a mountain. If you go to Guiana, you may see both lake and mountain to this day.

In all that land there was no lad so straight, so tall, so graceful as Aura, and, what is better still, he was kind and gentle. At the close of the day when he came from his fishing, he and his mother would sit in the cool of the evening, watching the glory of the sunset and listening to the music of the silver cascade which fell from the mountain into the lake. Often the forest animals would come and play about before their house. The lively little agouti[1] would sport with the black jaguar and the great armadillo would let the coral snake coil on his shell, while birds of wondrous beauty flashed through the leaves of the trees like living fire. Great butterflies with silky white and green wings fluttered about the flowers showing their beauty, and from them the old mother learned the way to weave bright designs into the hammocks that she made of silk grass. At such times, before the sun dropped into its purple bed of cloud, and before the million glowworms lit their lights, the queen ant would sing:

> "From forest and hill
> We come at your will.
> Call, Aura, call!"

---

[1] **agouti** (ə gōō′tē): a brown or dark gray rodent of tropical America.

Illustrated by Leslie Evans   393

All went very well until one day Aura, going to the lake, found his basket net broken and torn, and taking it from the water saw with surprise that the fish which had been in it were eaten. Such a thing had never happened before, for in forest and hill he knew no enemy. As he stood in wonderment, the torn basket in his hand, he heard a voice behind him say:

> "From forest and hill
> We come at your will.
> Call, Aura, call!"

Looking around he saw a woodpecker, and the bright beady eyes of the bird were looking at him. Thereupon, Aura told the wood-pecker to watch well, and setting a new basket net in the water he went a little way into the forest to gather wild fruits. Not far had he gone when he heard the watching woodpecker call, "Toc, Toc!" Swiftly he ran, but though he sped like a deer he was too late, for the second basket net was destroyed even more completely than the first and again the fish were devoured.

A third net was set, and this time he called upon the cuckoo to watch while he gathered his fruits. Very soon he heard the "Pon, pon!" of his new watcher and Aura lost no time in running to the lakeside. There in the water and close to the basket net was the flat, mud-coloured head of a swamp alligator with its dull and heavy-lidded eyes. Quick as lightning, Aura fitted an arrow to his bow and let fly, and the shaft struck the reptile between the eyes. A moment later the beast disappeared into the water.

The basket net had been partly broken by the alligator, but Aura mended it and again entered the forest. But before long he heard the cuckoo call, and much louder this time, so he ran like the wind, fitting an arrow to his bow as he went. On the lake-bank

stood a beautiful Indian maiden in a gown that looked like silver, and she was weeping bitterly. At that Aura's heart was touched with pity, for he could see no living thing unhappy and remain happy himself. Gently he took her by the hand and asked her to tell him her name.

"Anu-Anaitu," she said, and smiled through her tears like the sun after a summer rain.

"From where do you come?" was his next question.

"Far, far away, where the great owl lives," she made reply, and pointed in the direction of the dark forest.

"And who is your father?" he asked, and at that there was a ripple of water rings on the lake and Aura thought he saw the nose of the alligator.

But she made no answer to his question. Instead, she covered her face with her hands and bent her head, so that her hair fell about her like a cloud.

Seeing her strange grief Aura said no more, but led her to his mother who received her kindly, and for many months the three of them dwelt together very happily. Yet whenever Anaitu thought of her father, she wept bitterly.

At last there came a day when Aura asked the maiden to be his wife and told her that if she would give him her hand, the two of them would make a journey to her own land so that she might say farewell to her people, telling them that she had made her home in

a land of peace and brightness with those who loved her. Hearing that, little Anaitu wept with terror, telling Aura of the fearful journey that would be theirs, through a place where were great bats and gray hairy spiders and centipedes, and harmful and fearful things.

"Then stay with my mother and I shall go alone," said Aura, seeing her fear. "And I will seek out your father and tell him that all is well with you."

"That is worse still," cried the maiden, "for there is an evil spirit in my land and my father is bewitched. Seeing you, he will destroy you and your mother and me as well, once he learns where we are."

Greatly puzzled with all this, Aura went to see a wise old hermit who lived at the end of the lake, and to him he told his troubles and fears. After much thought, the hermit told Aura that he would make his journey in safety if he feared not and carried himself like a man. "And," said he, "if it should come to pass that you are offered the choice of things, see to it that you choose the simplest."

More than that the wise man would not say, so Aura went home and straightway prepared his canoe, persuaded Anaitu to go with him, and presently they set off.

The way was fearful enough, as the maiden had said, for much of it was through dark forests and between high river banks where

the tree roots reached out black and twisted like evil serpents. Again, they had to pass through swamps where alligators slept and strange yellow beasts with heads large as houses lay hidden. And for many long hours they wound in and out of tangled jungles where the sun never shone and in the depths of which were strange things that roared so that the very trees trembled.

After many days they came to a smooth stretch of sand, and then the maiden told him that they had arrived in the land of her father.

"And now I must leave you," she said, "but my mother will come and offer you one of three things. See to it, dear Aura, that you choose wisely, for all depends upon your choice." At that she waved him a farewell and went up the bank and so passed from his sight.

Before long there came down the bank a wrinkled old woman with sorrowful eyes, and she bore three gourds. Setting them down by the side of the canoe, she bade Aura choose one. On the top of one gourd was a cover of gold, on the second a cover of silver, and on the third a cover of clay. Lifting the covers, Aura saw in the first fresh blood. In the gourd with the silver top he saw flesh, and in the third, a piece of cassava bread. Aura bore in mind the words of the old hermit and quickly chose the gourd that held the bread.

"You have done well," said the old woman. "This is a land where men believe in gold alone, and much blood is spilled because of it. Far better is it that men should choose that which is in the earth. Now having so chosen, I will lead you to my husband, whose name is Kaikoutji. But here cruelty reigns everywhere and he may tear you to pieces."

Aura had no mind to do otherwise than go through with his task and so told the old woman. Whereupon she led him to the top of the bank, where he again saw his Anaitu, and the maiden and her mother hid Aura in a forest near the house, while they went in to prepare Kaikoutji for the visit. Hearing that the young man who loved his daughter was near, the old man fell into a most marvellous rage and so great was his anger that he rushed out and bent trees as though they were reeds and bit rocks as a man bites a crust of bread. So there was much trouble before he was persuaded to see the gentle Aura. Even then, Anaitu begged Aura to return, but he threw his arms around her and was gone before she could say a word.

Strange things happened as he ran to the house. Great branches broke and fell without hands touching them and stones leaped from the earth and whizzed close to his ears, but he hastened on and entered into a hall. Kaikoutji was not there; but as Aura looked round, he came in running. The bewitched old man was strangely decked out with bones and teeth which dangled at the ends of strings fastened to his arms and legs and his head was covered with a great calabash[2] painted green, in the front of which were two holes pierced, through which he looked. For a moment Kaikoutji stood, then giving a terrible howl he began to leap about, waving his arms and rattling the dangling bones and teeth — a very painful sight to Aura. The howling the man made was terrible. After much of this he stopped, turning the holes of his calabash on Aura.

---

[2]**calabash** (kăl′ə băsh′): a gourd that is often dried, hollowed out, and used as a scoop.

"What can you do?" he yelled. "What can you do? Can you bend trees? Can you bite rocks? Can you leap like this?" Again he commenced to dance up and down, each leap being higher than the one before it, so that at last his calabash struck the roof.

When he had quieted down again, Aura said:

"I cannot leap. I cannot bend trees and I cannot bite rocks as you do. But I can work with my hands and make whatever you wish made."

Hearing that, Kaikoutji whirled about and gave three mighty leaps, rattling his bones and dangling teeth furiously.

"Make me a magic stool," he shouted. "And carve it of wood, with the head of a jaguar at one end and my head carved at the other. And see to it that you have it finished by sunrise, or else you die." Then he gave a yell, whirled about and rushed from the hall.

Aura saw that the task would be hard, even if he did what he had been set to do in the quiet of his own home. But without having seen the face of Kaikoutji he wondered greatly how he would complete his work. For all that he took his knife, selected a block of wood and went to work, and he worked with such a will that by midnight he had it all finished but the rough place at the end where was to appear the likeness of Kaikoutji. So he went to the old wife who had brought him the gourds and begged her to describe the features of her husband. But that she refused to do, saying that if she did so, Kaikoutji, who knew everything, being an enchanted man, would kill them all. An hour passed and everything was the same, Aura's work unfinished, his will as strong as ever. Then to him came the gentle maiden who took him by the hand and led him into another chamber where the old man sat in a corner asleep, his green calabash over his head. In another corner of the room was a hammock and into that Aura crept, thinking that if he kept quiet and remained hidden, by some chance the calabash might fall off and the face of the

man be seen. But after looking long and seeing no move on the part of the sleeping man, he grew weak and weary.

Out of the corner near him came a small voice which said:

> "From forest and hill
> We come at your will.
> Call, Aura, call!"

and looking that way he saw a mouse. At that the heart of Aura was glad, the more as he saw the mouse run to the sleeping man and begin to nibble at his hand. For a moment it looked as if Kaikoutji would take off his calabash, for he was plainly annoyed. But instead, by chance, he set his hand on the mouse, caught it, and flung it to the end of the room.

Again a voice was heard and this time Aura saw a spider dropping from the ceiling, and as it dropped it said:

> "From forest and hill
> We come at your will.
> Call, Aura, call!"

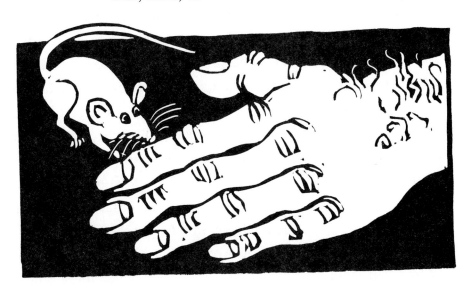

Over to the sleeper ran the spider, but matters were no better than before, for Kaikoutji dropped his hand, caught the spider, and threw it after the mouse.

No sooner had Kaikoutji fallen asleep again than there came into the room ants by hundreds and thousands, and leading them was the queen ant who sang:

> "From forest and hill
> We come at your will.
> Call, Aura, call!"

Like little soldiers they marched on the sleeper, swarming over his hands, his body, his legs. Under the calabash they went, a half hundred of them. That was too much even for Kaikoutji, and he leaped to his feet, dashed the calabash to the earth, and fell to brushing off the ants in lively manner. But the calabash was broken to pieces by the force of the fall, and for the rest of that night he slept with his face exposed.

From his hiding place it did not take long for Aura to learn his ugly features. Nor did it escape his notice that between the eyes was an arrow mark, and by that he knew that Kaikoutji was also the alligator he had shot in the lake. When he was sure that the old man was asleep, he slipped out quietly and went to his work, and with such spirit he wrought that before sunrise he had carved the face on the end of the stool. Better still, so exact was his work, that all who saw it knew the face of Kaikoutji the terrible. But when the old man saw it and noted the arrow mark between the eyes, he leaped higher than he had ever leaped before, having no calabash to hinder him, and declared that the task had been too easy and that another must be done.

"Build me," he said, "a house of feathers before sundown, and see to it that there is no bird in the forest from which there is not a

feather taken." Then, giving strict orders that no one should enter the part of the forest in which Aura was put, he leaped up and down several times, screaming horribly, after which he hastened away.

When all was quiet, Aura lifted his head and sang:

> "From forest and hill
> Oh, come. 'Tis my will.
> I call. I call."

Then there was a great rushing sound and from everywhere came birds: sea birds and land birds, river birds and lake birds, birds that flew, ran, and waded. There were sober brown birds, and birds more glorious than the rainbow. There was a cloud of humming-birds, glittering like powdered gold, and there were proud ostriches. Chakars dropped from the sky singing, and blood-red flamingoes raced with golden-crested wrens. There were song-birds, and silent birds, and birds whose cry was like the sound of a golden bell. There were storks, hawks, vultures, condors, swans, lapwings, and mocking-birds.

Not a moment did they lose. In and out and round about they went, weaving wonderfully, their busy beaks at work, and before an hour had passed there stood the most wonderful house of feathers

that the eye of man ever saw. In the light of the sun it shone green-gold, violet, purple, brown, white, and scarlet. And when the last feather was woven the condor called, and the beating of so many wings, as the birds left, made the very air throb. When all was again silent it seemed to Aura that the work had been done in the twinkling of an eye.

The minute the sun touched the edge of the world Kaikoutji came howling and leaping. When he saw the feather house he stood for a moment with open mouth. So angry he was at the sight that his tongue was dry and parched and he could say nothing. But the glory of what he saw dazzled and blinded him, and with a howl he turned and plunged into the depths of the forest and was seen no more. Some say that he was drowned in the Lake of Pitch.

But Aura and Anaitu lived in the house of feathers and from that day to this the people of that land have been kind and gentle and have forgotten the evil days when cruelty reigned everywhere. Also, they know now that there are things more glorious than gold.

Responding to The Calabash Man

Thinking and Discussing

How is Aura different from Kaikoutji?
Support your answer with examples from the folktale.

This story states that "there are things more glorious than gold."
What does it suggest is more glorious? List several things.
Compare your list with those of your classmates.

Choosing a Creative Response

Drawing a Mural With the help of birds, Aura built "the most wonderful house of feathers that the eye of man ever saw." With a group, draw a mural of the house of feathers or of what you think is the most beautiful scene from "The Calabash Man."

Creating Your Own Activity Plan and complete your own activity in response to "The Calabash Man."

Exploring Language

Notice the descriptive language that creates a mood of enchantment in "The Calabash Man." Choose your favorite images and put them together in a magical poem that captures this unique tone.

The Magic Muntr

retold by Elizabeth Jamison Hodges

 Long ago in the Deccan of western India, there lived a young prince who was kind, clever, and full of curiosity. His name was Vicram, and when he inherited the royal throne, he devoted himself with such zeal to the well-being of his people that they spoke of him as "Maharajah," which means "Great King." But personally he was so modest that he never became used to this title.

His queen, called the "Ranee," was named Anarkali, for her lips were rosy like pomegranates and her eyes as black and shining as the seeds of the sitapurl. In addition to being exquisite to look upon, she was a perfect companion to the young king. Her words as well as her flower-like beauty filled him with joy.

But since he little reckoned his own worth, he often thought, "Can this enchanting lady love me for myself? Must she not have been dazzled by the sound of my title and the blaze of my power?"

As for the handsome palace in which he lived, he paid little attention to its colorful paintings, jeweled throne, and ebony furniture. Instead, he busied himself with building a forest temple to Saraswathi, the goddess of learning. It was delicately carved, and he adorned it with a tower of lights so brilliant that, after sunset, their glory swept through the thick jungle like a bath of golden rain. Moreover, when not engaged in affairs of state, Vicram liked to talk with the ranee of poetry, music, or plans for his people, and with wise men about magic or wisdom.

Illustrated by Krystyna Stasiak

One day two travelers who said they were philosophers came to the gates of the palace. The first was an old and truly learned seer, but the other was a demon rakshas in disguise. Both, however, were made welcome, given robes with golden threads, and a meal of curried rice, sweet figs, and almonds. The next morning, they were presented to the king, who kindly asked what he might do for them.

"O, Noble Maharajah," the rakshas said after he had knelt before the ruler and bowed so low that his chin touched the carpet while his robe flowed out around him, "I have heard that the post of prime minister in your kingdom now is vacant and beg to serve you in that capacity. Be assured that I read a great deal, and to gather wisdom I have traveled many yojanas under the moon."

Vicram thought, I should be fortunate indeed to have a wise philosopher to serve me. So after asking this visitor some difficult questions, all of which he answered without hesitation, the king appointed the rakshas to the post of prime minister with the title of "Prudhan."

The true philosopher likewise bowed very low and said, "I also read a great deal and seeking wisdom have traveled many yojanas under the moon. In so doing I heard everywhere of the kindness and learning of Vicram Maharajah. Nothing, therefore, would please me more than to talk with Your Majesty that happily we may share some jewels of wisdom. As is well known, so marvelous is an exchange of this kind that each of us may keep what we also give away."

Vicram was delighted by these words and consented to his plan.

The rakshas then became the prudhan of the land and immediately began plotting evil mischief, while the elderly philosopher visited the maharajah every day to learn from his store of wisdom. In turn, he told the ruler many strange things he had discovered while walking in cities with busy noise, and while resting in forests with quiet deeps.

One day, Vicram said, "Of all the wonders you have known, pray tell me what seemed to you most marvelous?"

The philosopher thought for just a moment.

"The most wondrous thing I ever saw," he said, his eyes shining like tourmalines, "happened one day when I journeyed toward the regions of the West."

"And what was that?" the king said.

The old seer replied, "While I reposed unobserved in the shade of a banyan tree, I noticed a young man walking alone on a dusty highway. Nearby, a small dog lay asleep. As soon as the young man saw him, he approached the animal on tiptoe, put a hand over its heart and softly said a muntr.

"I could not distinguish the words, Your Majesty, which, I might say, sounded like a hurrying brook or an old demon mumbling in sleep. But they were composed of such powerful magic that they allowed the young man's spirit to slip into that of the dog, leaving his human body lying apparently lifeless beside the road."

"How did you know this had happened?" Vicram asked.

"Because," the philosopher replied, "the dog began to sing and to dance, both in human fashion."

"Amazing indeed!" Vicram said.

"Yes, Your Majesty," continued the philosopher, "and after this had gone on for quite a long time, the animal approached the body of the man, placed one paw over its heart, and barked softly with sounds not unlike the muntr I had heard before. Again, however, the words were not clear enough to be distinguished. But immediately the spirit of the man returned to his own body, for he stood up and walked away, while the little dog, breathing gently, lay asleep just as before."

"What did you do then?" asked the maharajah.

"I arose, Your Majesty, ran after the young man and begged him to teach me the magic muntr. At first he was loath to do so, declaring it was a dangerous saying, but I offered in exchange for the secret to tell him a hundred absorbing tales. So much did he love good stories that he had not the heart to refuse my offer.

"Therefore I traveled with him for many yojanas while the moon waxed seven times and waned. After I had told him one hundred stories he taught me the secret words. I can now, at will, cause my spirit to pass into that of another living creature and continue as long as I choose in its likeness before returning to my own form."

Vicram said, "So amazing is a change about such as you have described that, humbly begging your pardon, I must see it with my own eyes to believe it entirely."

When he heard this, the philosopher said, "In that case, Your Majesty, pray watch, and I shall perform the kind of feat I have just described."

He opened a window. Through it a small sparrow flew into the room and alighted on the carpet. Then very softly, the learned seer crept up behind it. When he had caught the bird he placed one finger lightly over the tiny creature's heart, at the same time saying the muntr in a low voice.

Instantly, in front of the maharajah the body of the old man dropped as if lifeless to the carpet while the little bird flew to Vicram, perched on his hand with a friendly flutter and sang as sweetly

410

as a bulbul bird. When asked by the king to fly from a table to a painting and back to himself, it obeyed perfectly every command.

Finally, after one more song, it settled on top of the philosopher's body right over the heart and softly chirped the strange muntr. Immediately the seer revived, and a moment later, the sparrow's own spirit having returned to its body, the little bird flew out of the window.

The philosopher said to his royal host, "I hope Your Majesty can now believe what I have said."

"I do indeed," replied the maharajah, "for never have I seen any thing so extraordinary. Pray, teach this muntr to me. Though I have now heard it twice, both you and the sparrow spoke so softly and so swiftly that I could not make out the words."

"It is a dangerous saying," the philosopher declared, "but since Your Majesty has been exceedingly kind to men of learning, I shall tell it to you."

This he did, and once the maharajah had learned the muntr, he delighted in going out into the jungle, secretly turning himself into a little owl and in this guise visiting many parts of the kingdom. Sometimes he alighted on roof tops where washing had been hung out to dry by day and where at night women talked of hopes and dreams. Sometimes he visited the cities and heard men both argue and agree in busy bazaars. Thus he came to understand his people better than any maharajah in his land before him, and when he returned to royal shape could rule them with greater wisdom.

Because of this, however, the king was often gone from court. The demon rakshas, who had obtained the position of prudhan, noted his many absences, and one day followed the maharajah into the jungle hiding behind trees as he did so.

It happened that on the same day a sambar came bounding along. This deer had such handsome antlers, held his head so high and pranced through the woods as if filled with so much joy, that Vicram decided it would be great sport to change himself into that happy creature.

He climbed, therefore, part way up an acacia tree, which grew in a hilly part of the jungle, and remained very still. When the sambar passed nearby, the maharajah reached his hands out quickly, held him and placed a finger on his back at a spot over the heart. At the same time he recited the magic muntr in a normal voice, not knowing that his prudhan was lurking close by and could overhear. No sooner had he spoken the words than the king's spirit passed into that of the sambar, while his own body fell lifeless to the ground under the acacia tree.

Now when the rakshas heard the muntr spoken aloud, he stored the words in his memory by saying them over and over to himself. Then after the maharajah, in the shape of the deer, had bounded off into another part of the jungle, the prudhan ran to the monarch's fallen body. Kneeling down, he placed a hand over its heart and firmly spoke the secret words he had just heard. At once, while his own form fell as if lifeless on the ground, the rakshas stood up in the guise of the maharajah, and hurried back to the palace to take the place of the king.

As for Vicram, at first he delighted in his new shape, and when a high and exciting wind streaked through the trees, he romped about the jungle as merry as a fawn. Finally, when the sun set he decided to return to his own body, but the wind had blown so many leaves from the trees that each one now looked different. Even the prudhan's body was nowhere to be seen. In the gale it had rolled down the hillside and lay buried under a sea of leaves.

So after he had looked a long time, Vicram, feeling himself lost indeed, gave up in despair and wandered through the jungle eating wild plants and fleeing from tigers, jackals, and other animals which chased him. When he lay down to sleep, small ants climbed

out of their nests and swarmed over him. When he wished to drink from forest streams, powerful lions bared their teeth and frightened him away.

In this desperate plight, he happened one day to see a parrot which had flown from the top of a banyan tree to a branch near the ground. If I could fly like a bird, Vicram thought, I could escape

from these troublesome animals. So he crept up softly behind the parrot which was asleep, placed his chin ever so lightly on the creature over his heart, spoke the magic muntr and forthwith entered the body of the parrot. That of the sambar fell to the ground and lay as if asleep for a few days, until it was found by its own wandering spirit which pranced away with it.

The head of the parrot that Vicram had entered was blue and yellow like a summer sea edged with golden sand. The breast was rosy and the wings green like leaves of a palm tree. Vicram not only felt handsome, but now he could rise above tigers, jackals, lions and other ground creatures. Pleased with his greater freedom, he practiced flying short distances before attempting to search for his palace, and, to have company, he joined a flock of other birds living merrily in the jungle.

With great delight he found that he understood their language, and that they from wide travel could tell him many things. So on warm nights he listened carefully while cicadas sang and the moon slipped over the deeps of sky like a silver ship.

In this way Vicram learned much, not only concerning his own kingdom but about countries far away with rivers of golden fish and about distant oceans rich in pearls. Thus a few days passed not uncomfortably for the former ruler, who delighted in hearing of all that was strange and curious.

One night, however, when it was dark, he fell asleep on a low branch of a sicakai tree, not knowing, so lost had he become, that it was near the temple of Saraswathi. Nor did he awake when the lamps on its tower were lit for the night.

About the same time a fowler came through the woods in search of birds to snare and sell. By the lights of the tower he saw the brilliant plumage of the parrot. So he threw a net over the bird's sleepy head and thus caught Vicram in it.

Delighted with his colorful prize, the fowler put the parrot in a cage where he kept other captured birds and, bolting the door with a little wooden peg, carried them all to the edge of the capital city. But when the fowler went away for a short time, Vicram, with intelligence like a man's, pulled the peg out of its place, and using his beak, pushed open the door.

Next, he watched while with a great squawking, twittering, and flutter of feathers the other birds fought, scrambled, and pell-mell pushed their way out of the cage. Vicram alone remained inside it.

When the fowler returned and found birds gone and the cage open, he wrung his hands and said, "Woe is me, most unfortunate of fowlers. Gone, all gone, like drops of water under a hot sun."

"Cheer up. Not quite all," Vicram said. "I am here."

The fowler looked round about but saw not a single human being nearby.

"I am here in the cage," Vicram said, "the parrot you so admired. See, I have not deserted you."

When the fowler discovered that it was his bird which had spoken so well though it had been caught only that day, he was astounded. Even more was he surprised when the parrot answered difficult questions and of its own accord spoke brightly of golden fish in distant rivers and pearl-rich reefs in faraway oceans.

The birdcatcher thought, I can sell this extraordinary parrot for a good price. So he took it to a bazaar where people bought and sold strange and beautiful things.

Now not far away from where he stopped with Vicram there arose a great surge of angry voices. Placing a branch of a tree against the door of the cage, the fowler ran to the place of dispute to find out why the morning air was rent with such ugly sounds.

After he had worked his way to the inner circle of the crowd, he found a woman, dressed like a farmer's wife, shouting at a handsomely clad young man.

"How dare you treat a poor woman so?" she said, stamping her foot. Then turning to others for sympathy, she said, "Last night I dreamed that this same young man offered to pay me a hundred golden mohurs for seven cartloads of fresh bringals, from my husband's farm. We delivered these vegetables, mind you the freshest we had, and now he refuses to pay even a single anna for them."

The fowler heard a shuffling of feet as all the people murmured, some taking the side of the farmer's wife, others the part of the young man.

Then the birdcatcher raised his voice higher than these sounds, the way the clear notes of a flute soar bravely above the music of drums, and said, "I have a remarkable parrot, with so much sense I am sure he can decide your dispute justly if you will agree to what he says."

At this all the people laughed, but when the fowler said his newly caught parrot could not only ape the speech of humans, but converse most sweetly of distant rivers and faraway oceans, the quarreling pair agreed to ask the strange bird to settle the case.

Thus the matter came before the parrot, and as he sat behind the bars of his cage, he listened carefully while first the young man spoke and then the woman.

Next Vicram asked for a table, a mirror, and from the young man a hundred golden mohurs. When these were brought, he had the mirror propped up on the table with the money placed in front of it. Seeing the coins, the woman's eyes lighted up for she expected they would be hers, but the young man looked at them with much concern.

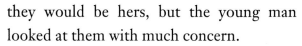

"Now," Vicram said to the woman, "you may have only the mohurs which you see in the mirror, for since the vegetables you delivered were dream bringals, which could not be eaten by the young man, it is fitting that your payment be only in coins which cannot be spent by you."

When he had spoken these words, the woman cried out in disappointment, but the young man was delighted, and the people laughed and applauded the wisdom of the parrot. Then the story flew in every direction like bees in a field full of sunflowers. Finally it reached the maharajah's palace.

On that day Anarkali, the ranee, was sitting in her own apartments feeling extremely downcast. For many days she had been worried about the ruler in whose body, unknown to her, the rakshas now was living. It seemed to the queen that her husband was so changed he was like another man. She had the royal cooks prepare his favorite foods; peppery curries of rice with onions, tamarind, and cucumbers, but the maharajah would not touch them and demanded strange unsavory dishes he had never requested before.

No longer did he speak to her of music and poetry or of how he might help his people. Instead, his conversation was all of war

and of gold. So, very much frightened, she had confined herself to her own apartments, bolting the door against everybody except one woman, a faithful attendant.

She, thinking it might amuse the ranee, now so sad and lonely, told her about the strange bird.

Anarkali was fascinated by the story of the clever parrot. She sent word to the fowler that she would pay a thousand golden mohurs if he would sell it to her.

But when he heard that the ranee had been sad for many days, he said, "Her Majesty may have the parrot as a gift. I do not wish to sell him for I should like to help make her happy. Besides, this bird seems too much like a human being to be bought or sold."

So Anarkali accepted the gift with many thanks and gave a little house and a generous pension to the fowler. After that he never went into the jungle to snare wild birds again.

For her part, the ranee was delighted with the parrot. She admired his colorful feathers and talked to him for a long time every day, marveling at the wonderful things he said. Also, she had built for him a large and spacious cage. It was decked with rubies, lined with red and purple velvet and furnished with silver swings. Round the room in which it was placed, she had several mirrors hung so that, seeing his reflection, he would be less lonely. She also had pictures of trees and flowers brought in, that even away from the jungle he might feel at home.

While the days passed the ranee came to love the parrot more and more. She fed him herself with food from her own table, and every day summoned three musical ladies of the court to play sweet tunes for him on stringed instruments.

Thus passed some time during which Vicram observed that no man came to the queen's apartments.

So, full of curiosity about how the country was being governed, he said, "Pray, tell me, Your Majesty, who is the king of this land?"

Anarkali said, "His name is Vicram, and he is called 'Maharajah,' but no longer is he like the man he was a short time ago. Then his words were full of poetry and music, and all his deeds were kindness. One day, however, he went away and on returning, conversed of naught but war and gold. This frightened me so that I have shut myself up here and refused to see him. Nor do I wish to go out again, though he has sent me strings of pearls and purple amethysts and entreats me to wear them before the court."

From these words, Vicram knew someone had taken his royal shape, but he was overjoyed to learn that the queen had not loved the impostor though his appearance, title, and power appeared the same as the real king's. So he told her the story of the magic muntr and of his strange wanderings. But who had taken his body and was now pretending to be Vicram Maharajah, he did not know.

The ranee, overjoyed to learn that her husband was still kind, said, "Dearest Husband, no wonder I felt such love for you even in your present shape as a bird, but who can have stolen your own form?"

Then Vicram asked if anyone was missing from the court the same day the king had first seemed so changed, and the queen remembered that the prudhan went away that very day and did not return. Indeed, the one who came back in the likeness of the king gave out that the prime minister had been lost and probably killed by a wild beast.

"Very likely then," Vicram said, "it is he who has taken my body."

At this the ranee wept and said, "O, my dear Husband. Alas! What can we do?"

Vicram said, "It is clear that whoever lives in my shape must also know the magic muntr. I pray you, have a hen brought to this apartment, and then invite hither the one who is called the 'Maharajah.'" He also explained more fully what she should do.

So the woman who attended the ranee was asked to get a hen, and when she brought it, Anarkali sent out word that she would like the maharajah to come to her apartments. The rakshas arrived in the guise of the king, his face shining for joy like a mound of melting butter.

The queen said, "Your Majesty, lately I have been very sad and bored. Pray tell me, can you divert me by doing something remarkable?"

Though much surprised by her question, the rakshas was so eager to please the ranee, who had been very cool to him, that he began to boast.

"I am able to do the most remarkable thing in the world," he said. "I can turn myself into another creature."

"Can you, indeed! Then pray," she said, indicating the hen, "let me see Your Majesty turn yourself into this chicken."

Thereupon, the rakshas picked up the hen, touched her over the heart and whispered the magic muntr. Immediately, the body of the maharajah lay still on the floor while the chicken began to fly round the room, clucking a sort of song as it did so.

Seeing this, the queen opened the door of the cage, and the parrot flew swiftly to the king's body, rested over its heart, and said the muntr. In less time than it takes a kitten to twitch his ears, Vicram resumed his own shape as the maharajah.

Then he caught the hen and put it into the small cage in which the parrot had been brought to the palace. A servant took it away with orders not to release the chicken except in the darkest part of the jungle.

The rakshas, when he had been freed there, flew about for a long time, but never found his own body. He lived the rest of his life a lonely hen in a dismal swamp.

As for Vicram, he appointed the true philosopher to the post of prudhan. And he rejoiced every day, because through the magic muntr and his strange adventures he now knew that Anarkali loved him for his own true self. His happiness made the ranee happy too, and they both lived long and merrily.

Pantoum for a Parrot

How wise the bird which speaks as man!
More royal than the rakshas's seeming,
He overthrows an evil plan
And ends a quarrel spun from dreaming.

More royal than the rakshas's seeming,
His wisdom shines like temple light,
And ends a quarrel spun from dreaming,
Yet knows a sambar's wild delight.

His wisdom shines like temple light;
He overthrows an evil plan,
Yet knows a sambar's wild delight.
How wise the bird which speaks as man!

Responding to The Magic Muntr

Thinking and Discussing

What does the king's ability to change his shape enable him to learn about his kingdom? How does this ability help him become a better ruler?

What qualities does the king have that help him defeat the evil rakshas? Explain how these qualities are revealed in the story.

Choosing a Creative Response

Making Characters Live Work with a group to dramatize a scene from this tale. You may want to start by creating character sketches of the main characters, including descriptions of their appearance and personalities. As you perform your scene, make sure that the characters behave as they are described in your sketches. Bring the characters to life.

Tracking Travels Create a collage, a map, or a travel guidebook showing the king's travels throughout his land.

Creating Your Own Activity Plan and complete your own activity in response to "The Magic Muntr."

Thinking and Writing

The good king decides that the best way to escape dangerous animals and hunters is to become a parrot. He realizes that in this shape, he can learn not only about his own kingdom but also about distant lands. Write diary entries that describe the king's travels and the knowledge he gains.

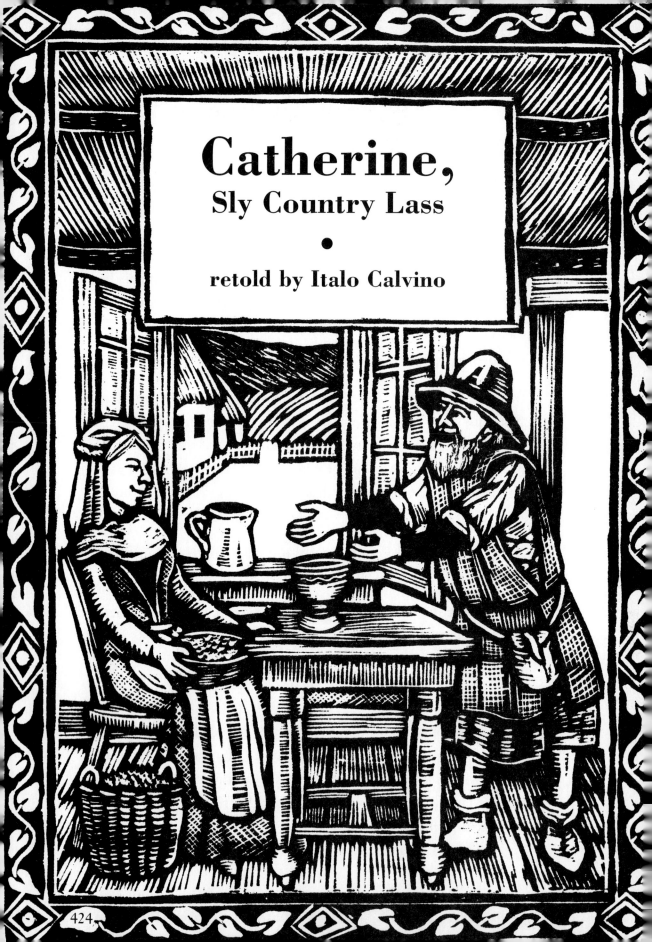

Catherine,
Sly Country Lass
•
retold by Italo Calvino

One day a farmer hoeing his vineyard struck something hard. He bent over and saw that he had unearthed a fine mortar.[1] He picked it up, rubbed the dirt off, and found the object to be solid gold.

"Only a king could own something like this," he said. "I'll take it to my king, who will most likely give me a handsome present in return!"

At home he found his daughter Catherine waiting for him, and he showed her the mortar, announcing he would present it to the king. Catherine said, "Beyond all doubt, it's as lovely as lovely can be. But if you take it to the king he'll find fault with it, since something is missing, and you'll even end up paying for it."

"And just what is missing? What could even a king find wrong with it, simpleton?"

"You just wait; the king will say:

'The mortar is big and beautiful,

But where, you dummy, is the pestle?'"[2]

The farmer shrugged his shoulders. "The idea of a king talking like that! Do you think he's an ignoramus like you?"

---

[1]**mortar (môr′tər):** a bowl in which substances are finely ground.
[2]**pestle (pĕs′əl):** a tool with a rounded end for grinding substances in a mortar.

Illustrated by Mary Azarian

He tucked the mortar under his arm and marched straight to the king's palace. The guards weren't going to let him in, but he told them he was bringing a wonderful gift, so they took him to His Majesty. "Sacred Crown," began the farmer, "in my vineyard I found this solid gold mortar, and I said to myself that the only place fit to display it was your palace. Therefore I am giving it to you, if you will have it."

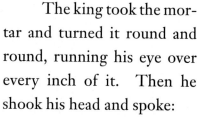

The king took the mortar and turned it round and round, running his eye over every inch of it. Then he shook his head and spoke:

> "The mortar is big and beautiful,
>
> But missing is its pestle."

Catherine's words exactly, except that the king didn't call him a dummy, since kings are well-bred persons. The farmer slapped his brow and couldn't help but exclaim, "Word for word! She guessed it!"

"Who guessed what?" asked the king.

"I beg your pardon," said the farmer. "My daughter told me the king would say just those words, and I refused to believe her."

"This daughter of yours," said the king, "must be a very clever girl. Let's see just how clever. Take her this flax and tell her to make me shirts for a whole regiment of soldiers. But tell her to do it quickly, since I need the shirts right now."

The farmer was stunned. But you don't argue with a king, so he picked up the bundle (which contained only a few measly strands of flax), bowed to the king, and set out for home, leaving the mortar without receiving a word of thanks, much less anything else.

"My daughter," he said to Catherine, "you are really in for it now." And he told her what the king had ordered.

"You get upset over nothing," replied Catherine. "Give me that bundle." She took the flax and shook it. As you know, there are always scalings in flax, even if it has been carded by an expert.[3] A few scalings dropped on the floor, so tiny you could scarcely see them. Catherine gathered them up and said to her father, "Here. Go right back to the king and tell him for me that I will make him the shirts. But since I have no loom to weave the cloth, tell him to have one made for me out of this handful of scalings, and his order will be carried out to the letter."

The farmer didn't have the nerve to go back to the king, especially with that message; but Catherine nagged him until he finally agreed.

Learning how cunning Catherine was, the king was now eager to see her with his own eyes. He said, "That daughter of yours is a clever girl! Send her to the palace, so that I'll have the pleasure of chatting with her. But mind that she comes to me neither naked nor clothed, on a stomach neither full nor empty, neither in the daytime nor at night, neither on foot nor on

---

[3]**scalings in flax . . . carded by an expert:** scalings are tiny particles in a fiber used to make material; to card means "to untangle the fibers."

horseback. She is to obey me in every single detail, or both your head and hers will roll."

The farmer arrived home in the lowest of spirits. But his daughter merrily said, "I know how, Daddy. Just bring me a fishing net."

In the morning before daybreak, Catherine rose and draped herself with the fishing net (that way she was neither naked nor clothed), ate a lupin (that way her stomach was neither empty nor full), led out the nanny goat and straddled it, with one foot dragging the ground and the other in the air (that way she was neither on foot nor on horseback), and reached the palace just as the sky grew lighter (it was neither day nor night). Taking her for a madwoman in that outlandish get-up, the guards barred the way; but on learning that she was just carrying out the sovereign's order, they escorted her to the royal chambers.

"Majesty, I am here in compliance with your order."

The king split his sides laughing, and said, "Clever Catherine! You're just the girl I was looking for. I am now going to marry you and make you queen. But in one condition, remember: you must never, never poke your nose into my business." (The king had realized that Catherine was smarter than he was.)

When the farmer heard about it, he said, "If the king wants you for his wife, you have no choice but to marry him. But watch your step, for if the king quickly decides what he wants, he can decide just as quickly what he no longer wants. Be sure to leave your workclothes hanging up here on a hook. In case you ever have to come home, you'll find them all ready to put back on."

429

But Catherine was so happy and excited that she paid little attention to her father's words, and a few days later the wedding was celebrated. There were festivities throughout the kingdom, with a big fair in the capital. The inns were filled to overflow, and many farmers had to sleep in the town squares, which were crowded all the way up to the king's palace.

One farmer, who had brought to town a pregnant cow to sell, found no barn to put the animal in, so an innkeeper told him he could put it under a shed at the inn and tether it to another farmer's cart. Lo and behold, in the night, the cow gave birth to a calf. In the morning the proud owner of the cow was preparing to lead his two animals away when out rushed the owner of the cart, shouting, "That's all right about the cow, she's yours. But hands off the calf, it's mine."

"What do you mean, it's yours? Didn't my cow have it last night?"

"Why wouldn't it be mine?" answered the other farmer. "The cow was tied to the cart, the cart's mine, so the calf belongs to the owner of the cart."

A heated quarrel arose, and in no time they were fighting. They grabbed props from under the cart and struck in blind fury at one another. At the noise, a large crowd gathered around them; then the constables ran up, separated the two men, and marched them straight into the king's court of justice.

It was once the custom in the royal city, mind you, for the king's wife also to express her opinion. But now with Catherine as queen, it happened that every time the king delivered a judgment, she opposed it. Weary of that in no time, the king said to her, "I warned you not to meddle in state business. From now on you'll stay out of the court of justice." And so she did. The farmers therefore appeared before the king alone.

After hearing both sides, the king rendered this decision: "The calf goes with the cart."

The owner of the cow found the decision too unjust for words, but what could he do? The king's judgment was final. Seeing the farmer so upset, the innkeeper advised him to go to the queen, who might find a way out.

The farmer went to the palace and asked a servant, "Could you tell me, my good man, if I might have a word with the queen?"

"That is impossible," replied the servant, "since the king has forbidden her to hear people's cases."

The farmer then went up to the garden wall. Spying the queen, he jumped over the wall and burst into tears as he told how unjust her husband had been to him. The queen said, "My advice is this. The king is going hunting tomorrow in the vicinity of a lake that is always bone-dry at this time of year. Do the following: hang a fish-dipper on your belt, take a net, and go through the motions of fishing. At the sight of someone fishing in that dry lake, the king will laugh and then ask why you're fishing where there's no water. You must answer: 'Majesty, if a cart can give birth to a calf, maybe I can catch a fish in a dry lake.'"

The next morning, with dipper dangling at his side and net in hand, the farmer went off to the dry

lake, sat down on the shore, lowered his net, then raised it as though it were full of fish. The king came up with his retinue[4] and saw him. Laughing, he asked the farmer if he had lost his mind. The farmer answered him exactly as the queen had suggested.

At that reply, the king exclaimed, "My good man, somebody else had a finger in this pie. You've been talking to the queen."

The farmer did not deny it, and the king pronounced a new judgment awarding him the calf.

Then he sent for Catherine and said, "You've been meddling again, and you know I forbade that. So now you can go back to your father. Take the thing you like most of all in the palace and go home this very evening and be a farm girl once more."

Humbly, Catherine replied, "I will do as Your Majesty wills. Only, I would ask one favor: let me leave tomorrow. Tonight it would be too embarrassing for you and for me, and your subjects would gossip."

"Very well," said the king. "We'll dine together for the last time, and you will go away tomorrow."

So what did sly Catherine turn around and do but have the cooks prepare roasts and hams and other heavy food that would make a person drowsy and thirsty. She also ordered the best wines brought up from the cellar.

---

[4]**retinue** (rĕt′n ōō′): the people accompanying an important person.

At dinner the king ate and ate and ate, while Catherine emptied bottle after bottle into his glass. Soon his vision clouded up; he started stuttering and at last fell asleep in his armchair, like a pig.

Then Catherine said to the servants, "Pick up the armchair with its contents and follow me. And not a word out of you, or else!"  She left the palace, passed through the city gate, and didn't stop until she reached her house, late in the night.

"Open up, Daddy, it's me," she cried.

At the sound of his daughter's voice, the old farmer ran to the window. "Back at this hour of the night? I told you so! I was wise to hold on to your work-clothes. They're still here hanging on the hook in your room."

"Come on, let me in," said Catherine, "and don't talk so much!"

The farmer opened the door and saw the servants bearing the armchair with the king in it. Catherine had him carried into her room, undressed, and put into her bed. Then she dismissed the servants and lay down beside the king.

Around midnight the king awakened. The mattress seemed harder than usual, and the sheets rougher. He turned over and felt his wife there beside him. He said, "Catherine, didn't I tell you to go home?"

433

"Yes, Majesty," she replied, "but it's not day yet. Go back to sleep."

The king went back to sleep. In the morning he woke up to the braying of the donkey and the bleating of the sheep, and saw the sunshine streaming through the window. He shook himself, for he no longer recognized the royal bedchamber. He turned to his wife. "Catherine, where on earth are we?"

She answered, "Didn't you tell me, Majesty, to return home with the thing I liked best of all? I took *you*, and I'm keeping you."

The king laughed, and they made up. They went back to the royal palace, where they still live, and from that day on, the king has never appeared in the court of justice without his wife.

Responding to
Catherine,
Sly Country Lass

Thinking and Discussing

How does the disagreement between the two farmers help reveal Catherine's admirable qualities?

How would you describe the personalities of the king and Catherine? What qualities enable Catherine to outwit the king?

Choosing a Creative Response

Speaking for the People Do you think that the king's subjects would want Catherine to help the king make decisions or not? Take the part of a subject, and prepare a speech or letter to the king expressing your opinion.

Making a Book of Clever Answers Catherine had to respond to the king's impossible requests before she became queen. With a group, discuss other possible solutions to the king's challenging requests. Collect your ideas in a book of clever answers to difficult riddles. You may wish to contribute your own riddles and witty solutions.

Creating Your Own Activity Plan and complete your own activity in response to "Catherine, Sly Country Lass."

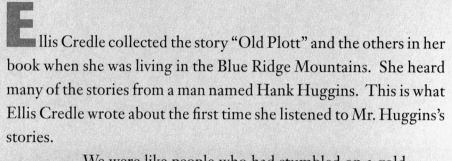

Ellis Credle collected the story "Old Plott" and the others in her book when she was living in the Blue Ridge Mountains. She heard many of the stories from a man named Hank Huggins. This is what Ellis Credle wrote about the first time she listened to Mr. Huggins's stories.

We were like people who had stumbled on a gold mine. We felt the excitement of a great discovery. Mr. Huggins was surely a man left over from a way of life now vanished, when people sat around a fire telling tales their grandparents had passed down to them, or making new ones out of half-forgotten lore. We sat entranced.

"However did you come to know so many stories?" I demanded at last. . . .

"It was like this. When I was a young fellow, I had a job driving a freight wagon from up here in the hills down to the low country. It was before the railroad was built through the mountains. Well, there used to be a lot of us fellows driving wagons, and we would go together in trains, so as to have help in case somebody got stuck in the mud or broke an axle. Nights we'd camp together in some nice grove. Whilst we were cooking our suppers and after we'd et them, we'd sit around swapping news or telling tales. The tales I've heard around those campfires! Every fellow trying to outdo the next one."

from *Tall Tales from the High Hills*

Old Plott

retold by Ellis Credle

Illustrated by Randall Enos

For as long as he could remember, young Jess Honeycutt had been hearing about the train. It passed through the city forty miles on yonder side of the mountain. Everybody that came back from there had something to tell about it.

"She's a sight to behold," they said. "She's got one eye right in the middle of her forehead. Go to see her in the nighttime. There she comes, down the track, glaring like a one-eyed wildcat staring into a pine torch. And racket. Whee! She comes a-raring[1] like a square dance on a tin roof!"

Jess sure did have a hankering[2] to see that train-critter, and one time when his wife went off to visit her folks he allowed it was

---

[1]**a-raring:** eager.
[2]**hankering:** longing, craving.

his chance and he was a-going. He stuck the frying pan up the chimney, hid the ax in a crotch of the tree, whistled up old Plott, his bear dog, and off he put. As he trudged on down the trail Jess got to thinking that it might not be a good idea to take his dog along. How could he prepare old Plott's mind for the sight of the train? The thing might scarify him to the point of addling his wits. He might run clean away and never come back. Jess didn't want anything like that to happen. Old Plott was the best bear dog anywhere in the Blue Ridge Mountains. Everybody knew it, and Jess loved him like a brother.

By this time, Jess had got down the mountain as far as the cabin where old man Gruber lived. The idea came to him that he might ask the old man to keep Plott until he got back from his

travels. Yes, that's what he'd do. No use taking chances with such a valuable dog.

He opened the front gate, walked up to Mr. Gruber's cabin and knocked at the door. It opened a crack and a gun barrel came poking through.

Young Jess gave a start. He backed away. "Hold on there, Mr. Gruber, hold on a minute. I don't mean you no harm."

"Who is it then?" came old man Gruber's voice from inside and it sounded mighty mean.

"It's me, Jess Honeycutt."

"Oh, so it's you, young Jess!" Old man Gruber stuck his head out the door. "Where are your raisings, young feller? That ain't no way to act, to come a-knocking at the door without even a whoop or a holler. How's a man to know if it's friend or foe? Mind your manners next time and give a holler before you open the gate."

"Yes, sir, Mr. Gruber, I sure will. I beg your pardon for giving you a scare."

"All right then, young Jess, all right. Now what is it you've come for?"

"I'm off for a trip, Mr. Gruber and I just wondered if you'd do me a favor while I'm away in foreign parts?"

"A favor? I don't know about that." Old man Gruber drew in his head and began to shut the door.

"I'll pay you well if you'll help me out, Mr. Gruber!" cried young Jess.

"Oh, that's different now." Mr. Gruber looked out again. "What is it you want me to do? What's the favor?"

"I was going to ask you to keep old Plott for me while I'm away."

"Old Plott? You want me to keep old Plott whilst you're away?" A greedy gleam came into old man Gruber's eyes. "Bring him right in, Jess. That's a favor I won't charge you for. I'll keep him here and treat him as kindly as if he were my own child. I sure will."

"That's mighty nice of you, Mr. Gruber." Jess was real pleased. He whistled old Plott into the cabin and shut the door on him. Then he went along on his journey, satisfied and easy in his mind. He clean forgot what folks said about old man Gruber, that he would steal the pennies outen a blind beggar's hat; that he was the meanest, stingiest, cheatin'est old man in seven counties.

A few days later, down the trail again came young Jess. He was footsore and dusty. He'd been over the mountain to the city.

He'd seen the train and he'd had enough of traveling. He stopped at old man Gruber's gate and gave a whoop and a holler.

Old man Gruber stuck his head out the door.

"Heigh-oh there, Mr. Gruber. Well, I'm back from my trip." He opened the gate and walked up the path.

"Howdy, young Jess, howdy. I reckon you've seen a sight, I reckon you have. Well, come around and tell me all about it one of these days." Old man Gruber drew in his head and began to shut the door.

"Hold on there, Mr. Gruber, hold on!" Young Jess stuck his foot in the crack. "What about my dog Plott? Where's old Plott? I've come for him."

"Old Plott, old Plott?" Mr. Gruber scratched his head and pretended to think. "Oh, yes, I declare I near 'bout forgot old Plott. Son, I sure am sorry to have to tell you about old Plott."

"What's the matter? What's happened? He ain't run away, has he?"

"Worse than that, son —"

"He ain't been hurt now, has he?"

Old man Gruber didn't say anything. He just looked down at the ground and shook his head in a mournful way.

"You ain't trying to tell me old Plott is dead now, are you, Mr. Gruber?" cried young Jess.

"I'm sorry to have to tell you, son, but he sure is. Dead as a doornail."

Tears came to young Jess' eyes. He felt as though a mule had kicked him right in the middle of his stomach. "Don't tell me, Mr. Gruber. That dog was everything to me. I wouldn't have taken a pretty³ for him."

"Well, son, it's the truth. He's dead."

"How did it happen, Mr. Gruber?"

"Why, son, the day you left I shut old Plott up in a little old house here on the place. I'd been renting it to some powerful dirty folks and they'd left it chockablock⁴ full of bedbugs. Those bugs hadn't had nothing to eat for the longest time. I reckon they were mortal hungry. Anyway, they set onto old Plott in the night and ate him up, hair, hide, and all. Wasn't anything left but his bones."

Jess turned about to go home. "Those bugs don't know what they've done to me!" He stumbled down the path with hanging head. He glanced back as he opened the gate. Mr. Gruber was grinning from ear to ear, as though he had done something mighty smart and was real pleased with himself.

That set young Jess to studying. He stood a minute with his hand on the gate, then he turned around and walked up the path again.

---

³**pretty:** a toy or decorative object.

⁴**chockablock** (chŏk′ə blŏk′): squeezed together.

"Mr. Gruber, I declare to goodness, this has hit me mighty hard. And I'm clean wore out with traveling. I feel so bad I don't know as I can get home. You know it's a mighty steep climb from here up to my cabin there on the mountain. Wouldn't you lend me your mule to ride on the rest of the way?"

"I don't know about that, now, young Jess. I need my mule here to home. Got to do some plowing today. Got to plow every day this week."

Young Jess stepped up on the porch. "Well then, Mr. Gruber, I reckon you'll just have to give me some dinner and some supper later on and put me up for the night. I haven't got the strength to go a step farther."

"Now, now, young Jess, you ain't that bad off." Mr. Gruber looked worried.

"I sure am, Mr. Gruber, I'm laid low. I'll have to stay the night with you, I sure will."

"No, young Jess, you can't do that. No, you can't. Maybe I'd better lend you my mule after all. Will you bring him back tomorrow sure and certain?"

"Sure as shootin', Mr. Gruber. Why would you ask such a thing? You know I'm as honest as the day is long, just like Pap and my old grandpap before me."

Old man Gruber led out his mule. Young Jess straddled him and off he went, plodding up the trail toward home.

On the following day, old man Gruber got up bright and early. He looked up the trail to see if young Jess was on the way with his mule. Not a sign of him did he see.

Now, that's no way to do — to keep my mule till half the day is gone! Maybe he won't get here till afternoon," he grumbled to himself and he found some work to do around the house.

When nighttime came and still no Jess and no mule, old man Gruber fussed and fumed. "That young scamp, a-keeping my mule right now during planting time. What's he up to, I'd like to know?"

The next day he leaped up as soon as the sun peeped over the ridge and ran out to see if young Jess was on the way. No, he wasn't. And the next day he didn't come either. Old man Gruber was mad a sight. "That cheating young rascal, I'll have the law on him, that I will. He'll pay me hard money for every day he keeps my mule!"

Well, day by day went by with never a sign of Jess and the mule. With his creaky joints, old man Gruber knew well enough he'd never make it up the steep trail to the cabin where Jess lived, and every day that passed he got madder and madder.

Then one morning, after the sun was well up in the sky, he looked out the window and there was young Jess sauntering along the road as though he didn't have a care in the world nor a thought for Mr. Gruber's mule.

Old man Gruber ran out of the house without even stopping to put his shoes on. "Oh there you are, you young scallawag! Where's my mule, now, where is he, I'd like to know?"

Young Jess stopped in the middle of the road. He looked at Mr. Gruber in a surprised sort of way. Then he scratched his head and pretended to think. "Your mule, Mr. Gruber? Oh, yes, I

declare I near 'bout forgot your mule. I sure am sorry to have to tell you about him, Mr. Gruber."

"What do you mean? What's happened to my mule?"

Young Jess didn't answer. He just looked down at the ground and shook his head in a mournful way.

"You haven't lost my mule in the mountains? You haven't let him fall off a cliff, have you?" shouted old man Gruber.

"Worse than that, Mr. Gruber. Worse than that," Jess said sadly.

"You ain't trying to tell me my mule is dead now, are you?" screamed the old man.

"I've got a mighty strong suspicion he is — dead as a doornail. But I don't know for sure, Mr. Gruber. No, I don't. A mighty curious thing happened to your mule. It sure did."

"I don't believe it! I don't believe nary a word you say, Jess Honeycutt. You've stole my mule and I'll have you jailed!" screeched old man Gruber. "Come on now, come right on. I'm going to haul you down the road to Squire Meekins' house. He'll fix you for stealing my mule." He grabbed young Jess by the arm and began to drag him down the road.

When they got to the crossroads where Squire Meekins lived, old man Gruber stood at his gate and hollered, "Squire Meekins! Come out, come out here right now. I want you to 'tend to this mule-thief!" And there he stood a-shouting and a-vaporing[5] until Squire Meekins came out on the porch to see what all the racket was about.

"I want you to throw young Jess in the jailhouse, Squire!" Old man Gruber shook his fist in the air and stomped his bare feet. "I want you to haul him off to jail right now!"

"Now, now, Mr. Gruber —" began Squire Meekins in a kindly voice.

"He stole my mule!" shrieked old man Gruber. "He borrowed my mule and won't bring him back. He says something curious happened to him. 'T ain't so. He's stole him. He's a plain mule-thief and I want the law on him!"

Squire Meekins held up his hand. "Calm yourself, Mr. Gruber, calm yourself. Let's get at both sides of this dispute. What's this all about, young Jess, what's happened to Mr. Gruber's mule? You tell me now, straight out."

"Well, it happened like this, Squire Meekins. As I was a-riding along home the other day after Mr. Gruber lent me that mule, I saw some turkey buzzards sort of sailing around up there in the sky. They kept circling lower and lower. I never thought nothing about it until they were right over my head. It came to me then that it was mighty peculiar how close they'd come. I could have reached

---

[5]**a-vaporing:** fuming with rage.

446

up and grabbed one. All of a sudden one of 'em swooped down. He grabbed Mr. Gruber's mule by the tail. He upended that mule and heaved me off, right over the critter's head. Then he went sailing off with that mule, a-flying fast and a-crowing like a rooster!"

"Hold on there, young Jess," exclaimed Squire Meekins. "I've seen many a turkey buzzard in my life, but nary one that could crow like a rooster!"

"As I'm a-living, that buzzard went a-flying off with that mule," young Jess insisted. "And with all the other buzzards following after. Last I saw of 'em they were a-clearing the top of Old Baldy Mountain. I reckon those buzzards hadn't had anything to eat in the longest time and they was mortal hungry. By this time you can be sure they've eaten Mr. Gruber's mule and picked his bones."

"You hear that, Squire Meekins?" yelled old man Gruber. "He expects us to believe a gally-whopper[6] like that. He stands there and tells such buncombe[7] with a straight face!"

"If a bunch of hungry bedbugs can eat up a full-grown dog like what happened to my old Plott, then a bunch of hungry buzzards can fly off with a mule and pick his bones," said young Jess.

It all came out then, how old man Gruber had acted about old Plott.

---

[6]**gally-whopper** (găl′ē-wŏp′ər): tall tale; lie.
[7]**buncombe** (bŭng′kəm): original form of the word *bunk*, "lies."

"What's sauce for the goose is sauce for the gander," said young Jess. "If my dog comes back after being eat by bedbugs, then maybe the mule will come back after being eat by the buzzards."

And that's just how it turned out. Squire Meekins made old man Gruber fetch Plott from the woods where he'd hid him and then young Jess brought back the mule. Maybe you think old man Gruber learned a lesson from all this. But no, folks in the mountains say he's still as mean and stingy and cheating as ever.

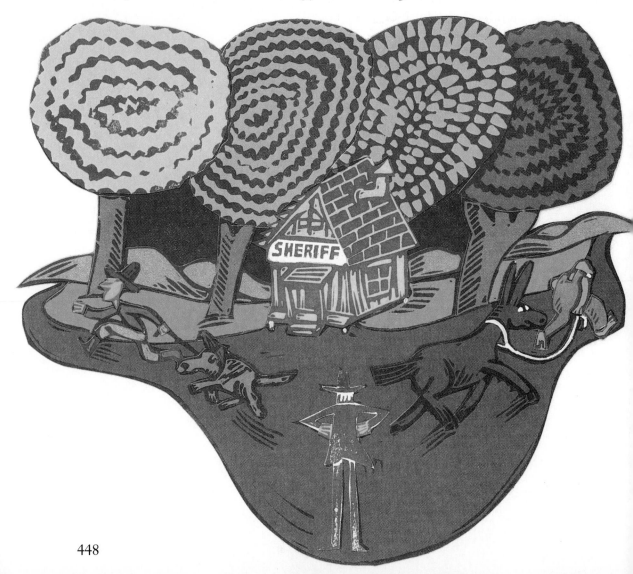

Responding to Old Plott

Thinking and Discussing

In what other ways could Jess have made Mr. Gruber reveal the truth about Old Plott? Do you think that the way Jess chose was the best way to do it? Why?

Why do you think Mr. Gruber does not learn a lesson from the events in this tale?

Choosing a Creative Response

Reading Aloud Which sentences and short passages capture the speech rhythms of the region especially well? With other students, take turns reading aloud these passages. You might also enjoy reading them to younger students.

Creating Your Own Activity Plan and complete your own activity in response to "Old Plott."

Thinking and Writing

Mr. Gruber's explanation of Old Plott's disappearance and Jess's explanation of the mule's fate are humorous and exaggerated. Such stories are often told in everyday life. Sometimes they form the basis of urban legends. Think of similar exaggerated stories that you've heard. Choose your favorite, and write a brief retelling of it, adding your own personal touches. Eventually, you may want to make a collection of these stories to share with your classmates.

THE MOON VALLEY

BY HELEN CHETIN

Neyroom is the wise and brave chief of an African tribe. He has been advised by the Scavenger Wives, strange and ugly old women who live in the trees deep in the forest, to search for a girl with a jewel in her head in the mythical land of Moon Valley. The other villagers fear and mistrust the Scavenger Wives because they believe that these women are witches who make magic medicines and cast spells. But Neyroom has realized their wisdom, and he has come to trust them. He follows their advice and begins to plan for the journey to Moon Valley.

In answer to his question, "Where is the Moon Valley?" Neyroom received many answers.

"Over the hills," Omuga said.

"Where you find it, it is," Zorkma said.

Only Bundar, who had traveled widely, made any sense to Neyroom. "I was there long ago," he said. "It is across a wide river, and you must lose your way before you find it. I think the people live in stone houses, but I am not sure. After one leaves the Moon Valley — which is not easy — he forgets everything about it."

Neyroom was so curious now that he knew he must find the Moon Valley. At his leave-taking, all the men came forward to see him depart. The elders of the village came, too, and no one asked why he was going. They seemed to understand that a chief must do things other men do not think of doing.

For many days Neyroom crossed the grasslands. Then he entered country he had never seen before. The sky seemed lower, and at night it was so purple and close that he would reach out, put his hand into it, and try to stir the stars about.

When Neyroom came to a wide, fast-flowing river, he was sure he would find the Moon Valley on the other side of it. He built a raft of logs bound firmly with vines. He cut and trimmed two long poles for steering, but as soon as he was on the water, he lost the poles — it was as if hands beneath the water pulled the poles from him. He was left helpless to float down the fast-running river. At night he heard the waters singing:

HO, NEYROOM, WHERE DO YOU GO?
WE KNOW, WE KNOW!
NEYROOM, WHAT WILL YOU DO THERE?
BEWARE! BEWARE!

The singing reminded him of the Scavenger Wives, and he wished it were those good women instead of river demons.

On the next night he heard a great thundering in the river ahead. As the noise grew louder, he feared he was approaching a waterfall, but there was nothing for him to do except hang onto the raft. Suddenly he felt himself lifted out of the water, then thrown back into the spray and foam. Down, down he fell until the night-black water closed over his head and he remembered nothing more.

When Neyroom awoke, he was lying face down on soft sand surrounded by thick reeds and rushes. First he heard the muted roar of a distant waterfall, and then he heard the tinkling sound of women's laughter. He guessed they were bathing nearby, for he could hear them splashing water, singing and calling one another.

When he heard someone coming, he closed his eyes.

"Oooo! Come, come!" he heard a girl's voice call. Soon he sensed that her companions were standing all around him.

"Is he dead?" one asked.

"Look at the mark on his back. He is either a king or a devil."

"Where did he come from?"

Then, very close to his ear, he heard the first voice whisper, "Are you alive, man?"

Neyroom opened his eyes to see a maiden more beautiful than any he had ever seen. "Yes," he answered, "but are you?"

"Eeee . . . !" she cried, startled and sitting back on her heels.

"Oooo! Oooo!" squealed the others, turning to run, yet calling back over their shoulders, "Run, Tawmoon! It's a river devil. Tawmoon, hurry!"

They were gone before Neyroom could stop them. "Tawmoon . . ." he called softly. "Tawmoon."

He stood up and looked over the rushes and reeds, but there was no sign of the maidens. Then Neyroom saw the circle of high snow-capped mountains and, in their cliffs, strange houses carved in the rock. This, he decided, must be the Moon Valley.

He crossed the rocky valley floor toward the cliff houses, and when he came quite near, he saw a huge arch — a gate, in fact. However, there was no wall on either side of it — just a gate that was being opened by men who wore long, lustrous white skirts.

Even from a distance, he could see the sparkle of jeweled necklaces on their bare brown chests. By the time he reached the gate, many men had gathered there.

Neyroom felt no fear as he approached them. Was it because they carried no weapons, he wondered. When he stood before them, they opened their hands as if they wished him to know they concealed nothing. He also opened his hands, and then their leader, an old man whose white beard grew out of a face that looked like dark, oiled leather, said, "Welcome. Come in peace."

"I come in peace," Neyroom said. "Is this the Moon Valley?"

"Yes. You came through the waterfall, which is the only way to enter the valley."

"How shall I leave?" Neyroom asked.

"You can never leave," the man replied, "but do not feel sorrow. You see, we have a gate, but no walls and no weapons. We live without war. Come, let me show you how we flourish."

What Neyroom saw in the days that followed astounded him. The cone-shaped houses carved in the rock were decorated inside with wondrous paintings. People ate from plates of gold, and whereas the men wore white, the women dressed in brilliant colors. Each young girl wore around her forehead a band embroidered with precious gems. The women were almost as beautiful as the

one called Tawmoon. Neyroom looked everywhere for her, but he never saw her.

Behind the houses, deep in the rocks, were tunnels from which miners took the sparkling stones. Never had Neyroom seen a place so rich, a town so clean, or a people so gentle. No one seemed ever to be sick. Clouds never darkened the sky, and angry voices were never heard. Delicate stringed instruments made beautiful music. But where, Neyroom wondered, was the beautiful Tawmoon?

One night he awakened to hear a scratching at the door. "Who is there?" he asked.

"I am Tawmoon," the voice replied.

"Come in, then," Neyroom said.

"I cannot," she replied.

"Tawmoon," he pleaded, "I have looked everywhere for you. How can I get to know you?"

"Ask to see where the word is kept," she said.

"The word? What does that mean?" he asked, but there was no answer, and he knew she had vanished into the night.

Neyroom was so excited that he could not go back to sleep. The next morning, first thing, he went to the great one with the white beard. He bowed down and said, "Tell me, is there something that I have done that makes you distrust me?"

"No," said the one with the beard. "Why do you ask?"

"You have shown me where you keep your gold and your jewels, how you weave rich cloths and rugs, how you carve stone and paint rock, yet there are some things you do not show me. If you should come to my country, this would not be so."

"What is it we have not shown you?" asked the great bearded one.

"Where you keep the word," Neyroom said.

"Ah . . . but it would have no meaning for you if you cannot read it or write it."

"Perhaps. But I would like to see where it is kept."

The great one clapped his hands. When men came forward, he ordered that Neyroom be shown the place of the word. Neyroom followed the men through many tunnels until they came to a great vaulted room where maidens stood in attendance. On a raised dais in the center sat the beautiful Tawmoon. She was dressed in white, and in the center of her forehead she wore a large, brilliant jewel that nearly blinded Neyroom with its light.

"Tell me," he said to her, "what it means to be the keeper of the word?"

"Everything we know is written on parchment scrolls," Tawmoon explained. "All recipes for foods and paints and medicines, all ways to make tools and metals and how to use them, all notes of music and lines of verse. When one wishes to learn something, he comes here, and we bring forth the scroll that he desires."

"But who writes it?" Neyroom asked. "And how does one learn to read it?"

"Our children learn to read and write when they are small. Whoever knows a thing well writes it down. Whoever wishes to learn it reads it."

"And you?" Neyroom persisted, aware that he was being told about a kind of miracle. "Do you know how to read the word and write it?"

"Yes, Neyroom, I know," she replied.

As Neyroom listened to the beautiful Tawmoon, he saw that the jewel that sparkled on her forehead was no brighter than her eyes. She was a beauty worthy of any great king, yet Neyroom felt humbled before her because she could both write words and read them while he could do neither. He bowed his head, ashamed before the beautiful Tawmoon.

"What is the matter, Neyroom?" she asked.

"I feel poor before you," he said.

456

Tawmoon took his hands in hers and said, "Each of us learns a thing at the time and place he has need of it. This is a new time for you, and if you wish, I shall be your teacher."

At first Neyroom felt too proud to allow this young girl to be his teacher, but then he remembered that everyone important in his life had been some kind of teacher to him — his parents, Grandfather Mawkoom, Omuga, Bundar, the Scavenger Wives, and all the others. If he could learn from them about men and stars, birds and beasts, forest and fish, then he knew he could learn the words, too.

So Neyroom agreed to be Tawmoon's pupil. In the days that followed, he listened well to what she said, trying to hide in his heart how much he loved her. The great bearded one came and listened and nodded with pleasure.

One day Tawmoon said, "Neyroom, soon you have only to go on reading for yourself. Soon there will be nothing more for me to teach you."

"When that happens," he said, "I shall return to my people."

"Oh, Neyroom," Tawmoon cried, tears coming to her eyes, "then I will never admit it because I could not bear to have you leave."

Astounded that she thought he could leave without her, he blurted out, "But you are coming with me! I plan to make you my wife."

"Oh, Neyroom," she said, pressing her hands against her cheeks, "nothing would please me more, but I can never leave the Moon Valley. Neither, alas, can you."

"We can and will," he replied, quite confident of himself. Then he reached up and tugged playfully at her ears. "You will like my people. They do not eat from gold plates, but they are quick to laugh with each other and are proud of the things they do well. They will welcome you, and by and by you will teach our children, yours and mine, all about the word, and they in turn will teach theirs until all in the land know how to read and write."

Tawmoon smiled and said, "The way you say it makes me believe it will be so."

Soon thereafter Neyroom went to the great bearded one and explained how it was written in the stars that he find the Moon Valley and the one with the jewel in her head. Then he explained how his people needed him and that he needed Tawmoon.

"For you who have so much," Neyroom said, "you should not mind sharing with the outside world."

The old one said he would speak with the wise men. After many days he called Neyroom and Tawmoon before the men of Moon Valley. He said it was agreed that the two of them could leave. No one, the old man said, should remain anywhere against his will.

"You will leave all Moon Valley possessions behind," he said, and when Tawmoon raised her hand to the jewel on her forehead, the old one said, "Inside your head is a jewel far brighter than that stone. The inner light you will carry with you always."

Then he called for a gold goblet of dark red wine. He said they should share the cup as they would share their lives, equally and together.

Neyroom and Tawmoon drank from the goblet and almost at once fell into a deep sleep. When they awoke, they were in a dark woods. Neyroom found his weapons beside him. He assured Tawmoon that by following the stars he could find his people.

The sun crossed the sky many times before they left the woods. Strange, wild beasts frightened Tawmoon, but she saw that Neyroom was fearless. He was also wise and knew how to hunt and fish for their food, how to light fires and cook, how to guard Tawmoon against dangers. He became her teacher, and she loved him greatly and was happy she had joined her life to his.

When they reached the grasslands, Neyroom's people came to meet them. Omuga said that word of their coming had carried on the wind, but Neyroom suspected the Scavenger Wives had ways of knowing.

All the tribesmen and their wives, all the braves and the maidens, showed Tawmoon that they were pleased she had come to live among them. The children carried flowers to Tawmoon as the procession went toward the center of the village. There, facing the green, grassy place, was a new house, and Neyroom saw by the pleased faces of his tribesmen that the house had been built for him. On the doorstep were three presents for Tawmoon: a bag of salt for a long life, a bag of sugar for a sweet life, and a basketful of eggs for many children.

The Moon Valley

THINKING AND DISCUSSING

What do Tawmoon and Neyroom learn from each other?

How is this modern tale like the earlier tales that were passed down from generation to generation?

CHOOSING A CREATIVE RESPONSE

Designing Costumes If you were to make a play out of "The Moon Valley," you would need to design costumes for the characters. Start by rereading the passages that describe the character's clothing. Then let your imagination add the details. Draw your designs and share them with your group.

Foretelling the Future People from Neyroom's village thought that the Scavenger Wives could foretell the future. If Neyroom were to go with Tawmoon to see the Scavenger Wives after their return, what would these women predict? Write a scene about that conversation.

Creating Your Own Activity Plan and complete your own activity in response to "The Moon Valley."

Organizing a Storytellers' Fair Suppose that you wanted to organize a fair at which storytellers from around the world might gather to tell their folktales. Here are some ideas and suggestions that you might like to develop.

- Research a tale, its background and its development into its present form. Make a display showing how the tale developed.
- Invite people from different parts of the world to share their own cultures' stories with you.
- Make a display showing how modern tales such as "The Moon Valley," "Batman," or "E.T." are similar to traditional folktales.
- Tape-record or videotape classmates telling stories.

You might eventually want to hold a Storytellers' Fair so that the rest of the school, parents, teachers, and friends can join in your fun and in your discoveries about folktales from yesterday and today.

Researching Folktales There are many known versions of the same folktales. The Brothers Grimm retold "Catherine, Sly Country Lass" as "The Clever Farmer's Daughter."

If you have the means of researching folktales in the library or in other sources, find versions of the same tale in different cultures. Show your findings to your class. You might even perform each story by having a different storyteller present each version.

Retelling a Folktale Traditional folktales have come down from generation to generation, changing each time they are retold. The stories maintain their universal themes, but their setting, characters, and storytelling tone change from one telling to the next.

If you were to retell one of the stories you have read here to your friends, which one would you choose? Would you make any changes in the stories? What would they be? With your group, discuss the things you would like changed as well as the things you would leave untouched.

Retell your own version of the story, trying to capture the sound and the tone of a storyteller in your performance.

Recreating the Oral Tradition With a group of classmates, demonstrate the process of change and development that occurs with the stories passed on in the oral tradition. Have one person whisper a short, simple story to another. Continue having each person whisper the story to the next, until everyone has had a turn. The last person should tell aloud the final version of the story. Discuss the changes that the story underwent through its various retellings. Try to determine where the changes occurred.

Genevieve Barlow was born in 1910 in Gardena, California. Her interest in other languages and countries has led to her varied career as a teacher of English and Spanish, translator for the Red Cross in Puerto Rico, speaker at international education conventions, and writer of several volumes of folktales from Latin America and from around the world.

Italo Calvino was born in Cuba in 1923 but grew up in Italy. *Italian Folktales* is one of Calvino's many collections of traditional folklore. He died in 1985.

Helen Chetin was born in 1922 and attended the University of Texas. She is currently an editor at a children's book publishing firm, and continues to write, mostly for adults. Her first book, *Tales from an African Drum*, was selected for the Child Study Association book list.

Ellis Credle was born in 1902 in North Carolina. She was brought up on the North Carolina coast and later lived in the Blue Ridge Mountains. *Down, Down the Mountain* includes tales and sayings of the mountain people. *Tall Tales from the High Hills* is a continuation of Credle's interest in the mountain country of Appalachia.

ichard Erdoes was born in 1912 in Vienna, Austria, but has lived most of his life in the United States. He has had a career as a freelance artist, illustrator, muralist, photographer, writer, and maker of educational films.

illiam J. Faulkner came from South Carolina, where as a boy he lived on a small farm with his widowed mother. His love for storytelling stems from his friendship with a former slave named Simon Brown, who told him "stories out of his imagination or the imagination of others he'd heard around the campfire in the slave quarters years ago." In *The Days When the Animals Talked*, Faulkner faithfully recorded the old stories that Simon Brown had told him.

harles J. Finger was born in England in 1869, but he came to America and became an American citizen as a young man. In 1925, he was awarded the Newbery Medal for *Tales from Silver Lands*, a collection of stories he had learned from the Indians of South America. Finger continued to contribute greatly to the literature for young people until his death in 1941.

lizabeth Jamison Hodges was born in Atlanta, Georgia. She remembers enjoying writing stories and poems as a child, and she was especially interested in English composition in school. She is the author of several books, including *The Three Princes of Serendip*, *Serendipity Tales*, *Free as a Frog*, and *A Song for Gilgamesh*.

TALES AND MORE TALES

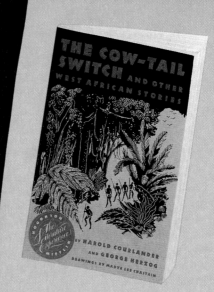

The Cow-Tail Switch, and Other West African Stories

The seventeen stories in this collection are full of laughter, with tricks played by clever and scheming animals and people. The authors gathered the tales on their trips to West Africa. By Harold Courlander and George Herzog (Houghton, 1991; Holt, 1947, 1987)

Sweet and Sour: Tales from China

Different periods in Chinese history are represented in unusual and timeless tales. Retold by Carol Kendall and Yao-wen Li (Clarion, 1979)

The Woman in the Moon and Other Tales of Forgotten Heroines

These stories from many different countries all feature courageous, strong, and clever women, such as the little-known Lone Star, Caterina the Wise, and Gulnara the Tartar Warrior. By James Riordan (Dial, 1985)

Womenfolk and Fairy Tales

This lively collection of tales from diverse cultures portrays girls and women as active, capable people in a variety of situations and roles. Edited by Rosemary Minard (Houghton, 1975)

They Dance in the Sky: Native American Star Myths

Long Ago, storytellers of North American Indian nations studied the night sky and created these exciting tales about the stars and constellations. By Jean Guard Monroe and Ray A. Williamson (Houghton, 1987)

The People Could Fly: American Black Folktales

Animal, fantasy, and supernatural stories, as well as slave tales of freedom, make up a collection by a well-known, award-winning author. Retold by Virginia Hamilton (Knopf, 1985)

NOVEL

BOOK 7

The Summer of the Swans

By
Betsy Byars

Illustrated by
Mark O'Neill

Sara Godfrey was lying on the bed tying a kerchief on the dog, Boysie. "Hold your chin up, Boysie, will you?" she said as she braced herself on one elbow. The dog was old, slept all the time, and he was lying on his side with his eyes closed while she lifted his head and tied the scarf.

Her sister Wanda was sitting at the dressing table combing her hair. Wanda said, "Why don't you leave Boysie alone?"

"There's nothing else to do," Sara answered without looking up. "You want to see a show?"

"Not particularly."

"It's called 'The Many Faces of Boysie.'"

"Now I know I don't want to see it."

Sara held up the dog with the kerchief neatly tied beneath his chin and said, "The first face of Boysie, proudly presented for your entertainment and amusement, is the Russian Peasant Woman. Taaaaaa-daaaaaa!"

"Leave the dog alone."

"He likes to be in shows, don't you, Boysie?" She untied the scarf, refolded it and set it carefully on top of the dog's head. "And now for the second face of Boysie, we travel half-way around the world to the mysterious East, where we see Boysie the Inscrutable Hindu. Taaaaaaa-daaaaaa!"

With a sigh Wanda turned and looked at the dog. "That's pathetic. In people's age that dog is eighty-four years old." She shook a can of hair spray and sprayed her hair. "And besides, that's my good scarf."

"Oh, all right." Sara fell back heavily against the pillow. "I can't do anything around here."

"Well, if it's going to make you that miserable, I'll watch the show."

"I don't want to do it any more. It's no fun now. This place smells like a perfume factory." She put the scarf over her face and stared up through the thin blue material. Beside her, Boysie lay back down and curled himself into a ball. They lay without moving for a moment and then Sara sat up on the bed and looked down at her long, lanky legs. She said, "I have the biggest feet in my school."

"Honestly, Sara, I hope you are not going to start listing all the millions of things wrong with you because I just don't want to hear it again."

"Well, it's the truth about my feet. One time in Phys Ed the boys started throwing the girls' sneakers around and Bull Durham got my sneakers and put them on and they fit perfectly! How do you think it feels to wear the same size shoe as Bull Durham?"

"People don't notice things like that."

"Huh!"

"No, they don't. I have perfectly terrible hands — look at my fingers — only I don't go around all the time saying, 'Everybody, look at my stubby fingers, I have stubby fingers, everybody,' to *make* people notice. You should just ignore things that are wrong with you. The truth is everyone else is so worried about what's wrong with *them* that —"

"It is very difficult to ignore the fact that you have huge feet when Bull Durham is dancing all over the gym in your shoes. They were not stretched the tiniest little bit when he took them off either."

"You wear the same size shoe as Jackie Kennedy Onassis if that makes you feel any better."

"How do you know?"

"Because one time when she was going into an Indian temple she had to leave her shoes outside and some reporter looked in them to see what size they were." She leaned close to the mirror and looked at her teeth.

"Her feet *look* littler."

"That's because she doesn't wear orange sneakers."

"I like my orange sneakers." Sara sat on the edge of the bed, slipped her feet into the shoes, and held them up. "What's wrong with them?"

"Nothing, except that when you want to hide something, you don't go painting it orange. I've got to go. Frank's coming."

She went out the door and Sara could hear her crossing into the kitchen. Sara lay back on the bed, her head next to Boysie. She looked at the sleeping dog, then covered her face with her hands and began to cry noisily.

"Oh, Boysie, Boysie, I'm crying," she wailed. Years ago, when Boysie was a young dog, he could not bear to hear anyone cry. Sara had only to pretend she was crying and Boysie would come running. He would whine and dig at her with his paws and lick her hands until she stopped. Now he lay with his eyes closed.

"Boysie, I'm crying," she said again. "I'm really crying this time. Boysie doesn't love me."

The dog shifted uneasily without opening his eyes.

"Boysie, Boysie, I'm crying, I'm so sad, Boysie," she wailed, then stopped and sat up abruptly. "You don't care about anybody, do you, Boysie? A person could cry herself to death these days and you wouldn't care."

She got up and left the room. In the hall she heard the tapping noise of Boysie's feet behind her and she said without looking at him, "I don't want you now, Boysie. Go on back in the bedroom. Go on." She went a few steps farther and, when he continued to follow her, turned and looked at him. "In case you are confused, Boysie, a dog is supposed to comfort people and run up and nuzzle them and make them feel better. All you want to do is lie on soft things and hide bones in the house because you are too lazy to go outside. Just go on back in the bedroom."

She started into the kitchen, still followed by Boysie, who could not bear to be left alone, then heard her aunt and Wanda arguing, changed her mind, and went out onto the porch.

Behind her, Boysie scratched at the door and she let him out. "Now quit following me."

Her brother Charlie was sitting on the top step and Sara sat down beside him. She held out her feet, looked at them, and said, "I like my orange sneakers, don't you, Charlie?"

He did not answer. He had been eating a lollipop and the stick had come off and now he was trying to put it back into the red candy. He had been trying for so long that the stick was bent.

"Here," she said, "I'll do it for you." She put the stick in and handed it to him. "Now be careful with it."

She sat without speaking for a moment, then she looked down at her feet and said, "I hate these orange sneakers. I just *hate* them." She leaned back against the porch railing so she wouldn't have to see them and said, "Charlie, I'll tell you something. This has been the worst summer of my life."

She did not know exactly why this was true. She was doing the same things she had done last summer — walk to the Dairy Queen with her friend Mary, baby-sit for Mrs. Hodges, watch television — and yet everything was different. It was as if her life was a huge kaleidoscope, and the kaleidoscope had been turned and now everything was changed. The same stones, shaken, no longer made the same design.

But it was not only one different design, one change; it was a hundred. She could never be really sure of anything this summer. One moment she was happy, and the next, for no reason, she was miserable. An hour ago she had loved her sneakers; now she detested them.

"Charlie, I'll tell you what this awful summer's been like. You remember when that finky Jim Wilson got you on the seesaw, remember that? And he kept bouncing you up and down and then he'd keep you up in the air for a real long time and then he'd drop you down real sudden, and you couldn't get off and you thought you never would? Up and down, up and down, for the rest of your life? Well, that's what this summer's been like for me."

He held out the candy and the stick to her.

"Not again!" She took it from him. "This piece of candy is so gross that I don't even want to touch it, if you want to know the truth." She put the stick back in and handed it to him. "Now if it comes off again — and I mean this, Charlie Godfrey — I'm throwing the candy away."

Charlie looked at the empty sucker stick, reached into his mouth, took out the candy, and held them together in his hand. Sara had said she would throw the candy away if this happened again and so he closed his fist tightly and looked away from her.

Slowly he began to shuffle his feet back and forth on the step. He had done this so many times over the years that two grooves had been worn into the boards. It was a nervous habit that showed he was concerned about something, and Sara recognized it at once.

"All right, Charlie," she said wearily. "Where's your sucker?"

He began to shake his head slowly from side to side. His eyes were squeezed shut.

"I'm not going to take it away from you. I'm going to fix it one more time."

He was unwilling to trust her and continued to shake his head. The movement was steady and mechanical, as if it would continue forever, and she watched him for a moment.

Then, with a sigh, she lifted his hand and attempted to pry his fingers loose. "Honestly, Charlie, you're holding onto this grubby piece of candy like it was a crown jewel or something. Now, let go." He opened his eyes and watched while she took the candy from him and put the stick in. The stick was now bent almost double, and she held it out to him carefully.

"There."

He took the sucker and held it without putting it into his mouth, still troubled by the unsteadiness of the bent stick. Sara looked down at her hands and began to pull at a broken fingernail. There was something similar about them in that moment, the same oval face, round brown eyes, brown hair hanging over the forehead, freckles on the nose. Then Charlie glanced up and the illusion was broken.

Still holding his sucker, he looked across the yard and saw the tent he had made over the clothesline that morning. He had taken an old white blanket out into the yard, hung it over the low clothesline, and then got under it. He had sat there with the blanket blowing against him until

Sara came out and said, "Charlie, you have to fasten the ends down, like this. It isn't a tent if it's just hanging in the wind."

He had thought there was something wrong. He waited beneath the blanket until she came back with some clothespins and hammered them into the hard earth, fastening the edges of the blanket to the ground. "Now, *that's* a tent."

The tent had pleased him. The warmth of the sun coming through the thin cotton blanket, the shadows of the trees moving overhead had made him drowsy and comfortable and now he wanted to be back in the tent.

Sara had started talking about the summer again, but he did not listen. He could tell from the tone of her voice that she was not really talking to him at all. He got up slowly and began to walk across the yard toward the tent.

Sara watched him as he walked, a small figure for his ten years, wearing faded blue jeans and a striped knit shirt that was stretched out of shape. He was holding the sucker in front of him as if it were a candle that might go out at any moment.

Sara said, "Don't drop that candy in the grass now or it's really going to be lost."

She watched while he bent, crawled into the tent, and sat down. The sun was behind the tent now and she could see his silhouette. Carefully he put the sucker back into his mouth.

Then Sara lay back on the hard boards of the porch and looked up at the ceiling.

In the house Wanda and Aunt Willie were still arguing. Sara could hear every word even out on the porch. Aunt Willie, who had been taking care of them since the death of their mother six years ago, was saying loudly, "No, not on a motorcycle. No motorcycle!"

Sara grimaced. It was not only the loudness of Aunt Willie's voice that she disliked. It was everything — the way she bossed them, the way she never really listened, the way she never cared what she said. She had once announced loud enough for everyone in Carter's Drugstore to hear that Sara needed a good dose of magnesia.

"It isn't a motorcycle, it's a motor *scooter*." Wanda was speaking patiently, as if to a small child. "They're practically like bicycles."

"No."

"All I want to do is to ride one half mile on this perfectly safe motor scooter —"

"No. It's absolutely and positively no. No!"

"Frank is very careful. He has never had even the tiniest accident."

No answer.

"Aunt Willie, it is perfectly safe. He takes his mother to the grocery store on it. Anyway, I am old enough to go without permission and I wish you'd realize it. I am nineteen years old."

No answer. Sara knew that Aunt Willie would be standing by the sink shaking her head emphatically from side to side.

"Aunt Willie, he's going to be here any minute. He's coming all the way over here just to drive me to the lake to see the swans."

"You don't care *that* for seeing those swans."

"I do too. I love birds."

"All right then, those swans have been on the lake three days, and not once have you gone over to see them. Now all of a sudden you *have* to go, can't wait one minute to get on this devil motorcycle and see those swans."

"For your information, I have been dying to see them, only this is my first chance." She went out of the kitchen and pulled the swinging door shut behind her. "And I'm going," she said over her shoulder.

Wanda came out of the house, slammed the screen door, stepped over Boysie, and sat by Sara on the top step. "She never wants anyone to have any fun."

"I know."

"She makes me so mad. All I want to do is just ride down to see the swans on Frank's motor scooter." She looked at Sara, then broke off and said, "Where did Charlie go?"

"He's over there in his tent."

"I see him now. I wish Frank would hurry up and get here before Aunt Willie comes out." She stood, looked down the street, and sat back on the steps. "Did I tell you what that boy in my psychology class last year said about Charlie?"

Sara straightened. "What boy?"

"This boy Arnold Hampton, in my psychology class. We were discussing children who —"

"You mean you talk about Charlie to perfect strangers? To your class? I think that's awful." She put her feet into the two grooves worn in the steps by Charlie. "What do you say? 'Let me tell you all about my retarded brother — it's so interesting'?" It was the first time in her life that she had used the term "retarded" in connection with her brother, and she looked quickly away from the figure in the white tent. Her face felt suddenly hot and she snapped a leaf from the rhododendron bush by the steps and held it against her forehead.

"No, I don't say that. Honestly, Sara, you —"

"And then do you say, 'And while I'm telling you about my retarded brother, I'll also tell you about my real hung-up sister'?" She moved the leaf to her lips and blew against it angrily.

"No, I don't say that because you're not all that fascinating, if you want to know the truth. Anyway, Arnold Hampton's father happens to be a pediatrician and Arnold is sincerely interested in working with boys like Charlie. He is even helping start a camp which Charlie may get to go to next summer, and all because I talked to him in my psychology class." She sighed. "You're impossible, you know that? I can't imagine why I even try to tell you anything."

"Well, Charlie's our problem."

"He's everybody's. There is no — Oh, here comes Frank." She broke off and got to her feet. "Tell Aunt Willie I'll be home later."

She started quickly down the walk, waving to the boy who was making his way slowly up the street on a green motor scooter.

"Wait, wait, you wait." Aunt Willie came onto the porch drying her hands on a dish towel. She stood at the top of the steps until Frank, a thin boy with red hair, brought the motor scooter to a stop. As he kicked down the stand she called out, "Frank, listen, save yourself some steps. Wanda's not going anywhere on that motorcycle."

"Aw, Aunt Willie," Frank said. He opened the gate and came slowly up the walk. "All we're going to do is go down to the lake. We don't even have to get on the highway for that."

"No motorcycles," she said. "You go break your neck if you want to. That's not my business. Wanda, left in my care, is not going to break her neck on any motorcycle."

"Nobody's going to break his neck. We're just going to have a very uneventful ride down the road to the lake. Then we're going to turn around and have a very uneventful ride back."

"No."

"I tell you what," Frank said. "I'll make a deal with you."

"What deal?"

"Have you ever been on a motor scooter?"

"Me? I never even rode on a bicycle."

"Try it. Come on. I'll ride you down to the Tennents' house and back. Then if you think it's not safe, you say to me, 'Frank, it's not safe,' and I'll take my motor scooter and ride off into the sunset."

She hesitated. There was something about a ride that appealed to her.

Sara said against the rhododendron leaf, "I don't think you ought to. You're too old to be riding up and down the street on a motor scooter."

She knew instantly she had said the wrong thing, for at once Aunt Willie turned to her angrily. "Too old!" She faced Sara with indignation. "I am barely forty years old. May I grow a beard if I'm not." She stepped closer, her voice rising. "Who says I'm so old?" She held the dish towel in front of her, like a matador taunting a bull. The dish towel flicked the air once.

"Nobody said anything," Sara said wearily. She threw the leaf down and brushed it off the steps with her foot.

"Then where did all this talk about my age come from, I'd like to know?"

"Anyway," Frank interrupted, "you're not too old to ride a motor scooter."

"I'll do it." She threw the dish towel across the chair and went down the steps. "I may break my neck but I'll do it."

"Hold on tight, Aunt Willie," Wanda called.

"Hold on! Listen, my hands never held on to anything the way I'm going to hold on to this motorcycle." She laughed, then said to Frank, "I never rode on one of these before, believe me."

"It's just like a motorized baby carriage, Aunt Willie."

"Huh!"

"This ought to be good," Wanda said. She called, "Hey, Charlie," waited until he looked out from the tent, and then said, "Watch Aunt Willie. She's going to ride the motor scooter."

Charlie watched Aunt Willie settle herself sidesaddle on the back of the scooter.

"Ready?" Frank asked.

"I'm as ready as I'll ever be, believe me, go on, go on."

Her words rose into a piercing scream as Frank moved the scooter forward, turned, and then started down the hill. Her scream, shrill as a bird's cry, hung in the still air. "Frank, Frank, Frank, Frankeeeeee!"

At the first cry Charlie staggered to his feet, staring in alarm at Aunt Willie disappearing down the hill. He pulled on one side of the tent as he got to his feet, causing the other to snap loose at the ground and hang limp from the line. He stumbled, then regained his balance.

Wanda saw him and said, "It's all right, Charlie, she's having a good time. She *likes* it. It's all right." She crossed the yard, took him by the hand, and led him to the steps. "What have you got all over yourself?"

"It's a gross red sucker," Sara said. "It's all over me too."

480

"Come on over to the spigot and let me wash your hands. See, Aunt Willie's coming back now."

In front of the Tennents' house Frank was swinging the scooter around, pivoting on one foot, and Aunt Willie stopped screaming long enough to call to the Tennents, "Bernie, Midge, look who's on a motorcycle!" Then she began screaming again as Frank started the uphill climb. As they came to a stop Aunt Willie's cries changed to laughter. "Huh, old woman, am I! Old woman!" Still laughing, she stepped off the scooter.

"You're all right, Aunt Willie," Frank said.

Sensing a moment of advantage, Wanda moved down the walk. She was shaking the water from her hands. "So can I go, Aunt Willie?"

"Oh, go on, go on," she said, half laughing, half scolding. "It's your own neck. Go on, break your own neck if you want to."

"It's not her neck you have to worry about, it's my arms," Frank said. "Honest, Aunt Willie, there's not a drop of blood circulating in them."

"Oh, go on, go on with you."

"Come on, Little One," Frank said to Wanda.

Aunt Willie came and stood by Sara, and they watched Wanda climb on the back of the motor scooter. As Wanda and Frank drove off, Aunt Willie laughed again and said, "Next thing, *you'll* be going off with some boy on a motorcycle."

Sara had been smiling, but at once she stopped and looked down at her hands. "I don't think you have to worry about that."

"Huh! It will happen, you'll see. You'll be just like Wanda. You'll be —"

"Don't you see that I'm nothing like Wanda at all?" She sat down abruptly and put her lips against her knees. "We are so different. Wanda is a hundred times prettier than I am."

"You are just alike, you two. Sometimes in the kitchen I hear you and I think I'm hearing Wanda. That's how alike you are. May my ears fall off if I can hear the difference."

"Maybe our *voices* are alike, but that's all. I can make my voice sound like a hundred different people. Listen to this and guess who it is. 'N–B–C! Beautiful downtown Burbank.'"

"I'm not in the mood for a guessing game. I'm in the mood to get back to our original conversation. It's not how you look that's important, let me tell you. I had a sister so beautiful you wouldn't believe it."

"Who?"

"Frances, that's who."

"She wasn't all that beautiful. I've seen her and —"

"When she was young she was. So beautiful you wouldn't believe it, but such a devil, and —"

"It is *too* important how you look. Parents are always saying it's not how you look that counts. I've heard that all my life. It doesn't matter how you look. It doesn't matter how you look. Huh! If you want to find out how much it matters, just let your hair get too long or put on too much eye makeup and listen to the screams." She got up abruptly and said, "I think I'll walk over and see the swans myself."

"Well, I have not finished with this conversation yet, young lady."

Sara turned and looked at Aunt Willie, waited with her hands jammed into her back pockets.

"Oh, never mind," Aunt Willie said, picking up her dish towel and shaking it. "I might as well hold a conversation with this towel as with you when you get that look on your face. Go on and see the swans." She broke off. "Hey, Charlie, you want to go with Sara to see the swans?"

"He'll get too tired," Sara said.

"So walk slow."

"I never get to do anything by myself. I have to take him everywhere. I have him all day and Wanda all night. In all this whole house I have one drawer to myself. *One drawer.*"

"Get up, Charlie. Sara's going to take you to see the swans."

Sara looked down into his eyes and said, "Oh, come on," and drew him to his feet.

"Wait, there's some bread from supper." Aunt Willie ran into the house and came back with four rolls. "Take them. Here. Let Charlie feed the swans."

"Well, come on, Charlie, or it's going to be dark before we get there."

"Don't you rush him along, hear me, Sara?"

"I won't."

Holding Sara's hand, Charlie went slowly down the walk. He hesitated at the gate and then moved with her onto the sidewalk. As they walked down the hill, his feet made a continuous scratching sound on the concrete.

When they were out of earshot Sara said, "Aunt Willie thinks she knows everything. I get so sick of hearing how I am exactly like Wanda when Wanda is beautiful. I think she's just beautiful. If I could look like anyone in the world, I would want to look like her." She kicked at some high grass by the sidewalk. "And it does too matter how you look, I can tell you that." She walked ahead angrily for a few steps, then waited for Charlie and took his hand again.

"I think how you look is the most important thing in the world. If you *look* cute, you *are* cute; if you *look* smart, you *are* smart, and if you don't look like anything, then you aren't anything.

"I wrote a theme on that one time in school, about looks being the most important thing in the world, and I got a D — a *D*! Which is a terrible grade.

"After class the teacher called me up and told me the same old business about looks not being important, and how some of the ugliest people in the world were the smartest and kindest and cleverest."

They walked past the Tennents' house just as someone inside turned on the television, and they heard Eddie Albert singing, "Greeeeeeen acres is —" before it was turned down. Charlie paused a moment, recognizing the beginning of one of his favorite programs, looked up at Sara, and waited.

"Come on," Sara said. "And then there was this girl in my English class named Thelma Louise and she wrote a paper entitled 'Making People Happy' and she got an A. An *A*! Which is as good as you can get. It was sickening. Thelma Louise is a beautiful girl with blond hair and naturally curly eyelashes, so what does she know? Anyway, one time Hazel went over to Thelma Louise's, and she said the rug was worn thin in front of the mirror in Thelma Louise's room because Thelma Louise stood there all the time watching herself."

She sighed and continued to walk. Most of the houses were set close together as if huddled for safety, and on either side of the houses the West Virginia hills rose, black now in the early evening shadows. The hills were as they had been for hundreds of years, rugged forest land, except that strip mining had begun on the hills to the north, and the trees and earth had been hacked away, leaving unnatural cliffs of pale washed earth.

Sara paused. They were now in front of Mary Weicek's house and she said, "Stop a minute. I've got to speak to Mary." She could hear Mary's record player, and she longed to be up in Mary's room, leaning back against the pink dotted bedspread listening to Mary's endless collection of records. "Mary!" she called. "You want to walk to the pond with me and Charlie and see the swans?"

Mary came to the window. "Wait, I'm coming out."

Sara waited on the sidewalk until Mary came out into the yard. "I can't go because my cousin's here and she's going to cut my hair," Mary said, "but did you get your dress yesterday?"

"No."

"Why not? I thought your aunt said you could."

"She did, but when we got in the store and she saw how much it cost she said it was foolish to pay so much for a dress when she could make me one just like it."

"Disappointment."

"Yes, because unfortunately she can't make one *just* like it, she can only make one *kind of* like it. You remember how the stripes came together diagonally in the front of that dress? Well, she already has mine cut out and I can see that not one stripe meets."

484

"Oh, Sara."

"I could see when she was cutting it that the stripes weren't going to meet and I kept saying, 'It's not right, Aunt Willie, the stripes aren't going to meet,' and all the while I'm screaming, the scissors are flashing and she is muttering, 'The stripes will meet, the stripes will meet,' and then she holds it up in great triumph and not one stripe meets."

"That's awful, because I remember thinking when you showed me the dress that it was the way the stripes met that looked so good."

"I am aware of that. It now makes me look like one half of my body is about two inches lower than the other half."

"Listen, come on in and watch my cousin cut my hair, can you?"

"I better not. I promised Aunt Willie I'd take Charlie to see the swans."

"Well, just come in and see how she's going to cut it. She has a whole book of hair styles."

"Oh, all right, for a minute. Charlie, you sit down right there." She pointed to the steps. "Right there now and don't move, hear me? Don't move off that step. Don't even stand up." Then she went in the house with Mary, saying, "I really can't stay but a minute because I've got to take Charlie down to see the swans and then I've got to get home in time to dye my tennis shoes —"

"Which ones?"

"These, these awful orange things. They make me look like Donald Duck or something."

Charlie sat in the sudden stillness, hunched over his knees, on the bottom step. The whole world seemed to have been turned off when Sara went into the Weiceks' house, and he did not move for a long time. The only sound was the ticking of his watch.

The watch was a great pleasure to him. He had no knowledge of hours or minutes, but he liked to listen to it and to watch the small red hand moving around the dial, counting off the seconds, and it was he who remembered every morning after breakfast to have Aunt Willie wind it for him. Now he rested his arm across his legs and looked at the watch.

He had a lonely feeling. He got this whenever he was by himself in a strange place, and he turned quickly when he heard the screen door open to see if it was Sara. When he saw Mrs. Weicek and another woman he turned back and looked at his watch. As he bent over, a pale half circle of flesh showed between the back of his shirt and his pants.

"Who's the little boy, Allie?"

Mrs. Weicek said, "That's Sara's brother, Charlie. You remember me telling you about him. He's the one that can't talk. Hasn't spoken a word since he was three years old."

"Doesn't talk at all?"

"If he does, no one's ever heard him, not since his illness. He can understand what you say to him, and he goes to school, and they say he can write the alphabet, but he can't talk."

Charlie did not hear them. He put his ear against his watch and listened to the sound. There was something about the rhythmic ticking that never failed to soothe him. The watch was a magic charm whose tiny noise and movements could block out the whole clamoring world.

Mrs. Weicek said, "Ask him what time it is, Ernestine. He is so proud of that watch. Everyone always asks him what time it is." Then without waiting, she herself said, "What time is it, Charlie? What time is it?"

He turned and obediently held out the arm with the watch on it.

"My goodness, it's after eight o'clock," Mrs. Weicek said. "Thank you, Charlie. Charlie keeps everyone informed of the time. We just couldn't get along without him."

The two women sat in the rocking chairs on the porch, moving slowly back and forth. The noise of the chairs and the creaking floor boards made Charlie forget the watch for a moment. He got slowly to his feet and stood looking up the street.

"Sit down, Charlie, and wait for Sara," Mrs. Weicek said.

Without looking at her, he began to walk toward the street.

"Charlie, Sara wants you to wait for her."

"Maybe he doesn't hear you, Allie."

"He hears me all right. Charlie, wait for Sara. Wait now." Then she called, "Sara, your brother's leaving."

Sara looked out the upstairs window and said, "All right, Charlie, I'm coming. Will you wait for a minute? Mary, I've got to go."

She ran out of the house and caught Charlie by the arm. "What are you going home for? Don't you want to see the swans?"

He stood without looking at her.

"Honestly, I leave you alone for one second and off you go. Now come on." She tugged his arm impatiently.

As they started down the hill together she waved to Mary, who was at the window, and said to Charlie, "I hope the swans are worth all this trouble I'm going to."

"We'll probably get there and they'll be gone," she added. They walked in silence. Then Sara said, "Here's where we cut across the field." She waited while he stepped carefully over the narrow ditch, and then the two of them walked across the field side by side, Sara kicking her feet restlessly in the deep grass.

There was something painfully beautiful about the swans. The whiteness, the elegance of them on this dark lake, the incredible ease of their movements made Sara catch her breath as she and Charlie rounded the clump of pines.

"There they are, Charlie."

She could tell the exact moment he saw them because his hand tightened; he really held her hand for the first time since they had left Mary's. Then he stopped.

"There are the swans."

The six swans seemed motionless on the water, their necks all arched at the same angle, so that it seemed there was only one swan mirrored five times.

"There are the swans," she said again. She felt she would like to stand there pointing out the swans to Charlie for the rest of the summer. She watched as they drifted slowly across the water.

"Hey, Sara!"

She looked across the lake and saw Wanda and Frank, who had come by the road. "Sara, listen, tell Aunt Willie that Frank and I are going over to his sister's to see her new baby."

"All right."

"I'll be home at eleven."

She watched as Wanda and Frank got back on the motor scooter. At the roar of the scooter, the startled swans changed direction and moved toward Sara. She and Charlie walked closer to the lake.

"The swans are coming over here, Charlie. They see you, I believe."

They watched in silence for a moment as the sound of the scooter faded. Then Sara sat down on the grass, crossed her legs yoga style, and picked out a stick which was wedged inside one of the orange tennis shoes.

"Sit down, Charlie. Don't just stand there."

Awkwardly, with his legs angled out in front of him, he sat on the grass. Sara pulled off a piece of a roll and tossed it to the swans. "Now they'll come over here," she said. "They love bread."

She paused, put a piece of roll into her own mouth, and sat chewing for a moment.

"I saw the swans when they flew here, did you know that, Charlie? I was out on our porch last Friday and I looked up, and they were coming over the house and they looked so funny, like frying pans with their necks stretched out." She handed him a roll. "Here. Give the swans something to eat. Look, watch me. Like that."

She watched him, then said, "No, Charlie, small pieces, because swans get things caught in their throats easily. No, that's *too* little. That's just a crumb. Like *that*."

She watched while he threw the bread into the pond, then said, "You know where the swans live most of the time? At the university, which is a big school, and right in the middle of this university is a lake and that's where the swans live. Only sometimes, for no reason, the swans decide to fly away, and off they go to another pond or another lake. This one isn't half as pretty as the lake at the university, but here they are."

She handed Charlie another roll. "Anyway, that's what Wanda thinks, because the swans at the university are gone."

Charlie turned, motioned that he wanted another roll for the swans, and she gave him the last one. He threw it into the water in four large pieces and put out his hand for another.

"No more. That's all." She showed him her empty hands.

One of the swans dived under the water and rose to shake its feathers. Then it moved across the water. Slowly the other swans followed, dipping their long necks far into the water to catch any remaining pieces of bread.

Sara leaned forward and put her hands on Charlie's shoulders. His body felt soft, as if the muscles had never been used. "The swans are exactly alike," she said. "Exactly. No one can tell them apart."

She began to rub Charlie's back slowly, carefully. Then she stopped abruptly and clapped him on the shoulders. "Well, let's go home."

He sat without moving, still looking at the swans on the other side of the lake.

"Come on, Charlie." She knew he had heard her, yet he still did not move. "Come *on*." She got to her feet and stood looking down at him. She held out her hand to help him up, but he did not even glance at her. He continued to watch the swans.

"Come on, Charlie. Mary may come up later and help me dye my shoes." She looked at him, then snatched a leaf from the limb overhead and threw it at the water. She waited, stuck her hands in her back pockets, and said tiredly, "Come on, Charlie."

He began to shake his head slowly back and forth without looking at her.

"Mary's coming up to help me dye my shoes and if you don't come on we won't have time to do them and I'll end up wearing these same awful Donald Duck shoes all year. Come *on*."

He continued to shake his head back and forth.

"This is why I never want to bring you anywhere, because you won't go home when I'm ready."

With his fingers he began to hold the long grass on either side of him as if this would help him if she tried to pull him to his feet.

"You are really irritating, you know that?" He did not look at her and she sighed and said, "All right, if I stay five more minutes, will you go?" She bent down and showed him on his watch. "That's to right there. When the big hand gets *there*, we go home, all right?"

He nodded.

"Promise?"

He nodded again.

"All right." There was a tree that hung over the water and she went and leaned against it. "All right, Charlie, four more minutes now," she called.

Already he had started shaking his head again, all the while watching the swans gliding across the dark water.

Squinting up at the sky, Sara began to kick her foot back and forth in the deep grass. "In just a month, Charlie, the summer will be over," she said without looking at him, "and I will be so glad."

Up until this year, it seemed, her life had flowed along with rhythmic evenness. The first fourteen years of her life all seemed the same. She had loved her sister without envy, her aunt without finding her coarse, her brother without pity. Now all that was changed. She was filled with a discontent, an anger about herself, her life, her family, that made her think she would never be content again.

She turned and looked at the swans. The sudden, unexpected tears in her eyes blurred the images of the swans into white circles, and she blinked. Then she said aloud, "Three minutes, Charlie."

Sara was lying in bed with the lights out when Wanda came into the bedroom that night. Sara was wearing an old pair of her father's pajamas with the sleeves cut out and the legs rolled up. She watched as Wanda moved quietly across the room and then stumbled over the dressing-table stool. Hobbling on one foot, Wanda opened the closet door and turned on the light.

"You can put on the big light if you want. I'm awake," Sara said.

"*Now* you tell me."

"Did you have a good time, Wanda?"

"Yes."

"Did you get to see the baby?"

"He was so cute. He looked exactly like Frank. You wouldn't have believed it."

"Poor baby."

"No, he was darling, really he was, with little red curls all over his head." She undressed quickly, turned off the closet light, and then got into bed beside Sara. She smoothed her pillow and looked up at the ceiling. "Frank is so nice, don't you think?"

"He's all right."

"Don't you like him?" She rose up on one elbow and looked down at Sara in the big striped pajamas.

"I said he was all right."

"Well, what don't you like?"

"I didn't say I didn't like him."

"I know, but I can tell. What don't you like?"

"For one thing, he never pays any attention to Charlie. When he came up the walk tonight he didn't even speak to him."

"He probably didn't see him in the tent. Anyway, he likes Charlie — he told me so. What else?"

"Oh, nothing, it's just that he's always so affected, the way he calls you Little One and gives you those real meaningful movie-star looks."

"I love it when he calls me Little One. Just wait till someone calls *you* Little One."

"I'd like to know who could call me Little One except the Jolly Green Giant."

"Oh, Sara."

"Well, I'm bigger than everyone I know."

"You'll find someone."

"Yes, maybe if I'm lucky I'll meet somebody from some weird foreign country where men value tall skinny girls with big feet and crooked noses. Every time I see a movie, though, even if it takes place in the weirdest, foreignest country in the world, like where women dance in gauze bloomers and tin bras, the women are still little and beautiful." Then she said, "Anyway, I hate boys. They're all just one big nothing."

"Sara, what's wrong with you?"

"Nothing."

"No, I mean it. What's really wrong?"

"I don't know. I just feel awful."

"Physically awful?"

"Now don't start being the nurse."

"Well, I want to know."

"No, not physically awful, just plain awful. I feel like I want to start screaming and kicking and I want to jump up and tear down the curtains and rip up the sheets and hammer holes in the walls. I want to yank my clothes out of the closet and burn them and —"

"Well, why don't you try it if it would make you feel better?"

"Because it wouldn't." She lifted the top sheet and watched as it billowed in the air and then lowered on her body. She could feel the cloth as it settled on the bare part of her legs. "I just feel like nothing."

"Oh, everybody does at times, Sara."

"Not like me. I'm not anything. I'm not cute, and I'm not pretty, and I'm not a good dancer, and I'm not smart, and I'm not popular. I'm not anything."

"You're a good dishwasher."

"Shut up, Wanda. I don't think that's funny."

"Welllll —"

"You act like you want to talk to me and then you start being funny. You do that to me all the time."

"I'm through being funny, so go on."

"Well, if you could see some of the girls in my school you'd know what I mean. They look like models. Their clothes are so tuff and they're invited to every party, every dance, by about ten boys and when they walk down the hall everybody turns and looks at them."

"Oh, those girls. They hit the peak of their whole lives in junior high school. They look like grown women in eighth grade with the big teased hair and the eye liner and by the time they're in high school they have a used look."

"Well, I certainly don't have to worry about getting a used look."

"I think it is really sad to hit the peak of your whole life in junior high school."

"Girls, quit that arguing," Aunt Willie called from her room. "I can hear you all the way in here."

"We're not arguing," Wanda called back. "We are having a peaceful little discussion."

"I know an argument when I hear one, believe me. That's one thing I've heard plenty of and I'm hearing one right now. Be quiet and go to sleep."

"All right."

They lay in silence. Sara said, "The peak of my whole life so far was in third grade when I got to be milk monitor."

Wanda laughed. "Just give yourself a little time." She reached over, turned on the radio, and waited till it warmed up. "Frank's going to dedicate a song to me on the Diamond Jim show," she said. "Will the radio bother you?"

"No."

"Well, it bothers me," Aunt Willie called from her room. "Maybe you two can sleep with the radio blaring and people arguing, but I can't."

"I have just barely got the radio turned on, Aunt Willie. I have to put my head practically on the table to even hear it." She broke off abruptly. "What was that dedication, did you hear?"

"It was to all the girls on the second floor of Arnold Hall."

"Oh."

"I mean what I say now," Aunt Willie called. "You two get to sleep. Wanda, you've got to be up early to get to your job at the hospital on time, even if Sara can spend the whole day in bed."

"I'd like to know how I can spend the whole day in bed when she gets me up at eight o'clock," Sara grumbled.

"Aunt Willie, I just want to hear my dedication and then I'll go to sleep."

Silence.

Sara turned over on her side with the sheet wrapped tightly around her body and closed her eyes. She was not sleepy now. She could hear the music from the radio, and the sound from the next room of Charlie turning over in his bed, trying to get settled, then turning over again. She pulled the pillow over her head, but she could not block out the noises. Oddly, it was the restless sounds from Charlie's room which seemed loudest.

Charlie was not a good sleeper. When he was three, he had had two illnesses, one following the other, terrible high-fevered illnesses, which had almost taken his life and had damaged his brain. Afterward, he had lain silent and still in his bed, and it had been strange to Sara to see the pale baby that had replaced the hot, flushed, tormented one. The once-bright eyes were slow to follow what was before them, and the hands never reached out, even when Sara held her brother's favorite stuffed dog, Buh-Buh, above him. He rarely cried, never laughed. Now it was as if Charlie wanted to make up for those listless years in bed by never sleeping again.

Sara heard his foot thump against the wall. It was a thing that could continue for hours, a faint sound that no one seemed to hear but Sara, who slept against the wall. With a sigh she put the pillow back beneath her head and looked up at the ceiling.

"That was my dedication. Did you hear it?" Wanda whispered. "To Little One from Frank."

"Vomit."

"Well, I think it was sweet."

The thumping against the wall stopped, then began again. It was a sound that Sara had become used to, but tonight it seemed unusually loud. She found herself thinking how this had been Charlie's first movement after his long illness, a restless kicking out of one foot, a weak movement then that could hardly be noticed beneath the covers, but now, tonight, one that seemed to make the whole house tremble.

"Don't tell me you don't hear that," she said to Wanda. "I don't see how you can all persist in saying that you don't hear Charlie kicking the wall."

Silence.

"Wanda, are you asleep?"

Silence.

"Honestly, I don't see how people can just fall asleep any time they want to. Wanda, are you really asleep?"

She waited, then drew the sheet close about her neck and turned to the wall.

In his room Charlie lay in bed still kicking his foot against the wall. He was not asleep but was staring up at the ceiling where the shadows were moving. He never went to sleep easily, but tonight he had been concerned because a button was missing from his pajamas, and sleep was impossible. He had shown the place where the button was missing to Aunt Willie when he was ready for bed, but she had patted his shoulder and said, "I'll fix it tomorrow," and gone back to watching a game show on television.

496

"Look at that," Aunt Willie was saying to herself. "They're never going to guess the name. How can famous celebrities be so stupid?" She had leaned forward and shouted at the panelists, "It's Clark Gable!" Then, "Have they never heard of a person who works in a store? A person who works in a store is a *clerk* — Clerk Gable — the name is *Clerk Gable!*"

Charlie had touched her on the shoulder and tried again to show her the pajamas.

"I'll fix it tomorrow, Charlie." She had waved him away with one hand.

He had gone back into the kitchen, where Sara was dyeing her tennis shoes in the sink.

"Don't show it to me," she said. "I can't look at anything right now. And Mary, quit laughing at my tennis shoes."

"I can't help it. They're so gross."

Sara lifted them out of the sink with two spoons. "I know they're gross, only you should have told me that orange tennis shoes could not be dyed baby blue. Look at that. That is the worst color you have ever seen in your life. Admit it."

"I admit it."

"Well, you don't have to admit it so quickly. They ought to put on the dye wrapper that orange cannot be dyed baby blue. A warning."

"They do."

"Well, they ought to put it in big letters. Look at those shoes. There must be a terrible name for that color."

"There is," Mary said. "Puce."

"What?"

"Puce."

"Mary Weicek, you made that up."

"I did not. It really is a color."

"I have never heard a word that describes anything better. Puce. These just look like puce shoes, don't they?" She set them on newspapers. "They're — Charlie, get out of the way, please, or I'm going to get dye all over you."

He stepped back, still holding his pajama jacket out in front of him. There were times when he could not get anyone's attention no matter what he did. He took Sara's arm and she shrugged free.

"Charlie, there's not a button on anything I own, either, so go on to bed."

Slowly, filled with dissatisfaction, he had gone to his room and got into bed. There he had begun to pull worriedly at the empty buttonhole until the cloth had started to tear, and then he had continued to pull until the whole front of his pajama top was torn and hung open. He was now holding the jacket partly closed with his hands and looking up at the ceiling.

It was one o'clock and Charlie had been lying there for three hours.

He heard a noise outside, and for the first time he forgot about his pajamas. He stopped kicking his foot against the wall, sat up, and looked out the window. There was something white in the bushes; he could see it moving.

He released his pajamas and held onto the window sill tightly, because he thought that he had just seen one of the swans outside his window, gliding slowly through the leaves. The memory of their soft smoothness in the water came to him and warmed him.

He got out of bed and stood by the other window. He heard a cat miaowing and saw the Hutchinsons' white cat from next door, but he paid no attention to it. The swans were fixed with such certainty in his mind that he could not even imagine that what he had seen was only the cat.

Still looking for the swans, he pressed his face against the screen. The beauty of them, the whiteness, the softness, the silent splendor had impressed him greatly, and he felt a longing to be once again by the lake, sitting in the deep grass, throwing bread to the waiting swans.

It occurred to him suddenly that the swan outside the window had come to find him, and with a small pleased smile he went around the bed, sat, and slowly began to put on his bedroom slippers. Then he walked out into the hall. His feet made a quiet shuffling sound as he passed through the linoleumed hall and into the living room, but no one heard him.

The front door had been left open for coolness and only the screen door was latched. Charlie lifted the hook, pushed open the door, and stepped out onto the porch. Boysie, who slept in the kitchen, heard the door shut and came to the living room. He whined softly when he saw Charlie outside on the porch and scratched at the door. He waited, then after a moment went back to the kitchen and curled up on his rug in front of the sink.

Charlie walked across the front porch and sat on the steps. He waited. He was patient at first, for he thought that the swans would come to the steps, but as time passed and they did not come, he began to shuffle his feet impatiently back and forth on the third step.

Suddenly he saw something white in the bushes. He got up and, holding the banister, went down the steps and crossed the yard. He looked into the bushes, but the swans were not there. It was only the cat, crouched down behind the leaves and looking up at him with slitted eyes.

He stood there, looking at the cat, unable to understand what had happened to the swans. He rubbed his hands up and down his pajama tops, pulling at the torn material. The cat darted farther back into the bushes and disappeared.

After a moment Charlie turned and began to walk slowly across the yard. He went to the gate and paused. He had been told again and again that he must never go out of the yard, but those instructions, given in daylight with noisy traffic on the street, seemed to have nothing to do with the present situation.

In the soft darkness all the things that usually confused him — speeding bicycles, loud noises, lawn mowers, barking dogs, shouting children — were gone, replaced by silence and a silvery moonlit darkness. He seemed to belong to this silent world far more than he belonged to the daytime world of feverish activity.

Slowly he opened the gate and went out. He moved past the Hutchinsons' house, past the Tennents', past the Weiceks'. There was a breeze now, and the smell of the Weiceks' flowers filled the air. He walked past the next house and hesitated, suddenly confused. Then he started through the vacant lot by the Akers' house. In the darkness it looked to him like the field he and Sara had crossed earlier in the evening on their way to see the swans.

He crossed the vacant lot, entered the wooded area, and walked slowly through the trees. He was certain that in just a moment he would come into the clearing and see the lake and the white swans gliding on the dark water. He continued walking, looking ahead so that he would see the lake as soon as possible.

The ground was getting rougher. There were stones to stumble over now and rain gullies and unexpected piles of trash. Still the thought of the swans persisted in his mind and he kept walking.

Charlie was getting tired and he knew something was wrong. The lake was gone. He paused and scanned the field, but he could not see anything familiar.

He turned to the right and began to walk up the hill. Suddenly a dog barked behind him. The sound, unexpected and loud, startled him, and he fell back a step and then started to run. Then another dog was barking, and another, and he had no idea where the dogs were. He was terribly frightened and he ran with increasing awkwardness, thrashing at the weeds with his hands, pulling at the air, so that everything about him seemed to be running except his slow feet.

The sound of the dogs seemed to him to be everywhere, all around him, so that he ran first in one direction, then in another, like a wild animal caught in a maze. He ran into a bush and the briers stung his face and arms, and he thought this was somehow connected with the dogs and thrashed his arms out wildly, not even feeling the cuts in his skin.

He turned around and around, trying to free himself, and then staggered on, running and pulling at the air. The dogs' barking had grown fainter now, but in his terror he did not notice. He ran blindly, stumbling over bushes and against trees, catching his clothing on twigs, kicking at unseen rocks. Then he came into a clearing and was able to gain speed for the first time.

He ran for a long way, and then suddenly he came up against a wire fence that cut him sharply across the chest. The surprise of it threw him back on the ground, and he sat holding his hands across his bare chest, gasping for breath.

Far down the hill someone had spoken to the dogs; they had grown quiet, and now there was only the rasping sound of Charlie's own breathing. He sat hunched over until his breathing grew quieter, and then he straightened and noticed his torn pajamas for the first time since he had left the house. He wrapped the frayed edges of the jacket carefully over his chest as if that would soothe the stinging cut.

After a while he got slowly to his feet, paused, and then began walking up the hill beside the fence. He was limping now because when he had fallen he had lost one of his bedroom slippers.

The fence ended abruptly. It was an old one, built long ago, and now only parts remained. Seeing it gone, Charlie felt relieved. It was as if the fence had kept him from his goal, and he stepped over a trailing piece of wire and walked toward the forest beyond.

Being in the trees gave him a good feeling for a while. The moonlight coming through the leaves and the soft sound of the wind in the branches were soothing, but as he went deeper into the forest he became worried. There was something here he didn't know, an unfamiliar smell, noises he had never heard before. He stopped.

He stood beneath the trees without moving and looked around him. He did not know where he was. He did not even know how he had come to be there. The whole night seemed one long struggle, but he could not remember why he had been struggling. He had wanted something; he could not remember what.

His face and arms stung from the brier scratches; his bare foot, tender and unused to walking on the rough ground, was already cut and sore, but most of all he was gripped by hopelessness. He wanted to be back in his room, in his bed, but home seemed lost forever, a place so disconnected from the forest that there was no way to get from one to the other.

He put his wrist to his ear and listened to his watch. Even its steady ticking could not help him tonight and he wrapped the torn pajamas tighter over his chest and began to walk slowly up the hill through the trees. As he walked, he began to cry without noise.

In the morning Sara arose slowly, letting her feet hang over the edge of the bed for a moment before she stepped onto the floor. Then she walked across the room, and as she passed the dressing table she paused to look at herself in the mirror. She smoothed her hair behind her ears.

One of her greatest mistakes, she thought, looking at herself critically, was cutting her hair. She had gone to the beauty school in Bentley, taking with her a picture from a magazine, and had asked the girl to cut her hair exactly like that.

"And look what she did to me!" she had screamed when she got home. "Look! Ruined!"

"It's not that bad," Wanda had said.

"Tell the truth. Now look at that picture. Look! Tell the truth — do I look anything, anything at *all*, even the tiniest little bit, like that model?"

Wanda and Aunt Willie had had to admit that Sara looked nothing like the blond model.

"I'm ruined, just ruined. Why someone cannot take a perfectly good magazine picture and cut someone's hair the same way without ruining them is something I cannot understand. I hope that girl fails beauty school."

"Actually, your *hair* does sort of look like the picture. It's your face and body that don't."

"Shut up, Wanda. Quit trying to be funny."

"I'm not being funny. It's a fact."

"I didn't make smart remarks the time they gave you that awful permanent."

"You did too. You called me Gentle Ben."

502

"Well, I meant that as a compliment."

"All right, girls, stop this now. No more arguing. Believe me, I mean it."

Sara now looked at herself, weighing the mistake of the hair, and she thought suddenly: I look exactly like that cartoon cat who is always chasing Tweetie Bird and who has just been run over by a steam roller and made absolutely flat. This hair and my flat face have combined to make me look exactly like —

"Sara!" Aunt Willie called from the kitchen.

"What?"

"Come on and get your breakfast, you and Charlie. I'm not going to be in here fixing one breakfast after another until lunch time."

"All right."

She went into the hall and looked into Charlie's room.

"Charlie!"

He was not in his bed. She walked into the living room. Lately, since he had learned to turn on the television, he would get up early, come in, and watch it by himself, but he was not there either.

"Charlie's already up, Aunt Willie."

In the kitchen Aunt Willie was spooning oatmeal into two bowls.

"Oatmeal again," Sara groaned. "I believe I'll just have some Kool-Aid and toast."

"Don't talk nonsense. Now, where's Charlie?"

"He wasn't in his room."

She sighed. "Well, find him."

"First I've got to see my shoes." She went over to the sink and looked at the sneakers. "Oh, they look awful. Look at them, Aunt Willie. They're gross."

"Well, you should have left them alone. I've learned my lesson about dyeing clothes, let me tell you. You saw me, I hope, when I had to wear that purple dress to your Uncle Bert's funeral."

"What color would you say these were?"

"I haven't got time for that now. Go get your brother."

"No, there's a name for this color. I just want to see if you know it."

"I don't know it, so go get your brother."

"I'll give you three choices. It's either, let me see — it's either pomegranate, Pomeranian, or puce."

"Puce. Now go get your brother."

"How did you know?"

"Because my aunt had twin Pomeranian dogs that rode in a baby carriage and because I once ate a piece of pomegranate. Go get your brother!"

Sara put down the shoes and went back into the hall.

"Charlie!" She looked into his room again. "Oh, Charlie!" She went out onto the front porch and looked at Charlie's tent. It had blown down during the night and she could see that he wasn't there.

Slowly she walked back through the hall, looking into every room, and then into the kitchen.

"I can't find him, Aunt Willie."

"What do you mean, you can't find him?" Aunt Willie, prepared to chide the two children for being late to breakfast, now set the pan of oatmeal down heavily on the table.

"He's not in his room, he's not in the yard, he's not anywhere."

"If this is some kind of a joke —" Aunt Willie began. She brushed past Sara and went into the living room. "Charlie! Where are you, Charlie?" Her voice had begun to rise with the sudden alarm she often felt in connection with Charlie. "Where could he have gone?" She turned and looked at Sara. "If this is a joke . . ."

"It's not a joke."

"Well, I'm remembering last April Fool's Day, that's all."

"He's probably around the neighborhood somewhere, like the time Wanda took him to the store without saying anything."

"Well, Wanda didn't take him this morning." Aunt Willie walked into the hall and stood looking in Charlie's room. She stared at the empty bed. She did not move for a moment as she tried to think of some logical explanation for his absence. "If anything's happened to that boy —"

"Nothing's happened to him."

"All right, where is he?"

Sara did not answer. Charlie had never left the house alone, and Sara could not think of any place he could be either.

504

"Go outside, Sara. Look! If he's not in the neighborhood, I'm calling the police."

"Don't call until we're sure, Aunt Willie, please."

"I'm calling. Something's wrong here."

Sara was out of her pajamas and into her pants and shirt in a minute. Leaving her pajamas on the floor, she ran barefoot into the yard.

"Charlie! Charlie!" She ran around the house and then stopped. Suddenly she remembered the swans and ran back into the house.

"Aunt Willie, I bet you anything Charlie went down to the lake to see the swans."

Aunt Willie was talking on the telephone and she put one hand over the receiver and said, "Run and see."

"You aren't talking to the police already?" Sara asked in the doorway.

"I'm not talking to the police, but that's what I'm going to do when you get back. Now quit wasting time."

"Just let me get my shoes."

She ran back into the kitchen and put on the sneakers, which were still wet. Then she ran out of the house and down the street. As she passed the Weiceks', Mary came out on the porch.

"What's the hurry?" she called.

"Charlie's missing. I'm going to see if he's down at the lake."

"I'll go with you." She came down the steps, calling over her shoulder, "Mom, I'm going to help Sara look for Charlie."

"Not in those curlers you're not."

"Mom, I've got on a scarf. Nobody can even tell it's rolled."

"Yeah, everyone will just think you have real bumpy hair," Sara said.

"Oh, hush. Now what's all this about Charlie?"

"We couldn't find him this morning and I think he might have got up during the night and gone to see the swans. He acted awful when we had to leave."

"I know. I saw you dragging him up the street last night."

"I had to. It was the only way I could get him home. It was black dark. You couldn't even see the swans and he still wouldn't come home."

"I hope he's all right."

"He's probably sitting down there looking at the swans, holding onto the grass, and I'm going to have to drag him up the hill screaming all over again. He's strong when he wants to be, you know that?"

"Hey, you've got your shoes on."

"Yeah, but they're still wet."

"You'll probably have puce feet before the day's over."

"That's all I need."

They turned and crossed the field at the bottom of the hill.

"Let's hurry because Aunt Willie is at this moment getting ready to call the police."

"Really?"

"She's sitting by the phone now. She's got her little card out with all her emergency numbers on it and her finger is pointing right to *POLICE*."

"Remember that time the old man got lost in the woods? What was his name?"

"Uncle somebody."

"And they organized a posse of college boys and the Red Cross brought coffee and everything, and then they found the old man asleep in his house the next morning. He was on a picnic and had got bored and just went home."

"Don't remind me. Probably as soon as Aunt Willie calls the police we'll find Charlie in the bathroom or somewhere."

They came through the trees and into the clearing around the lake. Neither spoke.

"Yesterday he was sitting right here," Sara said finally. "Charlie! Charlie!"

There was no answer, but the swans turned abruptly and began to glide to the other side of the lake. Sara felt her shoulders sag and she rammed her hands into her back pockets.

"Something really has happened to him," she said. "I know it now."

"Probably not, Sara."

"I *know* it now. Sometimes you just know terrible things. I get a feeling in my neck, like my shoulders have come unhinged or something, when an awful thing happens."

Mary put one hand on her arm. "Maybe he's hiding somewhere."

"He can't even do that right. If he's playing hide-and-seek, as soon as he's hidden he starts looking out to see how the game's going. He just can't —"

"Maybe he's at the store or up at the Dairy Queen. I could run up to the drugstore."

"No, something's happened to him."

They stood at the edge of the water. Sara looked at the swans without seeing them.

Mary called, "Charlie! Charlie!" Her kerchief slipped off and she retied it over her rollers. "Charlie!"

"I was so sure he'd be here," Sara said. "I wasn't even worried because I knew he would be sitting right here. Now I don't know what to do."

"Let's go back to the house. Maybe he's there now."

"I know he won't be."

"Well, don't get discouraged until we see." She took Sara by the arm and started walking through the trees. "You know who you sound like? Remember when Mary Louise was up for class president and she kept saying, 'I know I won't get it. I know I won't get it.' For three days that was all she said."

"And she didn't get it."

"Well, I just meant you sounded like her, your voice or something," Mary explained quickly. "Now, come on."

When Sara entered the house with Mary, Aunt Willie was still sitting at the telephone. She was saying, "And there's not a trace of him." She paused in her conversation to ask, "Did you find him?" and when Sara shook her head, she said into the telephone, "I'm hanging up now, Midge, so I can call the police. Sara just came in and he wasn't at the lake."

She hung up, took her card of emergency phone numbers and began to dial.

There was something final about calling the police and Sara said, "Aunt Willie, don't call yet. Maybe —"

"I'm calling. A hundred elephants couldn't stop me."

"Maybe he's at somebody's house," Mary said. "One time my brother went in the Hutchinsons' to watch TV and we —"

"Hello, is this the police department? I want to report a missing child."

She looked up at Sara, started to say something, then turned back to her telephone conversation. "Yes, a missing child, a boy, ten, Charlie Godfrey. G-o-d-f-r-e-y." Pause. "Eighteen-oh-eight Cass Street. This is Willamina Godfrey, his aunt. I'm in charge." She paused, then said, "Yes, since last night." She listened again. "No, I don't know what time. We woke up this morning, he was gone. That's all." She listened and as she answered again her voice began to rise with concern and anger. "No, I could not ask his friends about him because he doesn't have any friends. His brain was injured when he was three years old and that is why I am so concerned. This is not a ten-year-old boy who can go out and come home when he feels like it. This is not a boy who's going to run out and break street lights and spend the night in some garage, if that's what you're thinking. This is a boy, I'm telling you, who can be lost and afraid three blocks from home and cannot speak one word to ask for help. Now are you going to come out here or aren't you?"

She paused, said, "Yes, yes," then grudgingly, "And thank you." She hung up the receiver and looked at Sara. "They're coming."

"What did they say?"

"They said they're coming. That's all." She rose in agitation and began to walk into the living room. "Oh, why don't they hurry!"

"Aunt Willie, they just hung up the telephone."

"I know." She went to the front door and then came back, nervously slapping her hands together. "Where can he *be*?"

"My brother was always getting lost when he was little," Mary said.

"I stood right in this house, in that room," Aunt Willie interrupted. She pointed toward the front bedroom. "And I promised your mother, Sara, that I would look after Charlie all my life. I promised your mother nothing would ever happen to Charlie as long as there was breath in my body, and now look. Look! Where is this boy I'm taking such good care of?" She threw her hands into the air. "Vanished without a trace, that's where."

"Aunt Willie, you can't watch him every minute."

"Why not? Why can't I? What have I got more important in my life than looking after that boy? Only one thing more important than Charlie. Only one thing — that devil television there."

"Aunt Willie —"

"Oh, yes, that devil television. I was sitting right in that chair last night and he wanted me to sew on one button for him but I was too busy with the television. I'll tell you what I should have told your mother six years ago. I should have told her, 'Sure, I'll be glad to look after Charlie except when there's something good on television. I'll be glad to watch him in my spare time.' My tongue should fall out on the floor for promising to look after your brother and not doing it."

She went back to the doorway. "There are a hundred things that could have happened to him. He could have fallen into one of those ravines in the woods. He could be lost up at the old mine. He could be at the bottom of the lake. He could be kidnaped." Sara and Mary stood in silence as she named the tragedies that could have befallen Charlie.

Sara said, "Well, he could not have been kidnaped, because anybody would know we don't have any money for ransom."

"That wouldn't stop some people. Where are those policemen?"

Sara looked down at the table beside the television and saw a picture Charlie had drawn of himself on tablet paper. The head and body were circles of the same size, the ears and eyes overlapping smaller circles, the arms and legs were elongated balloons. He had started printing his name below the picture, but had completed only two letters before he had gone out to make the tent. The C was backward.

Wanda had bought him the tablet and crayons two days ago and he had done this one picture with the brown crayon. It gave Sara a sick feeling to see it because something about the picture, the smallness, the unfinished quality, made it look somehow very much like Charlie.

Aunt Willie said, "When you want the police they are always a hundred miles away bothering criminals."

"They're on their way. They said so," Mary said.

"All right then, where are they?"

Mary blinked her eyes at this question to which she had no answer, and settled the rollers beneath her scarf.

"I still can't get it out of my head that Charlie went back to see the swans," Sara said.

"He really was upset about having to go home. I can testify to that," Mary said.

Aunt Willie left the room abruptly. When she came back she was holding a picture of Charlie in one hand. It was a snapshot of him taken in March, sitting on the steps with Boysie in front of the house.

"The police always want a photograph," she said. She held it out so Mary and Sara could see it. "Mrs. Hutchinson took that with her Polaroid."

"It's a real good picture of him," Mary said.

Sara looked at the picture without speaking. Somehow the awkward, unfinished crayon drawing on the table looked more like Charlie than the snapshot.

"It was his birthday," Aunt Willie said mournfully, "and look how proud he was of that watch Wanda bought him, holding his little arm straight out in the picture so everyone would notice it. I fussed so much about Wanda getting him a watch because he couldn't tell time, and then he was so proud just to be wearing it. Everyone would ask him on the street, 'What time is it, Charlie? Have you got the time, Charlie?' just to see how proud he was to show them."

"And then those boys stole it. I think that was the meanest thing," Mary said.

"The watch was lost," Aunt Willie said. "The watch just got lost."

"Stolen," Sara snapped, "by that crook Joe Melby."

"I am the quickest person to accuse somebody, you know that. You saw me, I hope, when I noticed those boys making off with the Hutchinsons' porch chairs last Halloween; but that watch just got lost. Then Joe Melby found it and, to his credit, brought it back."

"Huh!"

"There was no stealing involved."

Mary said, giggling, "Aunt Willie, did Sara ever tell you what she did to Joe?"

"Hush, Mary," Sara said.

"What did she do?"

"She made a little sign that said *FINK* and stuck it on Joe's back in the hall at school and he went around for two periods without knowing it was there."

"It doesn't matter what I did. Nobody's going to pick on my brother and I mean it. That fink stole Charlie's watch and then got scared and told that big lie about finding it on the floor of the school bus."

"You want revenge too much."

"When somebody *deserves* revenge, then —"

"I take my revenge same as anybody," Aunt Willie said, "only I never was one to keep after somebody and keep after somebody the way you do. You take after your Uncle Bert in that."

"I hope I always do."

"No, your Uncle Bert was no good in that way. He would never let a grudge leave him. When he lay dying in the hospital, he was telling us who we weren't to speak to and who we weren't to do business with. His dying words were against Jeep Johnson at the used-car lot."

"Good for Uncle Bert."

"And that nice little Gretchen Wyant who you turned the hose on, and her wearing a silk dress her brother had sent her from Taiwan!"

"That nice little Gretchen Wyant was lucky all she got was water on her silk dress."

"Sara!"

"Well, do you know what that nice little Gretchen Wyant did? I was standing in the bushes by the spigot, turning off the hose, and this nice little Gretchen Wyant didn't see me — all she saw was Charlie at the fence — and she said, 'How's the *retard* today?' only she made it sound even uglier, 'How's the *reeeeetard*,' like that. Nothing ever made me so mad. The best sight of my whole life was nice little Gretchen Wyant standing there in her wet Taiwan silk dress with her mouth hanging open."

"Here come the police," Mary said quickly. "But they're stopping next door."

"Signal to them," Aunt Willie said.

Before Mary could move to the door, Aunt Willie was past her and out on the porch. "Here we are. This is the house." She turned and said over her shoulder to Sara, "Now, God willing, we'll get some action."

Sara sat in the living room wearing her cut-off blue jeans, an old shirt with *Property of State Prison* stamped on the back which Wanda had brought her from the beach, and her puce tennis shoes. She was sitting in the doorway, leaning back against the door with her arms wrapped around her knees, listening to Aunt Willie, who was making a telephone call in the hall.

"It's no use calling," Sara said against her knees. This was the first summer her knees had not been skinned a dozen times, but she could still see the white scars from other summers. Since Aunt Willie did not answer, she said again, "It's no use calling. He won't come."

"You don't know your father," Aunt Willie said.

"That is the truth."

"Not like I do. When he hears that Charlie is missing, he will . . ." Her voice trailed off as she prepared to dial the telephone.

Sara had a strange feeling when she thought of her father. It was the way she felt about people she didn't know well, like the time Miss Marshall, her English teacher, had given her a ride home from school, and Sara had felt uneasy the whole way home, even though she saw Miss Marshall every day.

Her father's remoteness had begun, she thought, with Charlie's illness. There was a picture in the family photograph album of her father laughing and throwing Sara into the air and a picture of her father holding her on his shoulders and a picture of her father sitting on the front steps with Wanda on one knee and Sara on the other. All these pictures of a happy father and his adoring daughters had been taken before Charlie's illness and Sara's mother's death. Afterward there weren't any family pictures at all, happy or sad.

When Sara looked at those early pictures, she remembered a laughing man with black curly hair and a broken tooth who had lived with them for a few short golden years and then had gone away. There was no connection at all between this laughing man in the photograph album and the gray sober man who worked in Ohio and came home to West Virginia on occasional weekends, who sat in the living room and watched baseball or football on television and never started a conversation on his own.

Sara listened while Aunt Willie explained to the operator that the call she was making was an emergency. "That's why I'm not direct dialing," she said, "because I'm so upset I'll get the wrong numbers."

"He won't come," Sara whispered against her knee.

As the operator put through the call and Aunt Willie waited, she turned to Sara, nodded emphatically, and said, "He'll come, you'll see."

Sara got up, walked across the living room and into the kitchen, where the breakfast dishes were still on the table. She looked down at the two bowls of hard, cold oatmeal, and then made herself three pieces of toast and poured herself a cup of cherry Kool-Aid. When she came back eating the toast Aunt Willie was still waiting.

"Didn't the operator tell them it was an emergency, I wonder," Aunt Willie said impatiently.

"Probably."

"Well, if somebody told me I had an emergency call, I would run, let me tell you, to find out what that emergency was. That's no breakfast, Sara."

"It's my lunch."

"Kool-Aid and toast will not sustain you five minutes." She broke off quickly and said in a louder voice, "Sam, is that you?" She nodded to Sara, then turned back to the telephone, bent forward in her concern. "First of all, Sammy, promise me you won't get upset — no, promise me first."

"He won't get upset. Even *I* can promise you that," Sara said with her mouth full of toast.

"Sam, Charlie's missing," Aunt Willie said abruptly.

Unable to listen to any more of the conversation, Sara took her toast and went out onto the front porch. She sat on the front steps and put her feet into the worn grooves that Charlie's feet had made on the third step. Then she ate the last piece of toast and licked the butter off her fingers.

In the corner of the yard, beneath the elm tree, she could see the hole Charlie had dug with a spoon; all one morning he had dug that hole and now Boysie was lying in it for coolness. She walked to the tree and sat in the old rope swing and swung over Boysie. She stretched out her feet and touched Boysie, and he lifted his head and looked around to see who had poked him, then lay back in his hole.

"Boysie, here I am, look, Boysie, look."

He was already asleep again.

"Boysie —" She looked up as Aunt Willie came out on the porch and stood for a minute drying her hands on her apron. For the occasion of Charlie's disappearance she was wearing her best dress, a bright green bonded jersey, which was so hot her face above it was red and shiny. Around her forehead she had tied a handkerchief to absorb the sweat.

Sara swung higher. "Well," she asked, "is he coming?" She paused to pump herself higher. "Or not?"

"He's going to call back tonight."

"Oh," Sara said.

"Don't say 'Oh' to me like that."

"It's what I figured."

"Listen to me, Miss Know-it-all. There is no need in the world for your father to come this exact minute. If he started driving right this second he still wouldn't get here till after dark and he couldn't do anything then, so he just might as well wait till after work and then drive."

"Might as well do the sensible thing." Sara stood up and really began to swing. She had grown so much taller since she had last stood in this swing that her head came almost to the limb from which the swing hung. She caught hold of the limb with her hands, kicked her feet free, and let the swing jerk wildly on its own.

"Anyway," Aunt Willie said, "this is no time to be playing on a swing. What will the neighbors think, with Charlie missing and you having a wonderful time on a swing?"

"I knew he wouldn't come."

"He is going to come," Aunt Willie said in a louder voice. "He is just going to wait till dark, which is reasonable, since by dark Charlie will probably be home anyway."

"It is so reasonable that it makes me sick."

"I won't listen to you being disrespectful to your father, I mean that," she said. "I know what it is to lose a father, let me tell you, and so will you when all you have left of him is an envelope."

Aunt Willie, Sara knew, was speaking of the envelope in her dresser drawer containing all the things her father had had in his pockets when he died. Sara knew them all — the watch, the twenty-seven cents in change, the folded dollar bill, the brown plaid handkerchief, the three-cent stamp, the two bent pipe cleaners, the half pack of stomach mints.

"Yes, wait till you lose your father. Then you'll appreciate him."

"I've already lost him."

"Don't you talk like that. Your father's had to raise two families and all by himself. When Poppa died, Sammy had to go to work and support all of us before he was even out of high school, and now he's got this family to support too. It's not easy, I'm telling you that. *You* raise two families and then I'll listen to what you've got to say against your father."

Sara let herself drop to the ground and said, "I better go. Mary and I are going to look for Charlie."

"Where?"

"Up the hill."

"Well, don't *you* get lost," Aunt Willie called after her.

From the Hutchinsons' yard some children called, "Have you found Charlie yet, Sara?" They were making a garden in the dust, carefully planting flowers without roots in neat rows. Already the first flowers were beginning to wilt in the hot sun.

"I'm going to look for him now."

"Sawa?" It was the youngest Hutchinson boy, who was three and sometimes came over to play with Charlie.

"What?"

"Sawa?"

"What?"

"Sawa?"

"What?"

"Sawa, I got gwass." He held up two fists of grass he had just pulled from one of the few remaining clumps in the yard.

"Yes, that's fine. I'll tell Charlie when I see him."

Sara and Mary had decided that they would go to the lake and walk up behind the houses toward the woods. Sara was now on her way to Mary's, passing the vacant lot where a baseball game was in progress. She glanced up and watched as she walked down the sidewalk.

The baseball game had been going on for an hour with the score still zero to zero and the players, dusty and tired, were playing silently, without hope.

She was almost past the field when she heard someone call, "Hey, have you found your brother yet, Sara?"

She recognized the voice of Joe Melby and said, "No," without looking at him.

"What?"

She turned, looked directly at him, and said, "You will be pleased and delighted to learn that we have not." She continued walking down the street. The blood began to pound in her head. Joe Melby was the one person she did not want to see on this particular day. There was something disturbing about him. She did not know him, really, had hardly even spoken to him, and yet she hated him so much the sight of him made her sick.

"Is there anything I can do?"

"No."

"If he's up in the woods, I could help look. I know about as much about those hills as anybody." He left the game and started walking behind her with his hands in his pockets.

"No, thank you."

"I *want* to help."

She swirled around and faced him, her eyes blazing. "I do not want your help." They looked at each other. Something twisted inside her and she felt suddenly ill. She thought she would never drink cherry Kool-Aid again as long as she lived.

Joe Melby did not say anything but moved one foot back and forth on the sidewalk, shuffling at some sand. "Do you —"

"Anybody who would steal a little boy's watch," she said, cutting off his words, and it was a relief to make this accusation to his face at last, "is somebody whose help I can very well do without." Her head was pounding so loudly she could hardly hear her own words. For months, ever since the incident of the stolen watch, she had waited for this moment, had planned exactly what she would say. Now that it was said, she did not feel the triumph she had imagined at all.

"Is that what's wrong with you?" He looked at her. "You think I stole your brother's watch?"

"I know you did."

"How?"

"Because I asked Charlie who stole his watch and I kept asking him and one day on the school bus when I asked him he pointed right straight at you."

"He was confused —"

"He wasn't that confused. You probably thought he wouldn't be able to tell on you because he couldn't talk, but he pointed right —"

"He *was* confused. I gave the watch *back* to him. I didn't take it."

"I don't believe you."

"You believe what you want then, but I didn't take that watch. I thought that matter had been settled."

"Huh!"

She turned and started walking with great speed down the hill. For some reason she was not as sure about Joe Melby as she had been before, and this was even more disturbing. He did take the watch, she said to herself. She could not bear to think that she had been mistaken in this, that she had taken revenge on the wrong person.

Behind her there were sudden cheers as someone hit a home run. The ball went into the street. Joe ran, picked it up, and tossed it to a boy in the field. Sara did not look around.

"Hey, wait a minute," she heard Joe call. "I'm coming."

She did not turn around. She had fallen into that trap before. Once when she had been walking down the street, she had heard a car behind her and the horn sounding and a boy's voice shouting, "Hey, beautiful!" And she had turned around. She! Then, too late, she had seen that the girl they were honking and shouting at was Rosey Camdon on the opposite side of the street, Rosey Camdon who was Miss Batelle District Fair and Miss Buckwheat Queen and a hundred other things. Sara had looked down quickly, not knowing whether anyone had seen her or not, and her face had burned so fiercely she had thought it would be red forever. Now she kept walking quickly with her head down.

"Wait, Sara."

Still she did not turn around or show that she had heard him.

"Wait." He ran, caught up with her, and started walking beside her. "All the boys say they want to help."

She hesitated but kept walking. She could not think of anything to say. She knew how circus men on stilts felt when they walked, because her legs seemed to be moving in the same awkward way, great exaggerated steps that got her nowhere.

She thought she might start crying so she said quickly, "Oh, all right." Then tears did come to her eyes, sudden and hot, and she looked down at her feet.

He said, "Where should we start? Have you got any ideas?"

"I think he's up in the woods. I took him to see the swans yesterday and I think he was looking for them when he got lost."

"Probably up that way."

She nodded.

He paused, then added, "We'll find him."

She did not answer, could not, because tears were spilling down her cheeks, so she turned quickly and walked alone to Mary's house and waited on the sidewalk until Mary came out to join her.

She and Mary were almost across the open field before Sara spoke. Then she said, "Guess who just stopped me and gave me the big sympathy talk about Charlie."

"I don't know. Who?"

"Joe Melby."

"Really? What did he say?"

"He wants to help look for Charlie. He makes me sick."

"I think it's nice that he wants to help."

"Well, maybe if he'd stolen your brother's watch you wouldn't think it was so nice."

Mary was silent for a moment. Then she said, "I probably shouldn't tell you this, but he didn't steal that watch, Sara."

"Huh!"

"No, he really didn't."

Sara looked at her and said, "How do you know?"

"I can't tell you how I know because I promised I wouldn't, but I *know* he didn't."

"How?"

"I can't tell. I promised."

"That never stopped you before. Now, Mary Weicek, you tell me what you know this minute."

"I promised."

"Mary, tell me."

"Mom would kill me if she knew I told you."

"She won't know."

"Well, your aunt went to see Joe Melby's mother."

"What?"

"Aunt Willie went over to see Joe Melby's mother."

"She didn't!"

"Yes, she did too, because my mother was right there when it happened. It was about two weeks after Charlie had gotten the watch back."

"I don't believe you."

"Well, it's the truth. You told Aunt Willie that Joe had stolen the watch — remember, you told everybody — and so Aunt Willie went over to see Joe's mother."

"She wouldn't do such a terrible thing."

"Well, she did."

"And what did Mrs. Melby say?"

"She called Joe into the room and she said, 'Joe, did you steal the little Godfrey boy's watch?' And he said, 'No.'"

"What did you expect him to say in front of his mother? 'Yes, I stole the watch'? Huh! That doesn't prove anything."

"So then she said, 'I want the truth now. Do you know who did take the watch?' and he said that nobody had *stolen* the watch."

"So where did it disappear to for a week, I'd like to know."

"I'm coming to that. He said some of the fellows were out in front of the drugstore and Charlie was standing there waiting for the school bus — you were in the drugstore. Remember it was the day we were getting the stamps for letters to those pen pals who never answered? Remember the stamps wouldn't come out of the machine? Well, anyway, these boys outside the store started teasing Charlie with some candy, and while Charlie was trying to get the candy, one of the boys took off Charlie's watch without Charlie noticing it. Then they were going to ask Charlie what time it was and when he looked down at his watch, he would get upset because the watch would be gone. They were just going to tease him."

"Finks! *Finks!*"

"Only you came out of the drugstore right then and saw what they were doing with the candy and told them off and the bus came and you hustled Charlie on the bus before anybody had a chance to give back the watch. Then they got scared to give it back and that's the whole story. Joe didn't steal the watch at all. He wasn't even in on it. He came up right when you did and didn't even know what had happened. Later, when he found out, he got the watch back and gave it to Charlie, that's all."

"Why didn't you tell me before this?"

"Because I just found out about it at lunch. For four months my mother has known all about this thing and never mentioned it because she said it was one of those things best forgotten."

"Why did she tell you now?"

"That's the way my mom is. We were talking about Charlie at the dinner table, and suddenly she comes up with this. Like one time she casually mentioned that she had had a long talk with Mr. Homer about me. Mr. Homer, the principal! She went over there and they had a long discussion and she never mentioned it for a year."

"That is the worst thing Aunt Willie has ever done."

"Well, don't let on that you know or I'll be in real trouble."

"I won't, but honestly, I could just —"

"You promised."

"I know. You don't have to keep reminding me. It makes me feel terrible though, I can tell you that." She walked with her head bent forward. "Terrible! You know what I just did when I saw him?"

"What?"

"Accused him of stealing the watch."

"Sara, you didn't."

"I did too. I can't help myself. When I think somebody has done something mean to Charlie I can't forgive them. I want to keep after them and keep after them just like Aunt Willie said. I even sort of suspected Joe Melby hadn't really taken that watch and I still kept on —"

"Shh! Be quiet a minute." Mary was carrying her transistor radio and she held it up between them. "Listen."

The announcer was saying: "We have a report of a missing child in the Cass section — ten-year-old Charlie Godfrey, who has been missing from his home since sometime last night. He is wearing blue pajamas and brown felt slippers, has a watch on one wrist and an identification bracelet with his name and address on the other. He is a mentally handicapped child who cannot speak and may become alarmed when approached by a stranger. Please notify the police immediately if you have seen this youngster."

The two girls looked at each other, then continued walking across the field in silence.

Mary and Sara were up in the field by the woods. They had been searching for Charlie for an hour without finding a trace of him.

Mary said, "I don't care how I look. I am taking off this scarf. It must be a hundred degrees out here."

"Charlie!" Sara called as she had been doing from time to time. Her voice had begun to sound strained, she had called so often. "Charlie!"

"Sara, do you know where we are?" Mary asked after a moment.

"Of course. The lake's down there and the old shack's over there and you can see them as soon as we get up a little higher."

"*If* we get up a little higher," Mary said in a tired voice.

"You didn't have to come, you know."

"I wanted to come, only I just want to make sure we don't get lost. I have to go to Bennie Hoffman's party tonight."

"I know. You told me ten times."

"So I don't want to get lost." Mary walked a few steps without speaking. "I still can't figure out why I was invited, because Bennie Hoffman hardly knows me. I've just seen him two times this whole summer at the pool. Why do you think he —"

"Come on, will you?"

"It seems useless, if you ask me, to just keep walking when we don't really know which way he went. Aunt Willie thinks he went in the old coal mine."

"I know, but she only thinks that because she associates the mine with tragedy because her uncle and brother were killed in that coal mine. But Charlie wouldn't go in there. Remember that time we went into the Bryants' cellar after they moved out, and he wouldn't even come in there because it was cold and dark and sort of scary."

"Yes, I do remember because I sprained my ankle jumping down from the window and had to wait two hours while you looked through old *Life* magazines."

"I was not looking through old magazines."

"I could hear you. I was down there in that dark cellar with the rats and you were upstairs and I was yelling for help and you kept saying, 'I'm going for help right now,' and I could hear the pages turning and turning and turning."

"Well, I got you out, didn't I?"

"Finally."

Sara paused again. "Charlie! Charlie!" The girls waited in the high grass for an answer, then began to walk again. Mary said, "Maybe we should have waited for the others before we started looking. They're going to have a regular organized posse with everybody walking along together. There may be a helicopter."

"The longer we wait, the harder it will be to find him."

"Well, I've got to get home in time to bathe and take my hair down."

"I know. I *know*. You're going to Bennie Hoffman's party."

"You don't have to sound so mad about it. I didn't *ask* to be invited."

"I am not mad because you were invited to Bennie Hoffman's party. I couldn't care less about Bennie Hoffman's party. I'm just mad because you're slowing me up on this search."

"Well, if I'm slowing you up so much, then maybe I'll just go on home."

"That suits me fine."

They looked at each other without speaking. Between them the radio began announcing: "Volunteers are needed in the Cass area in the search for young Charlie Godfrey, who disappeared from his home sometime during the night. A search of the Cheat woods will begin at three o'clock this afternoon."

Mary said, "Oh, I'll keep looking. I'll try to walk faster."

Sara shrugged, turned, and started walking up the hill, followed by Mary. They came to the old fence that once separated the pasture from the woods. Sara walked slowly beside the fence. "Charlie!" she called.

"Would he come if he heard you, do you think?"

Sara nodded. "But if they get a hundred people out here clomping through the woods and hollering, he's not going to come. He'll be too scared. I know him."

"I don't see how you can be so sure he came up this way."

"I just know. There's something about me that makes me understand Charlie. It's like I know how he feels about things. Like sometimes I'll be walking down the street and I'll pass the jeweler's and I'll think that if Charlie were here he would want to stand right there and look at those watches all afternoon and I know right where he'd stand and how he'd put his hands up on the glass and how his face would look. And yesterday I knew he was going to love the swans so much that he wasn't ever going to want to leave. I know how he feels."

"You just think you do."

"No, I *know*. I was thinking about the sky one night and I was looking up at the stars and I was thinking about how the sky goes on and on forever, and I couldn't understand it no matter how long I thought, and finally I got kind of nauseated and right then I started thinking, Well, this is how Charlie feels about some things. You know how it makes him sick sometimes to try to print letters for a long time and —"

"Look who's coming," Mary interrupted.

"Where?"

"In the trees, walking toward us. Joe Melby."

"You're lying. You're just trying to make me —"

"It is him. Look." She quickly began to tie her scarf over her rollers again. "And you talk about *me* needing eyeglasses."

"Cut across the field, quick!" Sara said. "No, wait, go under the fence. Move, will you, Mary, and leave that scarf alone. Get under the fence. I am not going to face him. I mean it."

"I am not going under any fence. Anyway, it would look worse for us to run away than to just walk by casually."

"I cannot walk by casually after what I said."

"Well, you're going to have to face him sometime, and it might as well be now when everyone feels sorry for you about your brother." She called out, "Hi, Joe, having any luck?"

He came up to them and held out a brown felt slipper and looked at Sara. "Is this Charlie's?"

Sara looked at the familiar object and forgot the incident of the watch for a moment. "Where did you find it?"

"Right up there by the fence. I had just picked it up when I saw you."

She took the slipper and, holding it against her, said, "Oh, I *knew* he came up this way, but it's a relief to have some proof of it."

"I was just talking to Mr. Aker," Joe continued, "and he said he heard his dogs barking up here last night. He had them tied out by the shack and he thought maybe someone was prowling around."

"Probably Charlie," Mary said.

"That's what I figured. Somebody ought to go down to the gas station and tell the people. They're organizing a big search now and half of the men are planning to go up to the mine."

There was a pause and Mary said, "Well, I guess I could go, only I don't know whether I'll have time to get back up here." She looked at Joe. "I promised Bennie Hoffman I'd come to his party tonight. That's why my hair's in rollers."

"Tell them I found the slipper about a half mile up behind the Akers' at the old fence," Joe said.

"Sure. Are you coming to Bennie's tonight?"

"Maybe."

"Come. It's going to be fun."

Sara cleared her throat and said, "Well, I think I'll get on with my search if you two will excuse me." She turned and started walking up the hill again. There seemed to be a long silence in which even the sound of the cicadas in the grass was absent. She thrashed at the high weeds with her tennis shoes and hugged Charlie's slipper to her.

"Wait a minute, Sara, I'll come with you," Joe Melby said.

He joined her and she nodded, still looking down at the slipper. There was a picture of an Indian chief stamped on the top of the shoe and there was a loneliness to the Indian's profile, even stamped crudely on the felt, that she had never noticed before.

She cleared her throat again. "There is just one thing I want to say." Her voice did not even sound familiar, a tape-recorded voice.

He waited, then said, "Go ahead."

She did not speak for a moment but continued walking noisily through the weeds.

"Go ahead."

"If you'll just wait a minute, I'm trying to think how to say this." The words she wanted to say — I'm sorry — would not come out at all.

They continued walking in silence and then Joe said, "You know, I was just reading an article about a guru over in India and he hasn't spoken a word in twenty-eight years. *Twenty-eight years* and he hasn't said one word in all that time. And everyone has been waiting all those years to hear what he's going to say when he finally does speak because it's supposed to be some great wise word, and I thought about this poor guy sitting there and for twenty-eight years he's been trying to think of something to say that would be the least bit great and he can't think of anything and he must be getting really desperate now. And every day it gets worse and worse."

"Is there supposed to be some sort of message in that story?"

"Maybe."

She smiled. "Well, I just wanted to say that I'm sorry." She thought again that she was going to start crying and she said to herself, You are nothing but a big soft snail. Snail!

"That's all right."

"I just found out about Aunt Willie going to see your mother."

He shrugged. "She didn't mean anything by it."

"But it was a terrible thing."

"It wasn't all that bad. At least it was different to be accused of something I *didn't* do for a change."

"But to be called in like that in front of Aunt Willie and Mary's mother. No, it was terrible." She turned and walked into the woods.

"Don't worry about it. I'm tough. I'm indestructible. I'm like that coyote in 'Road Runner' who is always getting flattened and dynamited and crushed and in the next scene is strolling along, completely normal again."

"I just acted too hastily. That's one of my main faults."

"I do that too."

"Not like me."

"Worse probably. Do you remember when we used to get grammar-school report cards, and the grades would be on one part of the card, and on the other side would be personality things the teacher would check, like 'Does not accept criticism constructively'?"

Sara smiled. "I always used to get a check on that one," she said.

"Who didn't? And then they had one, 'Acts impetuously and without consideration for others,' or something like that, and one year I got a double check on that one."

"You didn't."

"Yes, I did. Second grade. Miss McLeod. I remember she told the whole class that this was the first year she had ever had to give double checks to any student, and everyone in the room was scared to open his report card to see if he had got the double checks. And when I opened mine, there they were, two sets of double checks, on acting impetuously and on not accepting criticism, and single checks on everything else."

"Were you crushed?"

"Naturally."

"I thought you were so tough and indestructible."

"Well, I am" — he paused — "I think." He pointed to the left. "Let's go up this way."

She agreed with a nod and went ahead of him between the trees.

There was a ravine in the forest, a deep cut in the earth, and Charlie had made his way into it through an early morning fog. By chance, blindly stepping through the fog with his arms outstretched, he had managed to pick the one path that led into the ravine, and when the sun came out and the fog burned away, he could not find the way out.

All the ravine looked the same in the daylight, the high walls, the masses of weeds and wild berry bushes, the trees. He had wandered around for a while, following the little paths made by dirt washed down from the hillside, but finally he sat down on a log and stared straight ahead without seeing.

After a while he roused enough to wipe his hands over his cheeks where the tears and dirt had dried together and to rub his puffed eyelids. Then he looked down, saw his bare foot, put it on top of his slipper, and sat with his feet overlapped.

There was a dullness about him now. He had had so many scares, heard so many frightening noises, started at so many shadows, been hurt so often that all his senses were worn to a flat hopelessness. He would just sit here forever.

It was not the first time Charlie had been lost, but never before had there been this finality. He had become separated from Aunt Willie once at the county fair and had not even known he was lost until she had come bursting out of the crowd screaming, "Charlie, Charlie," and enveloped him. He had been lost in school once in the hall and could not find his way back to his room, and he had walked up and down the halls, frightened by all the strange children looking out of every door, until one of the boys was sent out to lead him to his room. But in all his life there had never been an experience like this one.

He bent over and looked down at his watch, his eyes on the tiny red hand. For the first time he noticed it was no longer moving. Holding his breath in his concern, he brought the watch closer to his face. The hand was still. For a moment he could not believe it. He watched it closely, waiting. Still the hand did not move. He shook his hand back and forth, as if he were trying to shake the watch off his wrist. He had seen Sara do this to her watch.

Then he held the watch to his ear. It was silent. He had had the watch for five months and never before had it failed him. He had not even known it could fail. And now it was silent and still.

He put his hand over the watch, covering it completely. He waited. His breathing had begun to quicken again. His hand on the watch was almost clammy. He waited, then slowly, cautiously, he removed his hand and looked at the tiny red hand on the dial. It was motionless. The trick had not worked.

Bending over the watch, he looked closely at the stem. Aunt Willie always wound the watch for him every morning after breakfast, but he did not know how she did this. He took the stem in his fingers, pulled at it clumsily, then harder, and it came off. He looked at it. Then, as he attempted to put it back on the watch, it fell to the ground and was lost in the leaves.

A chipmunk ran in front of him and scurried up the bank. Distracted for a moment, Charlie got up and walked toward it. The chipmunk paused and then darted into a hole, leaving Charlie standing in the shadows trying to see where it had gone. He went closer to the bank and pulled at the leaves, but he could not even find the place among the roots where the chipmunk had disappeared.

Suddenly something seemed to explode within Charlie, and he began to cry noisily. He threw himself on the bank and began kicking, flailing at the ground, at the invisible chipmunk, at the silent watch. He wailed, yielding in helplessness to his anguish, and his piercing screams, uttered again and again, seemed to hang in the air so that they overlapped. His fingers tore at the tree roots and dug beneath the leaves and scratched, animal-like, at the dark earth.

His body sagged and he rolled down the bank and was silent. He looked up at the trees, his chest still heaving with sobs, his face strangely still. After a moment, his eyelids drooped and he fell asleep.

"Charlie! Charlie!"

The only answer was the call of a bird in the branches overhead, one long tremulous whistle.

"He's not even within hearing distance," Sara said.

For the past hour she and Joe Melby had been walking deeper and deeper into the forest without pause, and now the trees were so thick that only small spots of sunlight found their way through the heavy foliage.

"Charlie, oh, Charlie!"

She waited, looking down at the ground.

Joe said, "You want to rest for a while?"

Sara shook her head. She suddenly wanted to see her brother so badly that her throat began to close. It was a tight feeling she got sometimes when she wanted something, like the time she had had the measles and had wanted to see her father so much she couldn't even swallow. Now she thought that if she had a whole glass of ice water — and she was thirsty — she probably would not be able to drink a single drop.

"If you can make it a little farther, there's a place at the top of the hill where the strip mining is, and you can see the whole valley from there."

"I can make it."

"Well, we can rest first if —"

"I can make it."

She suddenly felt a little better. She thought that if she could stand up there on top of the hill and look down and see, somewhere in that huge green valley, a small plump figure in blue pajamas, she would ask for nothing more in life. She thought of the valley as a relief map where everything would be shiny and smooth, and her brother would be right where she could spot him at once. Her cry, "There he is!" would ring like a bell over the valley and everyone would hear her and know that Charlie had been found.

She paused, leaned against a tree for a moment, and then continued. Her legs had begun to tremble.

It was the time of afternoon when she usually sat down in front of the television and watched game shows, the shows where the married couples tried to guess things about each other and where girls had to pick out dates they couldn't see. She would sit in the doorway to the hall where she always sat and Charlie would come in and watch with her, and the living room would be dark and smell of the pine-scented cleaner Aunt Willie used.

Then "The Early Show" would come on, and she would sit through the old movie, leaning forward in the doorway, making fun, saying things like, "Now, Charlie, we'll have the old Convict Turning Honest scene," and Charlie, sitting on the stool closer to the television, would nod without understanding.

She was good, too, at joining in the dialogue with the actors. When the cowboy would say something like, "Things are quiet around here tonight," she would join in with, "Yeah, *too* quiet," right on cue. It seemed strange to be out here in the woods with Joe Melby instead of in the living room with Charlie, watching *Flame of Araby*, which was the early movie for that afternoon.

Her progress up the hill seemed slower and slower. It was like the time she had won the slow bicycle race, a race in which she had to go as slow as possible without letting a foot touch the ground, and she had gone slower and slower, all the while feeling a strong compulsion to speed ahead and cross the finish line first. At the end of the race it had been she and T. R. Peters, and they had paused just before the finish line, balancing motionless on their bicycles. The time had seemed endless, and then T.R. lost his balance and his foot touched the ground and Sara was the winner.

She slipped on some dry leaves, went down on her knees, straightened, and paused to catch her breath.

"Are you all right?"

"Yes, I just slipped."

She waited for a moment, bent over her knees, then she called, "Charlie! Charlie," without lifting her head.

"Oh, Charleeeeee," Joe shouted above her.

Sara knew Charlie would shout back if he heard her, the long wailing cry he gave sometimes when he was frightened during the night. It was such a familiar cry that for a moment she thought she heard it.

She waited, still touching the ground with one hand, until she was sure there was no answer.

"Come on," Joe said, holding out his hand.

He pulled her to her feet and she stood looking up at the top of the hill. Machines had cut away the earth there to get at the veins of coal, and the earth had been pushed down the hill to form a huge bank.

"I'll never get up that," she said. She leaned against a tree whose leaves were covered with pale fine dirt which had filtered down when the machines had cut away the hill.

"Sure you will. I've been up it a dozen times."

He took her hand and she started after him, moving sideways up the steep bank. The dirt crumbled beneath her feet and she slid, skinned one knee, and then slipped again. When she had regained her balance she laughed wryly and said, "What's going to happen is that I'll end up pulling you all the way down the hill."

"No, I've got you. Keep coming."

She started again, putting one foot carefully above the other, picking her way over the stones. When she paused, he said, "Keep coming. We're almost there."

"I think it's a trick, like at the dentist's when he says, 'I'm almost through drilling.' Then he drills for another hour and says, 'Now, I'm really almost through drilling,' and he keeps on and then says, 'There's just one more spot and then I'll be practically really through.'"

"We must go to the same dentist."

"I don't think I can make it. There's no skin at all left on the sides of my legs."

"Well, we're really almost practically there now, in the words of your dentist."

She fell across the top of the dirt bank on her stomach, rested for a moment, and then turned and looked down the valley.

She could not speak for a moment. There lay the whole valley in a way she had never imagined it, a tiny finger of civilization set in a sweeping expanse of dark forest. The black treetops seemed to crowd against the yards, the houses, the roads, giving the impression that at any moment the trees would close over the houses like waves and leave nothing but an unbroken line of black-green leaves waving in the sunlight.

Up the valley she could see the intersection where they shopped, the drugstore, the gas station where her mother had once won a set of twenty-four stemmed glasses which Aunt Willie would not allow them to use, the grocery store, the lot where the yellow school buses were parked for the summer. She could look over the valley and see another hill where white cows were all grouped together by a fence and beyond that another hill and then another.

She looked back at the valley and she saw the lake and for the first time since she had stood up on the hill she remembered Charlie.

Raising her hand to her mouth, she called, "Charlie! Charlie! Charlie!" There was a faint echo that seemed to waver in her ears.

"Charlie, oh, Charlie!" Her voice was so loud it seemed to ram into the valley.

Sara waited. She looked down at the forest, and everything was so quiet it seemed to her that the whole valley, the whole world was waiting with her.

"Charlie, hey, Charlie!" Joe shouted.

"Charleeeeeee!" She made the sound of it last a long time. "Can you hear meeeeee?"

With her eyes she followed the trail she knew he must have taken — the house, the Akers' vacant lot, the old pasture, the forest. The forest that seemed powerful enough to engulf a whole valley, she thought with a sinking feeling, could certainly swallow up a young boy.

"Charlie! Charlie! Charlie!" There was a waver in the last syllable that betrayed how near she was to tears. She looked down at the Indian slipper she was still holding.

"Charlie, oh, Charlie." She waited. There was not a sound anywhere. "Charlie, where are you?"

"Hey, Charlie!" Joe shouted.

They waited in the same dense silence. A cloud passed in front of the sun and a breeze began to blow through the trees. Then there was silence again.

"Charlie, Charlie, Charlie, Charlie, Charlie."

She paused, listened, then bent abruptly and put Charlie's slipper to her eyes. She waited for the hot tears that had come so often this summer, the tears that had seemed so close only a moment before. Now her eyes remained dry.

I have cried over myself a hundred times this summer, she thought, I have wept over my big feet and my skinny legs and my nose, I have even cried over my stupid shoes, and now when I have a true sadness there are no tears left.

She held the felt side of the slipper against her eyes like a blindfold and stood there, feeling the hot sun on her head and the wind wrapping around her legs, conscious of the height and the valley sweeping down from her feet.

"Listen, just because you can't hear him doesn't mean anything. He could be —"

"Wait a minute." She lowered the slipper and looked down the valley. A sudden wind blew dust into her face and she lifted her hand to shield her eyes.

"I thought I heard something. Charlie! Answer me right this minute."

She waited with the slipper held against her breasts, one hand to her eyes, her whole body motionless, concentrating on her brother. Then she stiffened. She thought again she had heard something — Charlie's long high wail. Charlie could sound sadder than anyone when he cried.

In her anxiety she took the slipper and twisted it again and again as if she were wringing water out. She called, then stopped abruptly and listened. She looked at Joe and he shook his head slowly.

She looked away. A bird rose from the trees below and flew toward the hills in the distance. She waited until she could see it no longer and then slowly, still listening for the call that didn't come, she sank to the ground and sat with her head bent over her knees.

Beside her, Joe scuffed his foot in the dust and sent a cascade of rocks and dirt down the bank. When the sound of it faded, he began to call, "Charlie, hey, Charlie," again and again.

Charlie awoke, but he lay for a moment without opening his eyes. He did not remember where he was, but he had a certain dread of seeing it.

There were great parts of his life that were lost to Charlie, blank spaces that he could never fill in. He would find himself in a strange place and not know how he had got there. Like the time Sara had been hit in the nose with a baseball at the Dairy Queen, and the blood and the sight of Sara kneeling on the ground in helpless pain had frightened him so much that he had turned and run without direction, in a frenzy, dashing headlong up the street, blind to cars and people.

By chance Mr. Weicek had seen him, put him in the car, and driven him home, and Aunt Willie had put him to bed, but later he remembered none of this. He had only awakened in bed and looked at the crumpled bit of ice-cream cone still clenched in his hand and wondered about it.

His whole life had been built on a strict routine, and as long as this routine was kept up, he felt safe and well. The same foods, the same bed, the same furniture in the same place, the same seat on the school bus, the same class procedure were all important to him. But always there could be the unexpected, the dreadful surprise that would topple his carefully constructed life in an instant.

The first thing he became aware of was the twigs pressing into his face, and he put his hand under his cheek. Still he did not open his eyes. Pictures began to drift into his mind; he saw Aunt Willie's cigar box which was filled with old jewelry and buttons and knickknacks, and he found that he could remember every item in that box — the string of white beads without a clasp, the old earrings, the tiny book with souvenir fold-out pictures of New York, the plastic decorations from cakes, the turtle made of sea shells. Every item was so real that he opened his eyes and was surprised to see, instead of the glittering contents of the box, the dull and unfamiliar forest.

He raised his head and immediately felt the aching of his body. Slowly he sat up and looked down at his hands. His fingernails were black with earth, two of them broken below the quick, and he got up slowly and sat on the log behind him and inspected his fingers more closely.

Then he sat up straight. His hands dropped to his lap. His head cocked to the side like a bird listening. Slowly he straightened until he was standing. At his side his fingers twitched at the empty air as if to grasp something. He took a step forward, still with his head to the side. He remained absolutely still.

Then he began to cry out in a hoarse excited voice, again and again, screaming now, because he had just heard someone far away calling his name.

At the top of the hill Sara got slowly to her feet and stood looking down at the forest. She pushed the hair back from her forehead and moistened her lips. The wind dried them as she waited.

Joe started to say something but she reached out one hand and took his arm to stop him. Scarcely daring to believe her ears, she stepped closer to the edge of the bank. Now she heard it unmistakably — the sharp repeated cry — and she knew it was Charlie.

"Charlie!" she shouted with all her might.

She paused and listened, and his cries were louder and she knew he was not far away after all, just down the slope, in the direction of the ravine.

"It's Charlie, it's Charlie!"

A wild joy overtook her and she jumped up and down on the bare earth and she felt that she could crush the whole hill just by jumping if she wanted.

She sat and scooted down the bank, sending earth and pebbles in a cascade before her. She landed on the soft ground, ran a few steps, lost her balance, caught hold of the first tree trunk she could find, and swung around till she stopped.

She let out another whoop of pure joy, turned and ran down the hill in great strides, the puce tennis shoes slapping the ground like rubber paddles, the wind in her face, her hands grabbing one tree trunk after another for support. She felt like a wild creature who had traveled through the forest this way for a lifetime. Nothing could stop her now.

At the edge of the ravine she paused and stood gasping for breath. Her heart was beating so fast it pounded in her ears, and her throat was dry. She leaned against a tree, resting her cheek against the rough bark.

She thought for a minute she was going to faint, a thing she had never done before, not even when she broke her nose. She hadn't even believed people really did faint until this minute when she clung to the tree because her legs were as useless as rubber bands.

There was a ringing in her ears and another sound, a wailing siren-like cry that was painfully familiar.

"Charlie?"

Charlie's crying, like the sound of a cricket, seemed everywhere and nowhere.

She walked along the edge of the ravine, circling the large boulders and trees. Then she looked down into the ravine where the shadows lay, and she felt as if something had turned over inside her because she saw Charlie.

He was standing in his torn pajamas, face turned upward, hands raised, shouting with all his might. His eyes were shut tight. His face was streaked with dirt and tears. His pajama jacket hung in shreds about his scratched chest.

He opened his eyes and as he saw Sara a strange expression came over his face, an expression of wonder and joy and disbelief, and Sara knew that if she lived to be a hundred no one would ever look at her quite that way again.

She paused, looked down at him, and then, sliding on the seat of her pants, went down the bank and took him in her arms.

"Oh, Charlie."

His arms gripped her like steel.

"Oh, Charlie."

She could feel his fingers digging into her back as he clutched her shirt. "It's all right now, Charlie, I'm here and we're going home." His face was buried in her shirt and she patted his head, said again, "It's all right now. Everything's fine."

She held him against her for a moment and now the hot tears were in her eyes and on her cheeks and she didn't even notice.

"I know how you feel," she said. "I know. One time when I had the measles and my fever was real high, I got lost on my way back from the bathroom, right in our house, and it was a terrible feeling, terrible, because I wanted to get back to my bed and I couldn't find it, and finally Aunt Willie heard me and came and you know where I was? In the kitchen. In our kitchen and I couldn't have been more lost if I'd been out in the middle of the wilderness."

She patted the back of his head again and said, "Look, I even brought your bedroom slipper. Isn't that service, huh?"

She tried to show it to him, but he was still clutching her, and she held him against her, patting him. After a moment she said again, "Look, here's your slipper. Let's put it on." She knelt, put his foot into the shoe, and said, "Now, isn't that better?"

He nodded slowly, his chest still heaving with unspent sobs.

"Can you walk home?"

He nodded. She took her shirttail and wiped his tears and smiled at him. "Come on, we'll find a way out of here and go home."

"Hey, over this way," Joe called from the bank of the ravine. Sara had forgotten about him in the excitement of finding Charlie, and she looked up at him for a moment.

"Over this way, around the big tree," Joe called. "That's probably how he got in. The rest of the ravine is a mass of brier bushes."

She put one arm around Charlie and led him around the tree. "Everybody in town's looking for you, you know that?" she said. "Everybody. The police came and all the neighbors are out — there must be a hundred people looking for you. You were on the radio. It's like you were the President of the United States or something. Everybody was saying, 'Where's Charlie?' and 'We got to find Charlie.'"

Suddenly Charlie stopped and held up his hand and Sara looked down. "What is it?"

He pointed to the silent watch.

She smiled. "Charlie, you are something, you know that? Here we are racing down the hill to tell everyone in great triumph that you are found, *found*, and we have to stop and wind your watch first."

She looked at the watch, saw that the stem was missing, and shook her head. "It's broken, Charlie, see, the stem's gone. It's broken."

He held it out again.

"It's *broken*, Charlie. We'll have to take it to the jeweler and have it fixed."

He continued to hold out his arm.

"Hey, Charlie, you want to wear my watch till you get yours fixed?" Joe asked. He slid down the bank and put his watch on Charlie's arm. "There."

Charlie bent his face close and listened.

"Now can we go home?" Sara asked, jamming her hands into her back pockets.

Charlie nodded.

They walked through the woods for a long time, Joe in the lead, picking the best path, with Charlie and Sara following. From time to time Sara turned and hugged Charlie and he smelled of trees and dark earth and tears and she said, "Everybody's going to be so glad to see you it's going to be just like New Year's Eve."

Sara could not understand why she suddenly felt so good. It was a puzzle. The day before she had been miserable. She had wanted to fly away from everything, like the swans to a new lake, and now she didn't want that any more.

Down the hill Mr. Rhodes, one of the searchers, was coming toward them and Joe called out, "Mr. Rhodes, Sara found him!"

"Is he all right?" Mr. Rhodes called back.

"Fine, he's fine."

"Sara found him and he's all right. He's all right." The phrase passed down the hill from Dusty Rhodes, who painted cars at the garage, to Mr. Aker to someone Sara couldn't recognize.

Then all the searchers were joining them, reaching out to pat Charlie and to say to Sara, "Oh, your aunt is going to be so happy," or "Where *was* he?" or "Well, now we can all sleep in peace tonight."

They came through the woods in a big noisy group and out into the late sunlight in the old pasture, Sara and Charlie in the middle, surrounded by all the searchers.

Suddenly Sara sensed a movement above her. She looked up and then grabbed Charlie's arm.

The swans were directly overhead, flying with outstretched necks, their long wings beating the air, an awkward blind sort of flight. They were so low that she thought they might hit the trees, but at the last moment they pulled up and skimmed the air just above the treetops.

"Look, Charlie, look. Those are the swans. Remember? They're going home."

He looked blankly at the sky, unable to associate the heavy awkward birds with the graceful swans he had seen on the water. He squinted at the sky, then looked at Sara, puzzled.

"Charlie, those are the swans. Remember? At the lake?" she said, looking right at him. "They're going home now. Don't you remember? They were —"

"Hey, there's your aunt, Charlie. There's Aunt Willie coming."

Sara was still pulling at Charlie's arm, directing his attention to the sky. It seemed urgent somehow that Charlie see the swans once again. She said, "Charlie, those are —"

He looked instead across the field and he broke away from Sara and started running. She took two steps after him and then stopped. Aunt Willie in her bright green dress seemed to shine like a beacon, and he hurried toward her, an awkward figure in torn blue pajamas, shuffling through the high grass.

There was a joyous yell that was so shrill Sara thought it had come from the swans, but then she knew that it had come from Charlie, for the swans were mute.

"Here he is, Willie," Mrs. Aker called, running behind Charlie to have some part in the reunion.

Aunt Willie was coming as fast as she could on her bad legs. "I never thought to see him again," she was telling everyone and no one. "I thought he was up in that mine. I tell you, I never thought to see him again. Charlie, come here to your Aunt Willie."

Charlie ran like a ball rolling downhill, bouncing with the slope of the land.

"I tell you this has been the blackest day of my life" — Aunt Willie was gasping — "and I include every day I have been on earth. Charlie, my Charlie, let me look at you. Oh, you are a sight."

He fell into Aunt Willie's arms. Over his head Aunt Willie said through her tears to Mrs. Aker, "May you never lose your Bobby, that's all I got to say. May you never lose your Bobby, may none of you ever lose anybody in the woods or in the mine or anywhere."

Sara stood in the pasture by the old gray shack and watched the swans disappear over the hill, and then she watched Charlie and Aunt Willie disappear in the crowd of people, and she felt good and loose and she thought that if she started walking down the hill at that moment, she would walk with the light movements of a puppet and never touch the ground at all.

She thought she would sit down for a moment now that everyone was gone, but when she looked around she saw Joe Melby still standing behind her. "I thought you went with the others."

"Nope."

"It's been a very strange day for me." She looked at the horizon where the swans had disappeared.

"It's been one of my stranger days too."

"Well, I'd better go home."

Joe walked a few steps with her, cleared his throat, and then said, "Do you want to go to Bennie Hoffman's party with me?"

She thought she hadn't heard him right for a moment, or if she had, that it was a mistake, like the boy who shouted, "Hey, beautiful," at Rosey Camdon.

"What?"

"I asked if you wanted to go with me to the party."

"I wasn't invited." She made herself think of the swans. By this time they could probably see the lake at the university and were about to settle down on the water with a great beating of wings and ruffling of feathers. She could almost see the long perfect glide that would bring them to the water.

"I'm inviting you. Bennie said I could bring somebody if I wanted to. He begged me to bring someone, as a matter of fact. He and Sammy and John and Pete have formed this musical group and they're going to make everybody listen to them."

"Well, I don't know."

"Why not? Other than the fact that you're going to have to listen to some terrible guitar playing. Bennie Hoffman has had about one and a half lessons."

"Well . . ."

"It's not any big deal, just sitting in Bennie Hoffman's back yard and watching him louse up with a two-hundred-dollar guitar and amplifier."

"I guess I could go."

"I'll walk over and pick you up in half an hour. It won't matter if we're late. The last fifty songs will sound about the same as the first fifty."

"I'll be ready."

When Sara came up the walk Wanda was standing on the porch. "What is going on around here, will you tell me that? Where is Charlie?"

"We found him. He's with Aunt Willie, wherever that is."

"Do you know how I heard he was lost? I heard it on the car radio when I was coming home. How do you think that made me feel — to hear from some disc jockey that my own brother was missing? I could hardly get here because there are a hundred cars full of people jamming the street down there."

"Well, he's fine."

"So Mr. Aker told me, only I would like to see him and find out what happened."

"He got up during the night sometime — this is what I think happened — to go see the swans and ended up in a ravine crying his heart out."

Wanda stepped off the porch and looked across the street, leaning to see around the foliage by the fence. She said, "Is that them over there on the Carsons' porch?"

Sara looked and nodded.

"Honestly, Charlie still in his pajamas, and Aunt Willie in her good green dress with a handkerchief tied around her forehead to keep her from sweating, and both of them eating watermelon. That beats all."

"At least he's all right."

Wanda started down the walk, then paused. "You want to come?"

"No, I'm going to a party."

"Whose?"

"Bennie Hoffman's."

"I didn't think you were invited."

"Joe Melby's taking me."

"Joe Melby? Your great and terrible enemy?"

"He is not my enemy, Wanda. He is one of the nicest people I know."

"For three months I've been hearing about the evils of Joe Melby. Joe Melby, the thief; Joe Melby, the fink; Joe Melby, the —"

"A person," Sara said coldly, "can occasionally be mistaken." She turned and went into the living room, saw Boysie sleeping by the door and said, "Boysie, we found Charlie." She bent and rubbed him behind the ears. Then she went into the kitchen, made a sandwich, and was starting into the bedroom when the phone rang.

"Hello," she said, her mouth full of food.

"Hello, I have a long-distance call for Miss Willamina Godfrey," the operator said.

"Oh, she's across the street. If you'll wait a minute I'll go get her."

"Operator, I'll just talk to whoever's there," Sara heard her father say.

She said quickly, "No, I'll go get her. Just wait one minute. It won't take any time. She's right across the street."

"Sara? Is this Sara?"

"Yes, this is me." The strange feeling came over her again. "If you wait a minute I'll go get Aunt Willie."

"Sara, did you find Charlie?"

"Yes, we found him, but I don't mind going to get Aunt Willie. They're over on the Carsons' porch."

"Is Charlie all right?"

"He's fine. He's eating watermelon right now."

"Where was he?"

"Well, he went up into the woods and got lost. We found him in a ravine and he was dirty and tired and hungry but he's all right."

"That's good. I was going to come home tonight if he hadn't been found."

"Oh."

"But since everything's all right, I guess I'll just wait until the weekend."

"Sure."

"So I'll probably see you Saturday, then, if nothing turns up."

"Fine."

"Be sure to tell Willie I called."

"I will."

A picture came into her mind of the laughing, curly-headed man with the broken tooth in the photograph album, and she suddenly saw life as a series of huge, uneven steps, and she saw herself on the steps, standing motionless in her prison shirt, and she had just taken an enormous step up out of the shadows, and she was standing, waiting, and there were other steps in front of her, so that she could go as high as the sky, and she saw Charlie on a flight of small difficult steps, and her father down at the bottom of some steps, just sitting and not trying to go further. She saw everyone she knew on those blinding white steps and for a moment everything was clearer than it had ever been.

"Sara?"

"I'm still here."

"Well, that was all I wanted, just to hear that Charlie was all right."

"He's fine."

"And I'll see you on Saturday if nothing happens."

"Sure."

"Good-by."

She sat for a minute still holding the receiver and then she set it back on the telephone and finished her sandwich. Slowly she slipped off her tennis shoes and looked down at her feet, which were dyed blue. Then she got up quickly and went to get ready for the party.

Responding to *The Summer of the Swans*

Thinking and Discussing

What details make the Godfreys seem like a real family in the modern-day world? What do you learn about each family member through the dialogue? When and how do you get to know Charlie?

Why are the watch, the sneakers, and the swans important in the book? What makes them meaningful for certain characters?

What does Sara learn from the events in this novel? How does she change?

Choosing a Creative Response

Identifying Personal Treasures Most people own something they keep only because it comforts them. For Charlie, it is a watch. Make a list of things you treasure, such as an old sweatshirt, baseball mitt, or photograph, and circle your favorite one. Explain why you treasure this item.

Reporting Charlie's Rescue With your group, plan and act out a television newscast covering the story of Charlie's rescue. Members of your group can take the parts of the story characters, reporters, and camera operators. Then lead a discussion about how the portrayal of this event in the newscast differs from the way it is treated in the novel.

Creating Your Own Activity Plan and complete your own activity in response to *The Summer of the Swans*.

Thinking About Novels

Designing Book Covers Gather materials to make a collage that could be used to illustrate the cover of *The Summer of the Swans*. If necessary, look back in the book to recall details about the characters. Then, based on your ideas, select colored paper, photos, fabric, or anything else that can be glued to sturdy paper or cardboard. When you have finished the collage, compare it to those of your classmates.

Creating Chapter Titles Imagine you have been hired to write chapter titles for a reprint of *The Summer of the Swans*. Review each chapter and write a short phrase that could be used as its title. Consider two things: What happened in the chapter? How does it fit into the book as a whole? Your final chapter titles should roughly outline the plot of the story.

Weaving a Realistic Tale Byars says that she often draws inspiration from everyday life when writing her novels. She weaves her stories around ideas sparked by real-life events, people, or places. Find a photograph in a local museum, newspaper, or magazine that you are curious about and see if you can track down the facts behind it. When you have uncovered the events surrounding the photograph, make up a story based on your research to tell the class. Your audience might be interested in seeing a copy of the photograph.

About the Author

Betsy Byars

Betsy Byars was born in Charlotte, North Carolina, in 1928. She grew up in a family that enjoyed reading, and she herself learned to read when she was only four years old. Byars, however, had no desire to be a writer. She recalls, "Writing seemed boring. You sat in a room all day by yourself and typed." Finding herself home alone with two young children, however, she turned to writing to fill the quiet hours.

Byars's first book was published in 1962, but it was not successful. Still she pressed on, completing three other stories before writing *The Midnight Fox*, which was published in 1968. Byars says, "This is my favorite book, because it is very personal. A great deal of my own children and their activities went into it, and a great deal of myself. It came closer to what I was trying to do than any of my other books." In 1971 *The Summer of the Swans* won the Newbery Medal as well as several other awards. The idea for this popular story grew out of her actual experiences tutoring children with learning disabilities. Other books for children followed, including *The House of Wings*, *After the Goat Man*, *The Pinballs*, *The Cartoonist*, *The Night Swimmers*, *The Computer Nut*, and *The Not-Just-Anybody Family*. Byars now lives in Clemson, South Carolina, where she spends as much as eight hours a day at a word processor, hammering out her current book.

House events unfolded

551

Taking Flight

The House of Wings by Betsy Byars (Houghton, 1991; Viking, 1972)
Sammy doesn't understand why his eccentric grandfather seems to love only wild animals. It takes a blind and injured crane to teach him about caring.

Number the Stars by Lois Lowry (Houghton, 1989)
Annemarie Johansen and her family must endure the hated German occupation of Denmark. When the Nazis begin arresting and deporting Jews, the Johansens try to save their friends the Rosens. Their courage reflects the heroism of the Danish Resistance, which managed to smuggle nearly 7000 people to safety in Sweden.

The Midnight Fox by Betsy Byars (Viking, 1968)
The prospect of spending the summer on a farm is not pleasant for Tommy, who is afraid of animals. But one day he sees a beautiful black fox, and soon his whole life centers around the fox and her cub.

Jellybean by Tessa Duder (Viking, 1986)
Geraldine feels invisible in her mother's world of musicians and concert rehearsals until a new friend helps her make a secret ambition come true.

Cassie Binegar by Patricia MacLachlan (Harper, 1982)
Cassie is upset when she moves to a new home by the sea. Embarrassed by her large, noisy family, she decides to find a private space of her own.

NUMBER THE STARS
a novel by Lois Lowry

BETSY BYARS
THE
HOUSE OF WINGS

Glossary

Some of the words in this book may have pronunciations or meanings you do not know. This glossary can help you by telling you how to pronounce those words and by telling you the meanings with which those words are used in this book.

You can find out the correct pronunciation of any glossary word by using the special spelling after the word and the pronunciation key that runs across the bottom of the glossary pages.

The full pronunciation key opposite shows how to pronounce each consonant and vowel in a special spelling. The pronunciation key at the bottom of the glossary pages is a shortened form of the full key.

FULL PRONUNCIATION KEY

Consonant Sounds

b	**bib**	k	**c**at, **k**i**ck**, pi**que**	th	pa**th**, **th**in
ch	**ch**ur**ch**	l	**l**id, need**l**e	*th*	ba**th**e, **th**is
d	**d**ee**d**	m	a**m**, **m**an, **mum**	v	ca**v**e, **v**al**v**e,
f	**f**ast, **f**i**f**e, o**ff**,	n	**n**o, sudde**n**		**v**ine
	phase, rou**gh**	ng	thi**ng**	w	**w**ith
g	**g**a**g**	p	**p**o**p**	y	**y**es
h	**h**at	r	**r**oa**r**	z	**z**ose, si**z**e,
hw	**wh**ich	s	mi**ss**, **s**au**c**e, **s**ee		**x**ylophone,
j	**j**u**dg**e	sh	di**sh**, **sh**ip		**z**ebra
		t	**t**igh**t**	zh	gara**g**e,
					plea**s**ure, vi**s**ion

Vowel Sounds

ă	p**a**t	î	d**ea**r, d**ee**r,	ou	c**ow**, **ou**t
ā	**a**id, th**ey**, p**ay**		f**ie**rce, m**e**re	ŭ	c**u**t, r**ou**gh
â	**ai**r, c**a**re, w**ea**r	ŏ	p**o**t, h**o**rrible	û	f**i**rm, h**ea**rd,
ä	f**a**ther	ō	g**o**, r**ow**, t**oe**		t**e**rm, t**u**rn,
ĕ	p**e**t, pl**e**asure	ô	**a**lter, c**au**ght,		w**o**rd
ē	b**e**, b**ee**, **ea**sy,		f**o**r, p**aw**	y o͞o	ab**u**se, **u**se
	s**ei**ze	oi	b**oy**, n**oi**se, **oi**l	ə	**a**bout, sil**e**nt,
ĭ	p**i**t	o͝o	b**oo**k		penc**i**l, lem**o**n,
ī	b**y**, g**uy**, p**ie**	o͞o	b**oo**t		circ**u**s
				ər	butt**er**

STRESS MARKS

Primary Stress ′	Secondary Stress ′
bi•ol•o•gy [bī **ŏl′** ə jē]	bi•o•log•i•cal [bī′ə **lŏj′** ĭ kəl]

Pronunciation key © 1986 by Houghton Mifflin Company. Adapted and reprinted by permission from *The Houghton Mifflin Student Dictionary.*

A

The word **accusation** and its root *"accuse"* come from the Latin word accusare, *"to call to account."*

archaeologists

a•brupt•ly (ə **brŭpt′lē**) *adv.* Unexpectedly; suddenly: *Lightning caused the lights to go out* **abruptly.**

a•bun•dant (ə **bŭn′dənt**) *adj.* Existing in great supply; very plentiful: *In April there is usually* **abundant** *rainfall.*

ac•cu•sa•tion (ăk′yōo zā′shən) *n.* A statement or formal declaration that a person has been guilty of wrongdoing: *He vigorously denied the* **accusation.**

ac•knowl•edge (ăk **nŏl′ĭj**) *v.* **ac•knowl•edged, ac•knowl•edg•ing.** To admit the existence or truth of: *Did she* **acknowledge** *that we were right?*

ad•dle (**ăd′l**) *v.* **ad•dled, ad•dling.** To mix up, confuse, or muddle.

a•dorn (ə **dôrn′**) *v.* **a•dorned, a•dorn•ing.** To decorate with something beautiful or ornamental: *Her fingers were* **adorned** *with rings.*

af•ter•life (**ăf′tər lĭf′**) *or* (**äf′-**) *n.* Life or existence after death.

ag•i•ta•tion (ăj′ĭ tā′shən) *n.* Great emotional disturbance or excitement.

a•li•en (ā′lē ən) *or* (āl′yən) *adj.* Not natural; not characteristic: *The desert is an* **alien** *place to a person used to snow.*

a•mends (ə **mĕndz′**) *pl.n.* —**make amends.** To make up (to someone) for insult or injury: *He sent her roses to* **make amends.**

an•guish (**ăng′gwĭsh**) *n.* A pain of the body or mind that causes one agony.

ar•chae•ol•o•gist (är′kē **ŏl′ə** jĭst) *n.* A person engaged in the scientific study of the remains of past human activities, such as burials, buildings, tools, and pottery.

as•sur•ance (ə **shŏŏr′əns**) *n.* Self-confidence: *The best players act with great* **assurance.**

a•stound (ə **stound′**) *v.* **a•stound•ed, a•stound•ing.** To strike with sudden wonder; astonish: *The magician's trick* **astounded** *the crowd.*

ă pat / ā pay / â care / ä father / ĕ pet / ē be / ĭ pit / ī pie / î fierce / ŏ pot / ō go / ô paw, for /

as•trol•o•ger (ə strŏl′ə jər) *n.*
A person who practices the art of predicting the course of human events through the study of the positions of the stars and planets, which are believed to have a supernatural influence.

at•mos•phere (ăt′mə sfîr′) *n.*
A unit of pressure equal to the pressure of the air at sea level, about 14.7 pounds per square inch.

B

bar•ren (băr′ən) *adj.* **1.** Lacking or unable to produce growing plants or crops. **2.** Empty; bare: *With no furniture, the house looked barren.*

bea•con (bē′kən) *n.* A fire, light, radio signal, or any other signaling device used to guide ships, airplanes, etc.: *The ship's captain followed the flashing beacon to maintain his course in the fog.*

be•fall (bĭ fôl′) *v.* **be•fell, be•fall•en** (bĭ fôl′ən), **be•fall•ing.** To happen to: *Disasters have befallen many ships in these waters.*

bench•mark (bĕnch′märk′) *n.*
An established standard with which other things can be compared: *The Declaration of Independence is a benchmark in American history.*

be•witch (bĭ wĭch′) *v.*
be•witched, be•witch•ing.
1. To cast a spell over: *The fairy bewitched the elves.*
2. To fascinate; charm.

blun•der (blŭn′dər) *n.* A foolish or stupid mistake: *Carelessness caused the blunder.*

bois•ter•ous (boi′stər əs) *or* (-strəs) *adj.* Noisy and lacking restraint or discipline.

bolt (bōlt) *n.* A large roll of cloth, especially as it comes from the loom.

bot•a•nist (bŏt′n ĭst) *n.* A scientist who specializes in the study of plants.

bound•a•ry (boun′də rē) *or* (-drē) *n., pl.* **bound•a•ries.** An edge, limit, or dividing line marking the place where a region ends.

buoy (bōō′ē) *or* (boi) *n.* A float used to mark a channel or a place for boats to anchor.

*In surveying, a **benchmark** is a mark made on some stationary object for use as a reference point in figuring differences in level. Therefore, a personal **benchmark** would be an event or accomplishment by which all others are measured.*

buoy

oi **oil** / ōō **book** / ōō **boot** / ou **out** / ŭ **cut** / û **fur** / *th* **the** / th **thin** / hw **which** / zh **vision** / ə **ago, item, pencil, atom, circus**

557

Caress *comes from the French word* ca-resse, *which in turn came from the Italian* carezza, *meaning "endearment." These words are descended from the Latin* ca-rus, *"dear."*

Concentrate *probably comes from the Old French word* concentrer, *a combination of the Latin* com-, *"same," and* centrum, *"center."*

ca·ress (kə rĕs′) *v.* **ca·ressed, ca·ress·ing.** To touch or stroke affectionately: *The mother caressed her child's head.*

cas·cade (kăs kād′) *n.* A small waterfall that flows over steep rocks.

cas·ket (kăs′kĭt) *or* (kä′skĭt) *n.* A small case or chest for jewels or other valuables.

cas·u·al·ly (kăzh′ōō əl lē) *adv.* With little interest; unconcernedly; nonchalantly: *She casually tossed the wrapper into a trash can.*

cat·a·ract (kăt′ə răkt′) *n.* A very large waterfall formed from steep rapids.

chal·lenge (chăl′ənj) *v.* **chal·lenged, chal·leng·ing.** To call to engage in a contest or fight: *We challenged them to a game of basketball.*

cha·os (kā′ŏs′) *n.* Great disorder or confusion.

clam·or·ing (klăm′ər ĭng) *adj.* Making or full of a loud, continuous, and usually confused noise: *The clamoring crowd disrupted the speech.*

coarse (kôrs) *or* (kōrs) *adj.* Not refined; crude; rude.

col·lec·tive (kə lĕk′tĭv) *adj.* Of a number of persons or things acting as one: *Our collective opinion will add weight.*

com·mit (kə mĭt′) *v.* **com·mit·ted, com·mit·ting.** To pledge (oneself) to a position: *He committed himself to the project.*

com·pas·sion (kəm păsh′ən) *n.* The feeling of sharing the suffering of another, together with a desire to give aid or show mercy.

com·pli·ance (kəm plī′əns) *n.* The act of complying; action or obedience in accordance with a rule, request, command, etc.

con·cen·trate (kŏn′sən trāt′) *v.* **con·cen·trat·ed, con·cen·trat·ing.** To keep or direct one's thoughts, attention, or efforts: *She was concentrating on making the free throw.*

con·di·tion (kən dĭsh′ən) *n.* Something stated as necessary or desirable; a requirement; provision: *He agreed on the condition that he would be paid.*

ă pat / ā pay / â care / ä father / ĕ pet / ē be / ĭ pit / ī pie / î fierce / ŏ pot / ō go / ô paw, for /

con•sent (kən sĕnt′) *v.*
con•sent•ed, con•sent•ing.
To give permission; agree:
*They finally **consented** to
help me.*

con•toured (kŏn′tŏŏrd′) *adj.*
Shaped on the surface: *The
field is **contoured** in ridges
and furrows.*

crest (krĕst) *n.* The top of
something, such as a mountain
or wave.

crude•ly (krōōd′lē) *adv.* In an
unskilled manner; roughly.

cru•el•ty (krōō′əl tē) *n.* The
condition or quality of causing
pain or suffering; unkindness;
mercilessness.

crust (krŭst) *n.* Any hard
outer layer or covering.

cun•ning (kŭn′ĭng) *adj.* Sly;
crafty; clever: *He had a
cunning scheme to get his
money back.*

cu•ri•os•i•ty (kyŏŏr′ē ŏs′ĭ tē)
n. A desire to know or learn:
*He burned with **curiosity** over
what was in the box.*

curl•i•cue (kûr′lĭ kyōō′) *n.* A
fancy twist or curl, such as a
flourish made with a pen.

cur•rent (kûr′ənt) *or* (kŭr′-)
n. A mass of liquid or gas
that is in motion: *Swimmers
can be swept off-balance by
a river's **currents**. —adj.* Com-
monly accepted; in wide-
spread use.

de•bris (də brē′) *or* (dā′brē′)
n. The scattered remains of
something broken, destroyed,
or discarded; fragments;
rubble.

de•ci•pher (dĭ sī′fər) *v.*
**de•ci•phered,
de•ci•pher•ing.** To change (a
message) from a code or cipher
to ordinary language; decode.

ded•i•cate (dĕd′ĭ kāt′) *v.*
ded•i•cat•ed, ded•i•cat•ing.
To set apart for a special purpose, such as worship: *The
ministers and members
dedicated the new church last
Sunday.*

de•fi•ance (dĭ fī′əns) *n.* Open
resistance to authority; refusal
to obey: *The prisoner made a
last gesture of **defiance**.*

del•ta (dĕl′tə) *n.* A usually triangular mass of sand, mud,
and earth at the mouth of a
river.

> **Curious** *comes from
the Old French word*
curios. *That word is
descended from the
Latin* curiosus,
*meaning "diligent,
careful, inquisitive."*

curlicue

---

oi **oil** / ŏŏ **book** / ōō **boot** / ou **out** / ŭ **cut** / û **fur** / *th* **the** / th **thin** / hw **which** /
zh **vision** / ə **ago, item, pencil, atom, circus**

dem•on•stra•tion
(dĕm′ən strā′shən) *n*. A display of how something proceeds or operates: *We gave a **demonstration** of debating skills.*

de•plor•a•ble (dĭ **plôr′**ə bəl) *or* (**-plōr′-**) *adj.* Worthy of strong disapproval or reproach.

de•pot (dē′pō) *n.* A railroad station.

de•pres•sion (dĭ **prĕsh′**ən) *n.* An area that is sunk below its surroundings; a hollow.

depth (dĕpth) *n.* A distance downward or inward from a surface.

de•scend (dĭ **sĕnd′**) *v.* **de•scend•ed, de•scend•ing.** To come down from a source or origin, as from an ancestor: *She is **descended** from the founder of this city.*

des•o•la•tion (dĕs′ə **lā′**shən) *n.* Loneliness or misery.

de•spair•ing•ly (dĭ **spâr′**ĭng lē) *adv.* With an utter lack of hope: *He spoke **despairingly** of their slim chance of survival.*

diadem

des•per•ate•ly (dĕs′pər ĭt lē) *adv.* Extremely; very strongly: *She wanted **desperately** to see her childhood friend.*

des•per•a•tion (dĕs′pə **rā′**shən) *n.* Despair or extreme action resulting from it.

des•tine (dĕs′tĭn) *v.* **des•tined, des•tin•ing.** To determine beforehand, as if by some force or power over which one has no control: *She was **destined** to become a great ruler.*

de•ter•mi•na•tion (dĭ tûr′mə **nā′**shən) *n.* Firmness of purpose: *He had a strong **determination** to win.*

de•test (dĭ **tĕst′**) *v.* **de•test•ed, de•test•ing.** To dislike strongly; abhor; loathe.

de•vour (dĭ **vour′**) *v.* **de•voured, de•vour•ing.** To swallow or eat up greedily.

di•a•dem (dī′ə dĕm′) *n.* A crown or ornamental band worn on the head as a sign of royalty.

di•et (dī′ĭt) *n.* The usual food and drink consumed by a person or animal.

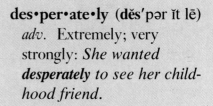

Depot *comes from the French word dé-pôt,* which is descended from the Latin depositum; *this was the neuter past participle of de-ponere, meaning "to deposit."*

ă pat / ā pay / â care / ä father / ĕ pet / ē be / ĭ pit / ī pie / î fierce / ŏ pot / ō go / ô paw, for /

dil•i•gence (dĭl′ə jəns) *n.* Long, steady effort in one's job or studies.

dis•mal (dĭz′məl) *adj.* Causing gloom or depression; dreary.

dis•man•tle (dĭs măn′tl) *v.* **dis•man•tled, dis•man•tling.** To take apart: *Workers were* **dismantling** *the exhibits at the museum.*

dis•o•ri•ent•ed (dĭs ôr′ē ĕnt′ĕd) *or* (-ōr′-) *adj.* Having lost awareness of one's relationship with one's surroundings, as with respect to time or place: *After the accident, the man seemed* **disoriented.**

dis•pute (dĭ spyo͞ot′) *n.* A quarrel.

dis•tin•guish (dĭ stĭng′gwĭsh) *v.* **dis•tin•guished, dis•tin•guish•ing.** To perceive distinctly; make out; discern: *The words of the song could not be* **distinguished** *through the radio's static.*

doomed (do͞omd) *adj.* Fated for an unhappy end, especially death.

dredg•ing (drĕj′ĭng) *n.* The act of fishing up from or as if from the bottom of a river, lake, etc., with a machine that uses scooping or suction devices.

dy•nas•ty (dī′nə stē) *n.* A succession of rulers from the same family or line.

e•la•tion (ĭ lā′shən) *n.* An intense feeling of happiness or joy.

el•e•gance (ĕl′ĭ gəns) *n.* Refinement and grace in appearance or manner: *He always noticed her unaffected* **elegance.**

em•balm (ĕm bäm′) *v.* **em•balmed, em•balm•ing.** To treat (a corpse) with substances that prevent or retard decay.

e•merg•ing (ĭ mûrj′ĭng) *adj.* Coming into view; appearing.

en•dure (ĕn do͝or′) *or* (-dyo͝or′) *v.* **en•dured, en•dur•ing.** To undergo; bear up under: *Astronauts must* **endure** *long hours in a cramped space.*

The earliest use of **dismal** *in Modern English was in the phrase "in the dismal," meaning "at an unlucky time" or "in the evil days." The concept of evil days appears in many early literary works. Also called "Egyptian days," the phrase refers to the two days a month that were considered unlucky and were said to have been discovered by Egyptian astrologers. Some medieval writers felt that the phrase referred to the plagues of ancient Egypt.* **Dismal** *ultimately comes from Latin dies mali, "evil days."*

Emerge *is from the Latin* ēmergere, *"to un-sink, to rise to the surface, to come out":* ē-, *"out,"* + merg- ere, *"to sink."*

oi **oil** / o͝o **book** / o͞o **boot** / ou **out** / ŭ **cut** / û **fur** / *th* **the** / th **thin** / hw **which** / zh **vision** / ə **ago, item, pencil, atom, circus**

en•dur•ing (ĕn dŏŏr′ĭng) *or* (-dyŏŏr′-) *adj.* Continuing to exist; lasting: *The Bill of Rights is of enduring value.*

en•vel•op (ĕn vĕl′əp) *v.* **en•vel•oped, en•vel•op•ing.** To enclose completely with or as if with a covering: *Clouds enveloped the mountains.*

e•rode (ĭ rōd′) *v.* **e•rod•ed, e•rod•ing.** To wear away or become worn away by or as if by rubbing or bombardment with small particles: *High winds can erode the hillside.*

ex•ca•va•tor (ĕks′kə vā′tər) *n.* One who uncovers or exposes to view by digging.

ex•pres•sion•less (ĭk sprĕsh′ən lĭs) *adj.* Not revealing feelings or emotion; impassive.

ex•traor•di•nar•y (ĭk strôr′dn ĕr′ē) *or* (ĕk′strə ôr′-) *adj.* Very unusual; exceptional; remarkable: *We watched a magician perform extraordinary tricks.*

F

fam•ine (făm′ĭn) *n.* A serious shortage of food resulting in widespread hunger and starvation.

fea•ture (fē′chər) *n.* A prominent part, quality, or characteristic: *The main features of the desert are rock, sand, and wind.*

feu•dal•ism (fyŏŏd′l ĭz′əm) *n.* A political and economic system in Europe during the Middle Ages, under which land was granted by a landowner to a person called a vassal in exchange for military service and various other duties.

fi•nal•i•ty (fī năl′ĭ tē) *n., pl.* **fi•nal•i•ties.** The quality of being at the end; decisiveness: *At the end of the game, the buzzer sounded with finality.*

flaunt (flônt) *v.* **flaunt•ed, flaunt•ing.** To show off.

flax (flăks) *n.* A light-colored fiber from plant stems used to make linen.

floun•der (floun′dər) *v.* **floun•dered, floun•der•ing.** To move clumsily or with difficulty.

flour•ish (flûr′ĭsh) *or* (flŭr′-) *v.* To fare well; succeed, prosper: *Carpenters flourish when many new houses are being built.*

---

*The word **erode** comes from the Latin* erodere, *meaning "to eat away" or "to gnaw off."*

Flounder is possibly a blend of blunder, *"to move clumsily or blindly," and* founder, *"to fall or stumble."*

ă pat / ā pay / â care / ä father / ĕ pet / ē be / ĭ pit / ī pie / î fierce / ŏ pot / ō go / ô paw, for /

fo•li•age (fō′lē ĭj) *n.* The leaves of plants or trees; leaves in general.

frag•ment (frăg′mənt) *n.* A piece or part broken off or detached from a whole.

furl (fûrl) *v.* **furled, furl•ing.** To roll up and fasten (a flag or sail) to a pole, yard, or mast: *While the ship was in port, its sails were furled.*

fur•row (fûr′ō) *or* (fŭr′ō) *n.* A long, narrow rut, groove, or depression: *The water cut furrows in the dirt road.*

gale (gāl) *n.* A very strong wind, especially one having a speed between 32 and 63 miles per hour.

gouge (gouj) *n.* A hole or groove that has been scooped out of a surface.

grin•go (grĭng′gō) *adj. Slang.* In Latin America, having to do with a foreigner, especially an American or Englishman. The word *gringo* is often considered offensive.

grop•ing•ly (grōp′ĭng lē) *adv.* Blindly or uncertainly: *When soap got in her eyes, she reached gropingly for a towel.*

gruff•ly (grŭf′lē) *adv.* In a stern or surly manner: *The man gruffly refused to return the dog's ball.*

hal•lu•ci•nate (hə lōō′sə nāt′) *v.* To see, hear, or otherwise sense something that does not really exist.

haunch (hônch) *or* (hänch) *n.* The hip, buttock, and upper thigh of a person or animal: *The dog settled back on its haunches.*

hes•i•ta•tion (hĕz′ĭ tā′shən) *n.* The act of pausing in doubt or uncertainty: *His hesitation over his clothes made him miss the bus.*

hi•er•o•glyph•ics (hī′ər ə glĭf′ĭks) *or* (hī′rə-) *n.* A system of writing, used in ancient Egypt, in which pictures or symbols are used to represent words or sounds.

hieroglyphics

---

oi **oil** / o͝o **book** / o͞o **boot** / ou **out** / ŭ **cut** / û **fur** / *th* **the** / th **thin** / hw **which** / zh **vision** / ə **ago, item, pencil, atom, circus**

host (hōst) *n.* A living plant or animal on or in which a parasite or other organism lives and from which it usually gets its nourishment.

hos•tile (hŏs′təl) *or* (-tīl′) *adj.* Not hospitable: *During a storm, the ocean can be hostile.*

Host *is from the Old French word* hoste, *which comes from the Latin* hospes; *this word meant simultaneously "host" and "guest."*

I

il•lu•sion (ĭ lōo′zhən) *n.* An appearance or impression that has no real basis; false perception: *The artist used shading to create the illusion of depth.*

im•i•tate (ĭm′ĭ tāt′) *v.* **im•i•tat•ed, im•i•tat•ing.** To copy the actions, appearance, function, or sounds of.

in•de•struc•ti•ble (ĭn′dĭ strŭk′tə bəl) *adj.* Not capable of being destroyed.

inlay

in•lay (ĭn′lā′) *n.* Contrasting material set into a surface in pieces to form a design: *The bracelets were made of turquoise inlay.*

in•sig•nif•i•cant (ĭn′sĭg nĭf′ĭ kənt) *adj.* Of no importance; trivial: *In a large crowd, one person can feel insignificant.*

in•stinct (ĭn′stĭngkt′) *n.* **1.** An inner influence, feeling, or drive that is not learned and that results in complex animal behavior such as building of nests, incubation of eggs, nursing of young, etc. **2.** A natural talent or ability.

in•stinc•tive•ly (ĭn stĭngk′tĭv lē) *adv.* In a manner showing instinct: *Many birds instinctively fly south for the winter.*

in•sti•tu•tion (ĭn′stĭ tōo′shən) *or* (-tyōo′-) *n.* An organization or foundation, especially one dedicated to public service.

in•tact (ĭn tăkt′) *adj.* Not impaired, injured, or damaged.

in•ter•pret (ĭn tûr′prĭt) *v.* **in•ter•pret•ed, in•ter•pret•ing.** To translate from one language to another.

in•ver•te•brate (ĭn vûr′tə brĭt) *or* (-brāt′) *adj.* Having no backbone: *Worms and jellyfish are invertebrate animals.*

J

ju•bi•lant (jōo′bə lənt) *adj.* Full of joy; rejoicing.

ă pat / ā pay / â care / ä father / ĕ pet / ē be / ĭ pit / ī pie / î fierce / ŏ pot / ō go / ô paw, for /

564

ka•lei•do•scope

(kə lī′də skōp′) *n.* A tube-shaped toy in which bits of loose, colored glass contained at one end reflect light into changing patterns visible from a hole at the other end.

la•goon (lə gōōn′) *n.* A body of water, usually connecting with the ocean, especially one bounded by sandbars or coral reefs.

laugh•ing•stock (lăf′ĭng stŏk′) or (lä′fĭng-) *n.* An object of mocking laughter, jokes, or ridicule.

lin•guist (lĭng′gwĭst) *n.* A specialist in the science of language and the study of the nature and structure of human speech.

list•less (lĭst′lĭs) *adj.* Lacking energy or enthusiasm; lethargic: *You will feel **listless** until the fever passes.*

log•i•cal (lŏj′ĭ kəl) *adj.* Reasonable: *The **logical** thing to do was to ask for help.*

long•ing (lông′ĭng) *or* (lŏng′-) *n.* A deep yearning; a strong desire: *The **longing** he felt to see his parents grew stronger.*

lout (lout) *n.* A foolish and stupid person.

lu•mi•nous (lōō′mə nəs) *adj.* Giving off light, especially light that is self-generated rather than reflected; shining.

lunge (lŭnj) *v.* **lunged, lung•ing.** To make a sudden, forceful movement forward: *The fielder **lunged** for the ball.*

lure (lōōr) *n.* Something that tempts or attracts with the promise of gaining pleasure or reward.

lurk•er (lûrk′ər) *n.* Someone or something that moves about furtively or sneaks.

lus•trous (lŭs′trəs) *adj.* Having a gloss or sheen; gleaming: *She wore a **lustrous** silk dress to the party.*

The **kaleidoscope** *was invented in 1816 by Sir David Brewster. He devised a toy in which mirrors in a tube reflected bits of colored glass to form beautiful patterns. The name came from a combination of Greek words: kalos, "beautiful"; eidos, "form"; and skopos, "watcher."*

Long *is from the Old English langian, which originally meant "to grow longer." It was used in phrases like "it longs me for (something)," meaning "it makes me wish for, I yearn for"; and later, "to long for" came to mean "to yearn for." The details are rather complex, but, simply put, the key idea is that when one yearns for something, it makes time seem to pass slowly.*

---

oi **oil** / ōō b**oo**k / ōō b**oo**t / ou **out** / ŭ c**u**t / û f**u**r / *th* **th**e / th **th**in / hw **wh**ich / zh vi**s**ion / ə **a**go, **i**tem, penc**i**l, at**o**m, circ**u**s

M

mag•ma (măg′mə) *n.* The hot molten material under the earth's crust that often cools and hardens to form igneous rock.

mas•sive (măs′ĭv) *adj.* Large, heavy and solid; bulky: *An elephant is a massive animal.*

maze (māz) *n.* A complicated, usually confusing network of passageways or pathways.

me•chan•i•cal (mə kăn′ĭ kəl) *adj.* Like a machine in operation: *He swung his arms repeatedly in a mechanical motion.*

med•dle (měd′1) *v.* **med•dled, med•dling.** To interfere in other people's business: *Don't meddle in affairs that don't concern you.*

men•ace (měn′əs) *n.* **1.** An appearance of being ready to do harm; a threatening quality: *The dark alleyway had an air of menace.* **2.** Someone or something that threatens harm; a threat: *A reckless driver is a menace to others.*

min•er•al (mĭn′ər əl) *n.* Any natural substance that has a definite chemical composition and characteristic physical structure: *The country is rich in minerals such as salt, zinc, and gold.*

mirth (mûrth) *n.* Gaiety and merriment, especially when expressed by laughter.

mite (mīt) *n.* Any of a group of very small animals related to the spiders.

mod•est (mŏd′ĭst) *adj.* Tending to play down one's talents or accomplishments: *She was too modest to boast about winning three tournaments.*

mol•ten (mōl′tən) *adj.* Made liquid by heat; melted.

mo•not•o•ny (mə nŏt′n ē) *n.* Tiresome lack of variety; dull sameness: *The monotony of hot weather was broken by a sudden rainstorm.*

mum•my (mŭm′ē) *n., pl.* **mum•mies.** The body of a human being or animal that was embalmed after death, according to the practice of the ancient Egyptians.

mush (mŭsh) *v.* **mushed, mush•ing.** To travel with a dog sled.

ă pat / ā pay / â care / ä father / ĕ pet / ē be / ĭ pit / ī pie / î fierce / ŏ pot / ō go / ô paw, for /

mut•ed (myoot′əd) *adj.* Muffled or softened: *His muted cries grew louder as the storm let up.*

myth•o•log•i•cal (mĭth′ə lŏj′ĭ kəl) *adj.* Of or existing in myths, legends, or traditional stories.

new-fan•gled (noo′făng′gəld) *or* **(nyoo′-)** *adj.* So new, recent, or modern as to be frowned on as a fad or too much of a novelty: *Many people once thought motion pictures were only a new-fangled idea.*

o•ce•a•nog•ra•pher (ō′shē ə nŏg′rə fər) *or* (ō′shə nŏg′-) *n.* A scientist who specializes in the study and exploration of the ocean.

om•i•nous (ŏm′ə nəs) *adj.* Seeming to foretell or be a sign of trouble, danger, or disaster; threatening: *Ominous clouds were the first sign of the approaching storm.*

op•pose (ə pōz′) *v.* **op•posed, op•pos•ing.** To offer resistance to or contend against: *The committee opposed changing the voting rules.*

op•pres•sive (ə prĕs′ĭv) *adj.* Causing physical or mental distress: *An oppressive silence fell upon the room.*

or•deal (ôr dēl′) *n.* A very difficult or painful experience, especially one that tests a person's character or endurance: *His stay in the hospital was an ordeal for the entire family.*

out•land•ish (out lăn′dĭsh) *adj.* Unusually strange in appearance or manner.

out•raged (out′rājd′) *adj.* Angry or offended: *The woman answered his questions in an outraged voice.*

oceanographer

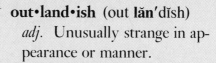

pa•py•rus (pə pī′rəs) *n., pl.* **pa•py•rus•es** or **pa•py•ri.** A tall, reedlike water plant of northern Africa and nearby regions from which a kind of paper was made by the ancient Egyptians.

papyrus

oi **oil** / oo b**oo**k / oo b**oo**t / ou **out** / ŭ **cut** / û f**ur** / *th* **th**e / th **th**in / hw **wh**ich / zh vi**s**ion / ə **a**go, it**e**m, penc**i**l, at**o**m, circ**u**s

The word **partition** existed in Middle English as particioun and in Old French as partition. These words came from the Latin partītio, a form of partīre, which means "to divide."

pleated

The name of the high-combed hairstyle known as the **pompadour** comes from the Marquise de Pompadour (1721–1764). The Marquise was a French noblewoman who influenced not only the fashions of her time but also the politics of the French court.

parch•ment (pärch′mənt) *n.* The skin of a sheep or goat prepared for writing or painting on.

par•ti•tion (pär tĭsh′ən) *n.* A usually thin structure, such as a panel or screen, that divides up a room or other enclosure.

pe•di•a•tri•cian (pē′dē ə trĭsh′ən) *n.* A physician who specializes in the care of infants and children and the treatment of their diseases.

per•sist (pər sĭst′) *v.* **per•sist•ed, per•sist•ing.** To insist or repeat obstinately; be tenacious: *The men persisted in declaring their innocence.*

pet•ri•fied (pĕt′rə fīd′) *adj.* Stunned or paralyzed, as with fear or astonishment.

phar•aoh (fâr′ō) *or* (fā′rō) *n.* A king of ancient Egypt.

phi•los•o•pher (fĭ lŏs′ə fər) *n.* An expert in the study by logical reasoning of the basic truths and laws governing the universe, nature, life, morals, etc.

pi•lón (pē lōn′) *n.* In Mexico, a treat such as a cookie or piece of candy.

pitch (pĭch) *v.* **pitched, pitch•ing.** To plunge forward and backward alternately.

plank•ton (plăngk′tən) *n.* Plants and animals, usually of very small size, that float or drift in great numbers in bodies of salt or fresh water.

plate (plāt) *n.* One of the huge, movable sections that form the earth's crust: *When earth's plates shift, they often cause earthquakes.*

pleat•ed (plēt′əd) *adj.* Arranged in flat folds made by doubling a material (such as cloth) on itself and pressing or sewing it in place.

plun•der•er (plŭn′dər ər) *n.* One who steals property or valuables; robber.

pom•pa•dour (pŏm′pə dôr′) *or* (-dōr′) *n.* A puffed-up hairstyle in which the hair is brushed straight up from the forehead.

pred•a•tor (prĕd′ə tər) *or* (-tôr′) *n.* An animal that lives by capturing and feeding on other animals; a preying animal: *The rancher protected his sheep from predators.*

pres•sure (prĕsh′ər) *n.* The amount of force applied per unit of area of a surface.

ă pat / ā pay / â care / ä father / ĕ pet / ē be / ĭ pit / ī pie / î fierce / ŏ pot / ō go / ô paw, for /

probe (prōb) *v.* **probed, prob•ing.** To explore or examine: *The dentist probed her teeth with a sharp tool.*

pro•claim (prō klām′) *or* (prə-) *v.* **pro•claimed, pro•claim•ing.** To announce officially and publicly; declare: *The mayor proclaimed tomorrow a holiday.*

pro•jec•tion (prə jĕk′shən) *n.* Something that thrusts or juts outward: *That insect uses the spiny projections on its back to trap its prey.*

prom•i•nent (prŏm′ə nənt) *adj.* Highly noticeable; readily evident; conspicuous: *The card catalog is in a prominent place in the library.*

pro•posed (prə pōzd′) *adj.* Put forward for consideration or acceptance; suggested.

pro•vi•sions (prə vĭzh′əns) *n.* Stocks of food and other necessary supplies.

psy•chol•o•gy (sī kŏl′ə jē) *n.* The scientific study of mental processes and behavior.

puce (pyo͞os) *n.* A deep, grayish red or purple.

quail (kwāl) *v.* **quailed, quail•ing.** To lose courage; cower: *The dog quailed when he saw the stranger.*

ra•tio (rā′shō) *or* (-shē ō′) *n.* A relationship between the amounts or sizes of two things; proportion: *The ratio of girls to boys in our class is three to one.*

re•as•sure (rē′ə sho͝or′) *v.* **re•as•sured, re•as•sur•ing.** To assure again; restore confidence to: *Seeing her father in the audience reassured her.*

re•cep•tion (rĭ sĕp′shən) *n.* A welcome, greeting, or acceptance: *The team got a wild reception from the fans.*

reed (rēd) *n.* Any of several tall, hollow-stemmed grasses or similar plants that grow in wet places.

reef (rēf) *n.* A strip or ridge of rock, sand, or coral that rises to or close to the surface of a body of water.

Quail *comes from the Middle English word* quailen, *"to give way, decline, fail." It may be descended from the Latin word* coāgulāre, *meaning "to curdle."*

Reef *was originally* riff *and was borrowed from Middle Dutch* rif, *meaning "ridge, ledge of rock."*

oi **oi**l / o͞o b**oo**k / o͞o b**oo**t / ou **ou**t / ŭ **cu**t / û f**ur** / *th* **th**e / th **th**in / hw **wh**ich / zh vi**s**ion / ə **a**go, it**e**m, penc**i**l, at**o**m, circ**u**s

ref•use (rĕf′yo͞os) *n.* Worthless matter; waste.

re•lent•less•ly (rĭ lĕnt′lĭs lē) *adv.* Steadily and persistently: *Crews worked **relentlessly** through the night searching for survivors.*

rel•ic (rĕl′ĭk) *n.* An object or custom surviving from a culture or period that has disappeared.

re•lief map (rĭ lēf′ măp′) *n.* A map that shows the physical features of land, as by using lines, colors, or shading.

re•luc•tant (rĭ lŭk′tənt) *adj.* Unwilling; averse: *They were **reluctant** to leave the park and go home.*

re•mote•ness (rĭ mōt′nəs) *n.* The state of being distant in manner; aloofness: *Few people spoke to the woman because of her quiet **remoteness**.*

ren•der (rĕn′dər) *v.* **ren•dered, ren•der•ing.** To pronounce; hand down, as a decision.

re•pul•sive (rĭ pŭl′sĭv) *adj.* Arousing a feeling of strong dislike or aversion; disgusting: *Rotting garbage has a **repulsive** odor.*

re•solve (rĭ zŏlv′) *v.* **re•solved, re•solv•ing.** To remove or dispel; explain away: *He **resolved** his concerns at the meeting.*

re•splen•dent (rĭ splĕn′dənt) *adj.* Shining with brilliance and splendor; dazzling: *She was **resplendent** in her jeweled gown.*

re•sume (rĭ zo͞om′) *v.* **re•sumed, re•sum•ing.** To begin again or continue after a break.

rev•er•ie (rĕv′ə rē) *n.* Abstracted thought; daydreaming.

rid•dled (rĭd′ld) *adj.* Pierced with numerous holes.

rig•id (rĭj′ĭd) *adj.* Not changing shape or bending; stiff; inflexible.

rush (rŭsh) *n.* Any of several tall plants that grow in wet places and have hollow or pithy stems.

sa•cred (sā′krĭd) *adj.* Dedicated or devoted to a religious use or purpose.

Relic *is from the Old French word* relique, *derived from the Latin* reliquiae, *"remains, relics," which in turn comes from* relinquere, *"to leave behind":* re-, *"back, behind,"* + linquere, *"to leave."*

Resume *comes from the Latin verb* sūmere, *"to take hold of." From* sūmere *was formed the compound verb that was borrowed by English:* resūmere, *meaning "to take up again."*

Riddle *originally meant "to sift something through a sieve" and only recently came to mean "to fill with holes." It comes from the Old English* hriddel, *meaning "sieve."*

ă pat / ā pay / â care / ä father / ĕ pet / ē be / ĭ pit / ī pie / î fierce / ŏ pot / ō go / ô paw, for /

sa•lin•i•ty (sə lĭn′ĭ tē) *n.* The degree to which something is saline or salty: *Ocean water has a high salinity.*

saun•ter (sôn′tər) *v.* **saun•tered, saun•ter•ing.** To walk at a leisurely pace; stroll.

scar•i•fy (skâr′ə fī′) *v.* **scar•i•fied, scar•i•fy•ing.** To shock or frighten: *He jumped out of the bushes to scarify the children on Halloween.*

scu•ba (skōō′bə) *n.* Equipment used by divers to breathe underwater, including a tank or tanks of compressed air worn on the back and fitted with a regulator, hose, and mouthpiece.

sed•i•ment (sĕd′ə mənt) *n.* Finely divided solid matter that falls to the bottom of a liquid.

seer (sîr) *n.* A person supposedly able to visualize, and thus predict, the future.

seine (sān) *n.* A large fishing net with weights at the lower edge and floats at the top.

sen•si•tive (sĕn′sĭ tĭv) *adj.* Responsive to or affected by something: *Delicate machinery often is sensitive to extreme heat or cold.*

ser•pent (sûr′pənt) *n.* A snakelike dragon or monster.

shrine (shrīn) *n.* **1.** A place devoted to worship or religious observances. **2.** A container or receptacle for sacred relics. **3.** A receptacle (as a casket or tomb) for the dead.

shroud (shroud) *n.* A cloth used to wrap a body for burial.

sieve (sĭv) *n.* A utensil for separating liquids and fine particles from more solid substances, consisting of a frame with wire mesh containing many small holes.

sig•ni•fy (sĭg′nə fī′) *v.* **sig•ni•fied, sig•ni•fy•ing.** To serve as a sign of: *The olive branch signified their hopes for peace.*

sil•hou•ette (sĭl′ōō ĕt′) *n.* An outline of something that appears dark against a light background.

sin•ew (sĭn′yōō) *n.* A tendon, or the tough fibrous tissue that connects a muscle and a bone.

smol•der•ing (smōl′dər ĭng) *adj.* Burning and producing heat, some smoke, and no visible flame: *Smoldering ashes were all that was left of the fire.*

Scuba *is an acronym, a word made up of the first letters of several words. It stands for "self-contained underwater breathing apparatus."*

sieve

Silhouette *comes from the name of Étienne de Silhouette (1709–1767), who served as French finance minister for nine months in 1759. He introduced a series of cutbacks to save France from bankruptcy. At about the same time, portraits drawn or cut from the outlines of projected shadows became popular. These cheap portraits were jokingly called "à la Silhouette," or "according to Silhouette."*

---

oi **oil** / ŏŏ **book** / ōō **boot** / ou **out** / ŭ **cut** / û **fur** / *th* **the** / th **thin** / hw **which** /
zh **vision** / ə **ago, item, pencil, atom, circus**

Sound *is from the Old English* sund, *originally meaning "the act of swimming, a swim"; hence, "a body of water narrow enough to swim across." This word (which is related to swim) was borrowed into Old French as* sonde, *"a line for measuring the depth of a body of water"; from this was formed* sonder, *"to measure depth," which was borrowed back into English as* **sound.**

sphinx

Stamina *comes from the Latin word* stā-men, *which means "thread of the warp" or "thread of human life."*

snor•kel (snôr′kəl) *v.* **snor•keled, snor•kel•ing.** To swim using a snorkel, which is a breathing apparatus consisting of a plastic tube curved at one end and fitted with a mouthpiece.

sound•ing (soun′dĭng) *n.* A measurement of depth, especially of a body of water by means of a weighted line.

source (sôrs) *or* **(sōrs)** *n.* A place or thing from which something comes; a point of origin: *This station is our main source of electricity.*

spe•cies (spē′shēz′) *or* **(-sēz′)** *n.* A group of similar animals or plants that are regarded as of the same kind and that are able to breed with one another.

spec•i•men (spĕs′ə mən) *n.* An element (such as an animal or plant) of a set (such as a species) taken as a representative of the whole set: *She captured many fine specimens of butterflies.*

spec•ter (spĕk′tər) *n.* A phantom; apparition.

sphinx (sfĭngks) *n.* An ancient Egyptian figure with the body of a lion and the head of a man, ram, or hawk.

spig•ot (spĭg′ət) *n.* A faucet.

stam•i•na (stăm′ə nə) *n.* The power to resist fatigue or illness while working hard; endurance: *Exercising daily will help you increase your stamina.*

stench (stĕnch) *n.* A strong, unpleasant smell; a stink.

strip min•ing (strĭp′ mī′nĭng) *n.* A method in which a mineral, especially coal, that lies close to the surface of the earth is mined by stripping off the topsoil, rock, etc., that covers it, leaving the earth barren after the mineral is removed.

sub•merge (səb mûrj′) *v.* **sub•merged, sub•merg•ing.** To cover with water: *At high tide the island was submerged.*

sum•mit (sŭm′ĭt) *n.* The highest point or part; the top, especially of a mountain: *From the summit, he could see for miles around.*

swell (swĕl) *n.* A long wave that moves continuously through the water without breaking.

ă pat / ā pay / â care / ä father / ĕ pet / ē be / ĭ pit / ī pie / î fierce / ŏ pot / ō go / ô paw, for /

sym•bol•ic (sĭm bŏl′ĭk) *adj.* Of or expressed by something that represents something else, as by association, resemblance, convention, etc.: *The bald eagle is* **symbolic** *of America's freedom.*

tar•nished (tär′nĭshd) *adj.* Dulled or discolored, as from exposure to air or dirt: *We cleaned the* **tarnished** *silverware.*

taunt (tônt) *n.* A scornful remark: *He ignored the* **taunts** *of the hostile crowd.*

te•di•ous (tē′dē əs) *adj.* Tiresome because of slowness or length; boring: *Filling the cracks in the wall was a* **tedious** *job.*

teem (tēm) *v.* **teemed, teem•ing.** To be full of; abound: *A tropical forest* **teems** *with plant and animal life.*

tel•e•graph (tĕl′ĭ grăf′) *or* (-gräf′) *n.* A communications system in which a message is sent, either by wire or radio, to a receiving station.

ther•mo•cline (thûr′mə klīn′) *n.* A layer of water in a body of water that separates an upper, warmer layer from a lower, colder layer and in which the temperature rapidly declines with increasing depth.

thresh•old (thrĕsh′ōld) *or* (-hōld) *n.* The place or point of beginning; the outset: *Scientists are on the* **threshold** *of a better understanding of the atmosphere.*

trace (trās) *n.* A visible mark or sign of the former presence or passage of some person, thing, or event: *The thief escaped without leaving a* **trace**.

trap•pings (trăp′ĭngz) *pl.n.* Articles of dress or ornamentation: *She wanted a wedding with all the* **trappings**.

trib•ute (trĭb′yo͞ot′) *n.* A gift or other acknowledgment of gratitude, respect, or admiration: *People bring flowers to the monument in* **tribute** *to those who died.*

trough (trôf) *or* (trŏf) *n.* A long, narrow depression, as between waves or ridges.

Teem comes from the Middle English temen or teamen, meaning "to give birth to" or "breed."

The word **trappings** *comes from the Middle English word* trappe *and the Old French* drap, *meaning "cloth." Its root probably extends back to the Late Latin* drappus, *for "drape or cloth."*

oi **oil** / o͞o **book** / o͞o **boot** / ou **out** / ŭ **cut** / û **fur** / *th* **the** / th **thin** / hw **which** / zh **vision** / ə **ago, item, pencil, atom, circus**

tu·mult (tōō′məlt) *or* (tyōō′-) *n*. Din and commotion: *Have you ever experienced the* **tumult** *of Times Square on New Year's Eve?*

un·ion (yōōn′yən) *n*. A combination formed by joining people or things together into a whole: *The states banded together to form a* **union**.

un·rav·el (ŭn răv′əl) *v*. **un·rav·eled** *or* **un·rav·elled**, **un·rav·el·ing** *or* **un·rav·el·ling**. To separate something snarled or entangled: *Only a bloodhound could* **unravel** *the correct trail from all the false leads.*

vague (vāg) *adj*. Lacking definite shape, form, or character: *Through the fog we could see the* **vague** *outline of a ship.*

val·iant (văl′yənt) *adj*. Possessing, showing, or acting with courage; brave: *Firefighters made a* **valiant** *attempt to save the building.*

Vague *comes from the Latin word* vagus, *meaning "wandering, undecided."*

Vigilant *is a Middle English word descended from the Latin* vigilāns, *which is the present participle of* vigilāre, *"to stay alert."*

winch

vein (vān) *n*. A long, regularly shaped deposit of an ore, mineral, etc., in the earth.

ven·ture (věn′chər) *v*. **ven·tured, ven·tur·ing**. To brave the dangers of: *Few cars* **ventured** *out onto the icy streets.*

vig·i·lant (vĭj′ə lənt) *adj*. On the alert; watchful; wary: *A security guard must always be* **vigilant**.

wa·ter moc·ca·sin (wô′tər mŏk′ə sĭn) *n*. A poisonous snake of swampy regions of the southern United States.

wa·ver (wā′vər) *v*. **wa·vered, wa·ver·ing**. To tremble or flicker, as sound or light: *The sound of the radio seemed to* **waver** *in the wind.*

winch (wĭnch) *n*. A machine for pulling or lifting, consisting of a drum around which a rope or cable attached to the load is wound as the load is moved.

ă pat / ā pay / â care / ä father / ĕ pet / ē be / ĭ pit / ī pie / î fierce / ŏ pot / ō go / ô paw, for /

win•now (wĭn′ō) *v.*
win•nowed, win•now•ing.
To separate the chaff from
(grain) by means of a current
of air.

with•er•ing (wĭth′ər ĭng) *adj.*
Causing to become speechless
or unable to act; stunning: *He
silenced his opponent with a
withering glance.*

wrought (rôt) *v. Archaic.* A
past tense and past participle
of **work.**

zeal (zēl) *n.* Enthusiasm; intense interest or devotion, as
in working toward a goal or
supporting a cause or belief:
*Her zeal for doing charity
work inspired everyone.*

zo•ol•o•gist (zō ŏl′ə jĭst) *n.* A
scientist who specializes in the
study of animals.

Winnow *comes from
the Old English word*
windwian, *for
"wind." To* **winnow**
*grain is to separate
the lighter chaff, or
husks, from the heav-
ier grain using the
air currents of the
wind.*

---

oi **oil** / o͞o **book** / o͞o **boot** / ou **out** / ŭ **cut** / û **fur** / *th* **the** / th **thin** / hw **which** /
zh **vision** / ə **ago, item, pencil, atom, circus**

action   The series of events that make up a **plot.**

alliteration   The repetition of a consonant sound, usually the first sound in a group of words, as in "trumpeted two times."

allusion   A brief mention of a person or thing with which the reader is presumed to be familiar.

anecdote   A short account that gives details of an interesting event.

antagonist   The character who opposes the main character, or **protagonist,** in a story, play, or poem.

archaic language   Words and expressions that once were part of the language, but are no longer in use.

author's purpose   What the author means to say or accomplish in his or her work.

autobiography   A person's account of his or her own life.

ballad   A fairly short poem that tells a story. Ballads typically consist of **stanzas** and a **refrain.** They were originally meant to be sung.

biography   The factual account of a person's life, written by someone else.

blank verse   A form of poetry that does not rhyme and has five beats per line.

chapter   One of the main sections of a book, usually labeled with a number or title.

characterization   The process of making a character seem real and lifelike. An author uses description of the character's physical features, personality traits, actions, thoughts, speech, and feelings to achieve characterization.

characters   The people or animals in a story. The main character handles the problem or **conflict** in the story. Minor characters help advance the **plot** and reveal information about the main character's personality.

character traits Qualities that make one character different from another. Such qualities — bravery, intelligence, stinginess, and so on — are as various in literature as they are in real life.

climax The point in a play or story where the **conflict** reaches its highest intensity and must be resolved. The climax is the most exciting moment in a story and holds the most interest for the reader. (See also **turning point.**)

comedy Writing that is designed to amuse. Comedy uses such devices as sarcasm, **exaggeration, satire,** and **wit.** Comedies typically have happy endings.

conclusion In dramatic structure, the part of a story or play that gives the final results; the ending.

conflict The problem in a story faced by the main character. The character may face one (or more) of the following four kinds of conflict: a struggle against nature, a struggle against another character, a struggle against society, or a struggle against himself or herself.

connotation The feelings, emotions, and ideas associated with a word, as opposed to its dictionary definition. (See also **denotation.**)

context The words and ideas that surround a particular word. A reader can often figure out the meaning of a new word from its context.

denotation The exact meaning of a word as it might appear in a dictionary. (See also **connotation.**)

description Writing that provides details of time, place, character, and setting. An author uses description to create images of the "world" in which the story takes place.

descriptive language Language that is rich in sensory details. It evokes sights, smells, sounds, and textures.

dialect   The way of speaking used by the people of a particular region or group. A writer achieves a dialect by using words that are spelled differently to show local or regional pronunciations, and by using words and sentence structures that are part of local or regional sayings and manners of speaking.

dialogue   The words spoken by characters to one another in a story or play.

diction   **1.** The choice and arrangement of words in a story or play. **2.** The quality of speech or singing judged by clearness and distinctness of pronunciation.

drama   A serious play designed to be acted on a stage.

dramatize   **1.** To turn a story into a play or screenplay. **2.** To relate an incident in a very dramatic way.

epic   A long poem or literary work, usually written in a formal style, about heroes and their adventures. Ancient epics, such as Homer's *Iliad* and *Odyssey*, are often written versions of the oral legends of a nation or culture.

essay   A brief piece of prose writing about a specific topic. An essay usually expresses the opinions of its author.

exaggeration   Deliberate overstatement used for emphasis, effect, or **humor.**

expository writing   Informational writing that enlightens or explains. Most **nonfiction prose** is expository.

fable   A short story, often with animal characters who speak and act like humans, that teaches a lesson about human nature.

falling action   In dramatic structure, the part of a story or play that tells what happens after the **climax.**

fantasy   Fiction that tells about events that are impossible in the real world because they do not obey known scientific laws. **Science fiction** and fairy tales are types of fantasy writing.

fiction   Stories created from the imagination of the author. **Novels, short stories,** and **fables** are all forms of fiction.

fictionalized biography An account of a person's life that is based on facts but includes some imagined elements.

figurative language Writing that uses figures of speech such as metaphors, similes, and personification. (See also **metaphor, simile,** and **personification.**)

figures of speech Various imaginative uses of language that create special effects or meanings. (See also **metaphor, simile,** and **personification.**)

first person The **point of view** from which one of the characters tells the story using the pronoun *I*. This character may experience the events of the story personally or may simply be a witness to them. (See also **narrator** and **third person.**)

flashback A writing technique that interrupts the present action to explain something that happened earlier.

folklore Traditions, beliefs, legends, customs, and stories handed down by a particular people from generation to generation by word of mouth. Folklore includes folk **ballads,** folk **dramas,** folk **heroes,** and **folktales.**

folktale A traditional story of a particular place or people, handed down from generation to generation and eventually written down.

foreshadowing A writing technique involving clues that a writer gives early in a selection to hint at future events.

formal language Careful, precise language, more frequently used in writing than in everyday speech. (See also **informal language.**)

free verse Poetry that does not follow a regular pattern of rhythm or line, and has either irregular rhyme or no rhyme.

genre A category or type of literary work. Works can be grouped into genres by form, technique, or type of subject. Thus, the adventure story, the **folktale,** and the **novel** are all examples of literary genres.

haiku A **lyric** poem of three lines and usually seventeen syllables. Traditionally, a haiku expresses a person's feelings inspired by nature.

hero/heroine **1.** The central character in a work of fiction, poetry, or drama. **2.** A strong and courageous man or woman who performs brave deeds or who risks his or her life for a good cause. In mythology, heroes and heroines were descended from gods.

historical fiction A story based partly on historical events and people and partly on the author's imagination.

humor **1.** A type of writing intended to make people laugh. **2.** The quality of being funny.

idiom A use of words, such as a **figure of speech** or a common saying, that is unique to one language and cannot be translated literally into another.

image A mental picture of something not present or real.

imagery Word pictures; mental images. In writing or speech, the use of **figurative language,** vivid **description,** or **sensory words** to produce **images.**

informal language Casual language used mainly in conversation. (See also **formal language.**)

interpretation The art of understanding what a work of literature means. Complex works can be interpreted in several different ways.

introduction In dramatic structure, the part of a story or play that creates the mood, presents some of the characters, and supplies background information.

irony The use of words or situations to contrast what is expected with what is actually meant or occurs. In *verbal irony,* the speaker says the opposite of what he or she means. In *dramatic irony,* the audience knows more about events than the characters do, which makes for **suspense** as the characters act out the story.

jargon Special or technical language used by people in a particular job or by people with a particular hobby or interest.

legend An imaginative story that is often connected with a national hero or a historical event and may be based on truth.

literature   Imaginative writing that possesses recognized artistic value.

lyric poetry   Poetry that expresses personal feelings and thoughts.

memoir   A form of **autobiography,** usually written by someone famous or by someone who has witnessed an important event. A memoir focuses on other people and events, rather than on the writer, as in autobiography.

metaphor   An implied comparison between very different things, used to add vividness to writing. In a metaphor, the two things compared are said to be the same, as in "Her mind is a computer." (See also **simile.**)

monologue   A long speech delivered by one character in a play, story, or poem.

mood   The effect of a story, poem, or play on the feelings of a reader or an audience; the emotional **tone** of a piece of writing.

moral   A lesson taught by a story or **fable.**

motivation   The combination of plot events and personality traits that determines a character's actions.

motive   A reason, a need, or an emotion that causes a character to act in a certain way.

mystery novel   Fiction that deals with a puzzling event, often a crime. (See also **novel.**)

myth   A story handed down from the past that gives an imaginary explanation of how certain things in nature, such as the moon, the sun, and the stars, came to be.

narration   The act or example of narrating, or telling a story.

narrative   In an account of an event, the description of characters, scenes, or events that is not dialogue.

narrative poetry   A type of poetry, sometimes rather long, that tells a story.

narrator   The character who tells the story or, in a play, who explains the events to the audience by addressing them directly. (See also **point of view, first person, third person.**)

nonfiction Writing that is about the real world rather than an imagined one.

novel A long fictional **narrative,** usually showing how a **character** develops as a result of events or actions, and organized around a **plot** or **theme.**

onomatopoeia The use of a word that imitates the sound it describes. *Buzz, splash,* and *honk* are all onomatopoetic words. In poetry, onomatopoeia may be more subtle, as the sound of the verses may help create a particular mood.

oral tradition A tradition in which songs and tales are passed by word of mouth from one generation to another.

outcome The final result; how something ends.

personification A **figure of speech** in which human traits are given to something that is not human.

plot The action or series of events in a story. The plot is traditionally divided into sections. The **introduction** creates the mood, presents some of the characters, and supplies background information. The **rising action** establishes and develops the **conflict.** At the **climax,** or turning point, the conflict is resolved through a key event or through the actions of the main character. In the **falling action,** the reader learns what happens as a result of the climax. The **conclusion** gives the final results.

point of view The position from which a story is told. A story may be told from the point of view of one of its characters, or from the position of an observer who is outside the action. (See also **first person, third person,** and **narrator.**)

prose Ordinary speech or writing as distinguished from verse or poetry.

protagonist The main character in a story. (See also **antagonist.**)

proverb A sentence or phrase that expresses a truth about life. "The early bird catches the worm" is a proverb.

realism Fiction that tells about true-to-life people, places, or events that could actually exist or happen.

582

refrain   A phrase or verse repeated several times, usually at regular intervals throughout a song or poem.

repetition   A writing technique in which a word or phrase is repeated for emphasis.

rhyme   The repetition of the same or similar sounds of syllables, often at the ends of lines of verse.

rhyme scheme   The pattern in which rhymes occur in a poem.

rhythm   In poetry, a regular pattern of accented and unaccented syllables.

rising action   In dramatic structure, the part of a story or play that establishes and develops the **conflict.**

romance novels   **Novels** about extraordinary events in extraordinary settings. Romance novels are more concerned with action — love, adventure, combat — than with characters.

satire   The use of **humor** or **irony** to expose hypocrisy or foolishness.

scene   A section of a novel or play that focuses on the actions of one or several characters in one place and time.

science fiction   Imaginative writing that has some basis in scientific fact and usually takes place in a time other than the present. Science fiction writing is sometimes used by an author as a vehicle for making a statement about society.

sensory words   Words that appeal to one or more of the five senses (hearing, sight, smell, touch, and taste).

setting   The time and place in which events in a story or play occur.

short story   A brief fictional **narrative** in prose. It has unity in **theme, tone, plot,** and **character.** Often a short story reveals a character's true nature through a series of events.

simile   A comparison of two unlike things, using *like* or *as*. "He was as brave as a lion" is a simile. (See also **metaphor.**)

slang   Words and phrases that occur most often in **informal language.**   Slang is often humorous, vivid, and extremely casual.   Slang tends to be in a state of constant change, words and phrases experiencing popularity for a time, only to be replaced by new terms.

stage directions   Instructions in the script of a play that tell the characters their movements on the stage.   They also describe use of props and sound effects.

stanza   In poetry, a group of lines united by a pattern of rhyme and rhythm.

subplot   An additional, but secondary **plot,** that makes the action in a work of fiction more complex and more interesting.

suspense   Uncertainty, on the part of the reader or the audience, about what will happen in a story or play.   Authors deliberately create suspense to hold the reader's or audience's interest.

symbolism   The use of an object, character, or incident to represent something else.

symbols   Objects, characters, or incidents that represent something else.

synopsis   A summary of a story's events.

theme   The underlying idea or message in a story.   The theme may be directly or indirectly stated.

third person   The **point of view** in which the author acts as an unidentified **narrator** to tell the story about the characters.   (See also **first person.**)

tone   The attitude toward the subject and the reader in a work of literature.   The tone of a work may be formal or informal, for example, or lighthearted or serious.   (See also **mood.**)

tragedy   A serious play that ends with a great misfortune that could not have been prevented.   In a classic tragedy, the main character, a worthy, noble person, meets his or her fate with courage and dignity.

turning point   An important moment in the **plot,** when events that have led to the moment of greatest intensity in the story come to a peak, and the main conflict must be resolved. (See also **climax.**)

universal themes   Themes that occur in the stories of every culture, in every time. The conflict between good and evil is a traditional theme. Universal themes are particularly apparent in traditional tales.

verse   **1.** A part of a poem, such as a line or a **stanza.**
2. Rhythmic, and usually rhymed, poetry.

wit   The ability to describe events that are amusing or odd, or to point out similarities in things that seem to be very different. Wit is a type of humor that depends mainly on the clever use of words.

Acknowledgments

For each of the selections listed below, grateful acknowledgment is made for permission to excerpt and/or reprint original or copyrighted material, as follows:

Major Selections

"Advice to Schoolboys," from *Wings of the Falcon: Life and Thought of Ancient Egypt*, translated and edited by Joseph Kaster. Copyright © 1968 by Joseph Kaster. Reprinted by permission of Henry Holt and Company, Inc.

"Akhenaten's Hymn to the Sun," from *Man and the Sun*, by Jacquetta Hawkes. Copyright © 1962 by Jacquetta Hawkes. Reprinted by permission of the Peters Fraser & Dunlop Group, Ltd.

From *Barrio Boy*, by Ernesto Galarza. Copyright © 1971 by University of Notre Dame Press, Notre Dame, Indiana 46556. Reprinted by permission.

"Brer Rabbit and Brer Cooter Race," from *The Days When the Animals Talked*, by William J. Faulkner. Copyright © 1977 by William J. Faulkner. Reprinted by permission of Marie F. Brown, Executor of the Estate of William J. Faulkner.

"The Calabash Man," from *Tales from Silver Lands*, by Charles J. Finger. Copyright © 1924 by Doubleday, a division of Bantam, Doubleday, Dell Publishing Group, Inc. Reprinted by permission of the publisher.

"Catherine, Sly Country Lass," from *Italian Folktales Selected and Retold by Italo Calvino*. Copyright © 1956 by Giulio Einaudi editore, s.p.a. Reprinted by permission of Wylie, Aitken & Stone, Inc. Translated and edited by George Martin. Copyright © 1980 by Harcourt Brace Jovanovich, Inc. Reprinted by permission of the publisher.

From *A Day in the Life of a Marine Biologist*, by William G. Jaspersohn. Copyright © 1982 by William G. Jaspersohn. Reprinted by permission of Little, Brown and Company.

"Discovering the Oceans," from *Under the High Seas: New Frontiers in Oceanography*, by Margaret Poynter and Donald Collins. Copyright © 1983 by Margaret Poynter and Donald Collins. Reprinted with permission of Atheneum Publishers, an imprint of Macmillan Publishing Company.

"The Lazy Fox," from *Latin American Tales*, by Genevieve Barlow. Copyright © 1989 by Checkerboard Press. Reprinted by permission of Genevieve Barlow.

Long Claws, by James Houston. Copyright © 1981 by James Houston. Reprinted by arrangement with Margaret K. McElderry, an imprint of Macmillan Publishing Company, and the Canadian publishers, McClelland and Stewart.

From *Lurkers of the Deep: Life Within the Ocean Depths*, by Bruce H. Robison. Copyright © 1978 by Dr. Bruce H. Robison (David McKay Company, New York). Reprinted by permission of Random House, Inc.

"The Magic Muntr," from *Serendipity Tales*, by Elizabeth Jamison Hodges. Copyright © 1966 by Elizabeth Jamison Hodges. Reprinted by permission of McIntosh and Otis, Inc.

"The Moon Valley," from *Tales from an African Drum*, by Helen Chetin. Copyright © 1970 by Helen Chetin. Reprinted by permission of Harcourt Brace Jovanovich, Inc.

"Oceans of the Earth," from *Scott, Foresman Earth Science*, by Jay M. Pasachoff, Naomi Pasachoff, and Timothy M. Cooney. Copyright © 1983 by Scott, Foresman and Company. Reprinted by permission.

"Old Plott," from *Tall Tales from the High Hills*, by Ellis Credle. Copyright © 1957 by Ellis Credle. Reprinted by permission of the author.

"Papa's Parrot," from *Every Living Thing*, by Cynthia Rylant. Copyright © 1985 by Cynthia Rylant. Reprinted with permission of Bradbury Press, an affiliate of Macmillan, Inc.

From *Race Against Death: A True Story of the Far North*, by Seymour Reit. Copyright © 1976 by Seymour Reit. Reprinted by permission of Seymour Reit.

"The Sea," from *Call It Courage*, written and illustrated by Armstrong Sperry. Copyright © 1940 by Macmillan Publishing Company, renewed © 1968 by Armstrong Sperry. Reprinted with permission of Macmillan Publishing Company and The Bodley Head, London.

The Cow-tail Switch and Other West African Stories, by Harold Courlander and George Herzog. Jacket art by Madye Lee Chastain, copyright © 1986. (Henry Holt and Company, Inc.)

The Great Barrier Reef: A Treasure in the Sea, by Alice Gilbreath. Cover art copyright © 1986 by Dillon Press, Inc.

The House of Wings, by Betsy Byars. Jacket art by Ted Lewin, copyright © 1982 by Viking Penguin Inc. Published simultaneously in Canada.

Mummies, Tombs, and Treasure: Secrets of Ancient Egypt, by Lila Perl. Jacket art by Erika Weihs. Copyright © 1987 by Erika Weihs.

Additional Recommended Reading

Houghton Mifflin Company wishes to thank the following publishers for permission to reproduce their book covers in Extended Reading lists.

Dillon Press, Inc.:
Incredible Facts About the Ocean: The Land Below, the Life Within, by W. Wright Robinson. Cover art copyright © 1987 by Dillon Press, Inc.

Houghton Mifflin Company:
The Black Pearl, by Scott O'Dell. Jacket art by Milton Johnson. Copyright © 1967.
Number the Stars, by Lois Lowry. Jacket photo by Lois Lowry. Copyright © 1989 by Lois Lowry.
Pyramid, by David Macaulay. Jacket art by David Macaulay, copyright © 1975 by David Macaulay.

J. B. Lippincott Junior Books, an imprint of Harper & Row Publishers, Inc.:
His Majesty, Queen Hatshepsut, by Dorothy Sharp Carter. Jacket art by Michele Chessare, copyright © 1987 by Michele Chessare. Published simultaneously in Canada by Fitzhenry & Whiteside Limited, Toronto.

National Geographic Society and Ed Robinson:
The Mysterious Undersea World, by Jan Leslie Cook. Jacket photograph by Ed Robinson, copyright © 1980.

Random House, Inc.:
Exploring the Sea: Oceanography Today, by Carvel Hall Blair. Jacket art by Harry McNaught, copyright © 1986. Published simultaneously in Canada by Random House of Canada Limited, Toronto.

Credits

Program Design Carbone Smolan Associates

Cover Design Carbone Smolan Associates

Design 13–111 Waters Design Associates, Inc.; 113–167 Studio Izbickas; 169–261 Liska & Associates, Inc.; 263–295 Martine Bruel; 297–299 Summerford Design; 300–313 Ligature, Inc.; 314–363 Summerford Design; 365–467 DeFrancis Studio

Illustration 13 Waters Design Associates, Inc.; 15 James Houston; 16–17 Waters Design Associates, Inc.; 18 Mark Lewis; 26–29 Waters Design Associates, Inc.; 30–37 (borders) Waters Design Associates, Inc.; 30 Armstrong Sperry; 38 Waters Design Associates, Inc.; 40–41 Bill Russell; 42 Mark Lewis; 43, 52–53 Bill Russell; 62, 66, 79 Mark Lewis; 81–104 James Houston, (borders) Waters Design Associates, Inc.; 106–107 Marlies Merk Najaka; 110–111 Waters Design Associates, Inc.; 114–115 Robert Hynes; 116, 118–124 Joseph Le Monnier; 125 Patricia Rossi; 129, 130, 133 George Ulrich; 137–139 James E. Taylor; 138 (map) Patricia Rossi; 142–148 Robert Hynes; 151 Robert Brooks; 157 George Ulrich; 172–183, 184–185 Stephan Daigle; 186–199 B. J. Johnson; 202–206 James Noel Smith; 208–221 Mary Azarian; 222–247 Barry Root; 250–255 Margaret Kasahara; 298–299 Carlos Llerena Aguirre; 301 Mapping Specialists; 302, 306 Precision Graphics; 304 Rebecca Merrilees; 305 Judy Reed; 312 Ligature, Inc.; 314, 327, 335 Reprinted with permission of GROLIER ENCYCLOPEDIA, 1955 © Grolier, Inc.; 338 Precision Graphics; 358–359 Carlos Llerena Aguirre; 365–367 Alphons Holtgreve; 368–369 Patti Green; 370–374 Paul Goble, (borders) Patti Green; 376–379 Alphons Holtgreve; 380–385 David Frampton; 386–391 Michael McCurdy; 392–405 Leslie Evans; 406–423 Krystyna Stasiak; 424–435 Mary Azarian; 436–449 Randall Enos; 450–461 James Kraus; 462–467 Alphons Holtgreve; 469–553 Mark O'Neill; 559, 560, 572 Robin Brickman; 563, 571 Christine Czernota

589

Photography   13 Comstock;   **13** (inset) Wide
World Photos;   **14** (left) Comstock;   **14–15**
(bottom) Wide World Photos;   **14–15** (center),
16–17 (all) Comstock;   **26–27** shark: The Image
Bank, diver: Comstock;   **28–29** Waters Design
Associates, Inc.;   **38** Comstock;   **62–63** Steve
McCutcheon;   **63** (inset),   **64, 70** Wide World
Photos;   **108** (left) Watson;   **108** (right) Courtesy
of Ariane Randall;   **108–109** Waters Design
Associates, Inc.;   **109** (top) Courtesy of Margo
Burns;   **109** (left) Courtesy of Seymour Reit;   **109**
(right) Courtesy of Colin Thiele;   **110–111** road:
Stan Wolenski Photography, lightning: Superstock,
horse: Superstock;   **113** (top) Superstock;   **113**
(bottom) William Curtsinger Photo Researchers,
Inc.;   **126–127** Superstock;   **136** (left) The
Cousteau Society;   **136** (right) Chuck Nicklin/
Ocean Images, Inc.;   **140–141** Bruce Robison;
149 Jeff Rotman;   **150** Al Giddings/Ocean
Images, Inc.;   **152–155, 158, 160** William
Jaspersohn;   **161** Superstock;   **162** (top) William
Jaspersohn;   **162** (bottom) Chuck Nicklin/Ocean
Images, Inc.;   **162–163** Superstock;   **164** Stan
Cobb;   **164–165** Superstock;   **165** (left) Courtesy
of Margaret Poynter;   **165** (right) University of
California Santa Barbara;   **166–167** Robert Frerck/
Odyssey Productions, (books) Gabor Demjen/Roy
Kirby, Aperture, Inc., Boston;
169 J. Taposchaner/FPG International;
170 © The Stock Market/Margaret Kois;
171 Richard Hutchings/Photo Researchers, Inc.;
201 Tom Rosenthal/Superstock;   **248–249** Terry
Donnelly/TSW-CLICK/Chicago Ltd.;   **256–257**
Brian Leng/West Light;   **258** (top) Courtesy of
New Mexico Highlands University of Alumni
Foundation;   **258** (center) Courtesy of Dan
D'Amelio;   **258** (bottom) Robert Neitsch;   **258–
259** Culver Pictures;   **259** (top) Gregory
Robertson;   **259** (center) Courtesy of Sophie S.
Rawls;   **259** (bottom) Courtesy of Cynthia Rylant;
260–261 Donald Dietz/Stock Boston;   **261** (book)
Gabor Demjen/Roy Kirby, Aperture, Inc., Boston;
265 Matisse, Henri. "The Blue Window." (summer
1913). Oil on canvas, 51½ x 35⅝". Collection, The
Museum of Modern Art. Abby Aldrich Rockefeller
Fund;   **266** Vincent van Gogh Foundation/
National Museum Vincent van Gogh, Amsterdam;
267 Courtesy of the New York Historical Society,

New York City;   **268** "Sudden Shower at Ohashi"
(3rd state). Hiroshige, Utagawa (Japanese, 1797–
1858). 1857. Color woodcut, 13⅜ x 8⅞".
Philadelphia Museum of Art: The Samuel S.
White, 3rd, and Vera White Collection;   **270** The
Tate Gallery, London/Art Resource, NY;   **271**
David Smith, "Lectern Sentinel," 1961. Stainless
steel, 8 feet ¾ inches x 33 x 20½ inches (2.58445m
x 83.82cm x 52.07cm). Collection of Whitney
Museum of American Art. Purchase, with funds
from the Friends of the Whitney Museum of
American Art. 62.15;   **275** van Gogh, Vincent."
"The Starry Night." (1889) Oil on canvas, 29 x
36¼". Collection, The Museum of Modern Art,
New York. Acquired through the Lillie P. Bliss
Bequest;   **277** Maurice and Margo Cohen
Collection;   **278** Klee, Paul. "Mask of Fear." (1932)
Oil on burlap, 39½ x 22½". Collection, The
Museum of Modern Art, New York. Nelson A.
Rockefeller Fund;   **280** Enrico Baj, "Angry
General with Decorations." Collection of the
Museum of Contemporary Art, Chicago. Promised
Gift of Joseph and Jory Shapiro;   **283** Joan Miró,
"Carnival of Harlequin," 1924–25. Oil on canvas, 26
x 36⅝". Albright-Knox Art Gallery, Buffalo, New
York. Room of Contemporary Art Fund, 1940;
284 David Smith (American, 1906–1965), "The
Hero," 1952. Steel sculpture, 73¹¹⁄₁₆ x 25½ x
11¾". The Brooklyn Museum, 57.185. Dick S.
Ramsay Fund;   **288** Abby Aldrich Rockefeller
Folk Art Center;   **289** Scala/Art Resource, NY,
Modigliani, *Louise*, 1915, Milan, Coll. Mazzotta;
291 Courtesy, Museum of the American Indian,
Heye Foundation;   **292** Wassily Kandinsky,
"Violet-Orange." October 1935. Oil on canvas, 35 x
45¼". Collection, the Solomon R. Guggenheim
Museum, New York. Photo: Myles Aronowitz,
Photograph © 1990 The Solomon R. Guggenheim
Foundation;   **295** Art Resource, NY/Copyright
1989 ARS NY/ADAGP;   **297** Alain Choisnet/The
Image Bank;   **300** © Allan Seiden, The Image
Bank;   **302** Collection, British Museum, Photo ©
Michael Holford;   **303** Borromeo, Art Resource,
NY;   **305** Egyptian Museum, Cairo, Giraudon,
Art Resource, NY;   **307** © Louis Goldman, Photo
Researchers, Inc.;   **308** Giraudon, Art Resource,
NY;   **309, 311, 313** Collection, British Museum,
Photo © Michael Holford;   **315** Julius Fekete/The